New Theology No. 3

New Theology No. 3

Edited by
Martin E. Marty
and Dean G. Peerman

The Macmillan Company, New York
Collier-Macmillan Ltd., London

Permission to reprint the following is gratefully acknowledged:
Daniel Callahan, Copyright © 1965 Commonweal Publishing
Kenneth Hamilton, © 1965 by American Academy of Religion
Daniel Berrigan, © Copyright 1965 by Justus George Lawler
Paul Peachey, Copyright © 1965 by Union Theological Seminary in Virginia. All rights reserved

SECOND PRINTING 1966

Library of Congress Catalog Card Number: 64-3132

The Macmillan Company, New York
Collier-Macmillan Canada, Ltd., Toronto, Canada

Printed in the United States of America

Acknowledgments

WE THANK the ten authors and ten editors who graciously permitted reprint of the articles which form the substance of this book. By now over thirty journals have been represented in the three annuals; *Theology Today*, *Interpretation*, and *Religion in Life* are making third appearances and the *Union Seminary Quarterly Review* and *Continuum* are represented a second time. Their reappearance is a mark of our special regard, our special debt, and our special recommendation of these journals whose addresses—let him who reads take the hint—are provided with each article.

We are also grateful to Kyle Haselden, editor of *The Christian Century* who encouraged us on this and in previous work, and to Mrs. Joanne Younggren and Miss Nancy Hardesty for help in preparation of the manuscript.

Contents

New Theology No. 3

The Turn from Mere Anarchy

New Theology, now apparently a hardy perennial, is a representative anthology of contemporary work in theology. Some might question whether each succeeding year produces sufficient change in climate or subject matter to warrant another garnering of theological articles. To readers of daily newspapers in which religion now plays a daily part and to editors of a weekly journal in which each seven-day cycle offers newness and change, the span of a year seems almost leisurely and—to editors who must meet weekly deadlines—almost luxurious. Judging from the journals over which we pore, we would say that the first years of the 1960's have presented a demonstrably different theological concern from those of the 1950's. And each of the past three years has served to convince us of subtle but rapid changes in the way theology is being approached and in the themes which engross theologians.

Of course, Christian theology has been around for almost twenty centuries, and change must always be viewed in the light of a tradition which anticipates much of what appears to be new. Future historians of theology may understandably yawn now and then as they page through journals obsessed with talk about the death of God, the presence of the profane, the problems of the spiritual life. "We've been through all that before" is a proper rejoinder. Indeed, we have: when the church was young, or when it met enemies from without in the later centuries, or when it was troubled from within, especially in the nineteenth century. But the current cultural context for these problems is the only one we are allowed to inhabit; it is in the midst of these problems that Christians are called to reflect and to act responsibly. These may not be the best times to be alive theologically, but they are the only times we experience firsthand. So we confront, sometimes in fear and often with relish, the current version of classical themes.

While we may have determined to let the concerns of practicing theologians and journal editors (who reflect the times even as they help shape them by what they accept or reject) speak for themselves, it is clear to any thoughtful person that an element of subjectivity necessarily enters into the formation of the plot of each volume of *New Theology*. Those who disagree with this year's internal principle of selection may find many evidences of afterglow or throwback from previous trends and movements in the same journals. Who knows, we may be deceived and may be guessing wrong about significances.

To illustrate: Future church historians will certainly look back on the years of our days and of our copyrights—the latter years of the Vatican Council—as days in which a great intra-Christian theological upheaval took place. A four-and-one-half-century-old family quarrel in Western Christianity, between Roman Catholics and Protestants, was being addressed meaningfully as never before. The house was being put in order. Yet only three of forty-three essays in our three volumes have directly taken cognizance of the upheaval and the change. We have deliberately played down the Vatican Council, in part because reportage concerning it is so accessible and theological reflection in depth on it so rare—indeed, perhaps this early it is impossible—that we feel it is wise to wait. Even more, much of the ecumenical theology is not "new" in that it is addressed for the most part to problems inherited from ecclesiastical contexts of the sixteenth and nineteenth centuries. It is a truism among most theologians that the *basic* theological problems in today's pluralist and secular world affect Roman Catholicism and Protestantism similarly and are being addressed similarly to both. The profound issues today develop not between Catholics and non-Catholics, but within the various communions and within the cultures that surround them or the individual persons who adhere to them.

If we have slighted ecumenical issues, so too have we neglected the major domestic issue which has occasioned activity and thought in the American churches: the ethical recovery associated with the civil rights movements. Only two articles in three years, and again, none in this third volume, relate directly to this revolution. Are we not once more overlooking what church historians of the future will mark and journalists of the present are marking as the prime issue for the churches? Once again we can plead both a plethora of reportage elsewhere, making reportage here unnecessary, and the fact that theological reflection on the movement is so recent and so embryonic that little has appeared in the scholarly quarterlies. (Here we will be a bit immodest and point to Gibson Winter's brief article "A Theology of Demonstration" in *The Christian Century* for October 13, 1965, as a model of the kind of argument that has begun to appear on this matter.) We have chosen to concern ourselves with theological reflection on church and world in a larger context.

When politicians or statesmen want to inaugurate new policies, they issue press releases or experiment with trial balloons. When playwrights or artists venture, they turn out plays or paintings. When theologians want to test new and tentative ideas, they write books. The number of people who buy theological works is relatively small: from four thousand to forty thousand sales covers the range for most such books. But the books become events, are discussed in journals and seminaries and eventually in parishes; sometimes they become the theme for radio and television discussions, and fortunately their influence is much wider than their immediate market.

Three times during the years of *New Theology* such books have appeared in America. As we organized materials for *New Theology No. 1* we found theologians relating to the *cause célèbre* occasioned by Anglican Bishop John A. T. Robinson's *Honest to God*—certainly the most popular theological work of the decade. Robinson's book, we felt, looked chiefly to the past: It dealt with themes formed by men whose thought had been well established in seminaries and journals. Paul Tillich's "ground of being," Rudolf Bultmann's "demythologized" Christian message, and Dietrich Bonhoeffer's "world come of age" were familiar issues in the gray halls and smoky coffee shops of seminaries or lay study cells. But through Robinson they became coin of the larger realm and theologians were obliged to take them seriously in a new cultural context. So in our first venture we gathered comment on Christian thought without a metaphysical background, on Christian style without conventional piety, on Christian expression without much of its historic context.

The second year we found theologians wrestling with themes in Paul van Buren's *The Secular Meaning of the Gospel.* In it a linguistic analyst philosopher applied his empirical tools to "God-talk" and found that it did not serve as linguistic coin of the realm. As with Robinson, we feel that van Buren did not so much establish the terms for the many theologians who worked with what we called in *New Theology No. 2* "The Problem of God and the Godless" as he exemplified that problem. But his book occasioned study and served as a catalyst; it also helped us select and arrange the articles for *No. 2.*

During the year in which *New Theology No. 3* was gestating, one book again served as barometer. No argument about it, Harvey Cox's *The Secular City* served to crystallize issues. It served us as the spectacles through which to view the journals. As in the previous instance, the author's critics could rightfully say, "We know all that; we've been through it before." The long shadow of Bonhoeffer in the concentration camp falls across Cox's pages as it did across Robinson's and van Buren's (Bonhoeffer seems to be the only theologian acceptable in the main to all three and to most of the "pro" and "con" people who debate the book writers of the sixties). The fact that the meaning of "the secular" or "the world" is the first item on theologians' agenda in the 1960's, just as "the church" or "the message" might have been for a half-century previously, robbed Cox's book of some of its apparent novelty. But Cox, profiting from time spent in eastern Europe, brought a flair and a style, an organizing sense, and a provocative spirit to his writing and in the process both reflected and shaped many theological issues in the journals on which we have drawn. As in *New Theology No. 2,* we introduce the "book of the year" with a featured review, in this instance by Daniel Callahan.

In asking ourselves what was fresh about Cox and the ensuing debates, what precisely was its appeal, we learned something pertinent to the "plot" of this annual. Why was Cox so popular in Protestant and Catholic journals, in seminaries, among younger priests and ministers, in circles of renewed laymen and laywomen? Why did his "celebration" of the secular city seem so attractive to people in the churches? A careful reading of the book suggests to us that it manifests enough of the "far-out" and revolutionary spirit of the younger churchmen of the 1960's to address one side of their needs and that it hints at or even offers programs for Christian thought and action which serve to inform the other side of their needs—their responsibilities to the church.

From this viewpoint *The Secular City* is a rather conservative book. It gives the reader a sense that, though he has traversed the same no-God's land where the "death of God" theologians (William Hamilton, Paul van Buren, Thomas J. J. Altizer, and others) would take them, he has also been counseled to return to the very ordinary "structures" (Cox's favored term, not ours) in which he must spend his life. The liturgy, the parish, the churches themselves, the possibility of God-talk, the regard for Christian tradition, are not here abolished so much as radically questioned, with the hope that they can be radically transformed.

To put it as pithily as possible: During the composing of *No. 1* and *No. 2* we were taken by the centrifugality and apparent anarchy of much theological discussion. Not that the people who were writing were necessarily destructive or anarchic in intent. But because they were working on a different set of assumptions than those shared by the neo-liberals or neo-orthodox of the 1950's, the effect of their work seemed disruptive. For some time it was difficult to sense the constructive purpose in some of the directions theology took. This year we have noticed a kind of centripetal direction, a hunger for order, a courage to make affirmations in the context of Christian tradition, a hesitant but visible first step toward new construction. One gets the impression that other theologians, who share so much of the cultural analysis of the God-is-dead theologians, are for the most part saying of these theologians' conclusions, "But that is not what *we* meant!" They refuse to concede that the godless life in a world come of age—a life marked by clear but sparse language about freedom in Jesus, the faith of the Easter community, the ethics of a servant church—demands or produces more courage or enterprise than does a theology that ventures into God-talk, that gropes to give expression to many features of human spirituality, that seeks to see Jesus and the Christian community and the servant church somehow in contexts more varied, in settings more complex, than the death-of-God reductionists see them.

The preceding paragraph, alas, cannot be viewed as a definitive theological judgment concerning the truth of the one "school" or of other schools. We are trying to be reporters and hope that our own mild reservations about the death-of-God men's cultural analysis and our more serious reservations about their theology have not misled us and will not thus mislead readers who look to this book for an accurate and honest reflection. The Hamiltons, van Burens, and Altizers would not, we are sure, be impressed by truth claims based on nose count or on content analysis of scores of theological journals. They might, for example, argue that editors have a vested interest in God-talk, churchiness, the conventional, the safe, the orderly. But if they were to canvass the contents of journals as we do, we are confident they would recognize that during the past eighteen months, more than during the previous three years, the interest in renewal of talk about God and of some sense of program for church life in the "secular city" has marked the writings of people who in many other respects breathe with, literally "conspire" with them!

Why the turn, apart from the hypothetical vested interest of editors? For one thing, the travel-light "secular" theology has thus far largely failed in its apologetic purpose. That is, secular intellectuals and other nonchurched compatriots have not been visibly more drawn to the "secular" theology than to its more burdened and apparently arcane antecedents in orthodoxy or neo-orthodoxy. Atheist Marghanita Laski, writing in the June 23, 1965, issue of the popular magazine *Punch*, was as typical as philosopher Alasdair MacIntyre had been in *Encounter* a few years ago: *Honest to God*-talk did not impress either of them. They wanted their agnosticism or their atheism straight, uncluttered by reference to Bible or incarnation or classic Christian themes in modern dress. They see no reason to bring Jesus or the faith of the Easter community to bear on the determination of their lives. Stated another way, if they were to be attracted to Jesus Christ and Christian claims, they would prefer to confront something of the sometimes embarrassing and often inspiring context and tradition in which they have appeared and have been affirmed. They averred that they preferred a more misfit, angular type—the spiritual people who seem to be related to a spiritual depth not easily accessible outside the tradition—to those who seem to opt for facile accommodationism, who want to be immediately relevant to the secularists but who still want to talk about Jesus and the servant church.

The MacIntyres and Laskis do not decide truth and falsehood for us; they serve as representatives marking an apologetic failure. As Miss Laski put it:

> Useful creative dialogue between religious people and unbelievers . . . will not be achieved by their inventing a mishmash of apparently less controversial religion, but by starting from a common core of needs and experiences, no matter what we suppose to be their source.

. . . . .

> Religionless Christianity, though often profoundly exciting to those who have hitherto taken an organized church for granted, seems to the unbeliever a natural response to the often noted fact that the vitality of impulses atrophy as they become institutionalized, no less true of churches than of literary societies or nuclear disarmament movements. It is the greatest tribute to Christianity's success in meeting so wide a range of needs that it has for so long proved capable of periodically revivifying the impulses within the structure of the institution. . . .

The Laskis in the intellectual community may, of course, be decoys, may mislead us. An obviously irrelevant Christianity in an obviously implausible context is easier to dismiss than Christianity which motivates and informs ecclesiastical change, especially if it inspires inconveniences like freedom movements or expression as eloquent as *The Secular City* has seemed to some to be. But such atheist witness against the apologetic intention of radical, religionless theology has prompted other theologians to take a second and longer look.

Couple this apologetic limitation with other features often criticized in "the new theology," and the background for this year's articles becomes more visible. To many, the newer theology has been proved to be short-range, sterile, devoid of content, has inspired little curiosity. "What do you do for an encore" after a book which, supposedly in the interest of theology, rules out virtually all theological content except for a few lines about a Jesus (concerning whom critical historians are nervous) or an Easter community or a servant church whose every empirical form seems indefensible on the face of things? We are treated to "calls" for nonreligious interpretations of biblical theology or new theologies of freedom and secularity: then what?

A cynic might say that theologians have been frightened away by anarchic signs in the culture, signs not directly related to radical theology but produced in the same constellation of experiences: the "new morality" of simple permissiveness in the interest of Christian love; campus revolt sometimes inspired by *anomie* more than by creative restlessness and humane concern; contrived and sensationalist experiment in Christian expression under the guise of "relevance" and witness. These questions are too complicated for brief treatment: We leave them to the theologians and the psychologists. Perhaps another kind of sense of responsibility, one matching the intensity and creativity of the theologians who in the early 1960's spoke of the death of God, is manifesting itself. In any case, countertrends are visible, reaction is setting in, options are present, issues are joined, a debate is in progress. The signs of new order—though not of a new conservativism or repressivism—impress us as we read these journals' pages.

As for the outline of the book: Britisher Ninian Smart speaks of a kind of "box" he thinks Anglo-American theology has gotten itself into. Following Smart's essay is Daniel Callahan's generally favorable review of Harvey Cox's book offering a way out of that "box." John Macquarrie, so far the only author to make a second appearance in these annuals, poses a question, "How Can We Think of God?" and then gives an ordered and constructive answer. Kenneth Hamilton enters the debate concerning whether man today is or should be "religious" and outlines a fresh approach to this part of the larger question.

Since so much of the reconstructive or ordered theological conversation has to do with ethics, we include three essays in the field: James Gustafson, in a conciliatory mood, seeks to dispel what he sees as a false dilemma in contemporary Christian ethics; Paul Peachey believes that Christian theology has something constructive to say in world affairs; and Tom F. Driver in a provocative article relates sexuality and Jesus in order to inform an aspect of personal ethics. John Killinger is typical of the numerous theologians who have explored contemporary literature for signs of negation and marks of affirmation. George Webber, speaking for and to churchmen at the "grass roots" level, corrects an imbalance for which we have been faulted in previous annuals. And Father Daniel Berrigan employs a very different theological genre—a kind of aphoristic prose-poem—to meditate on the freedom-in-obedience of today's Christian.

After our lungs, full of library dust, become clear again and the circles around our eyes disappear, we shall take another look and try to discern whether the theological scene warrants another annual summary. If not, we are sure that in the second half of the 1960's other observers will find what we have been finding: enough contentiousness to reassure us that theologians are alive and kicking; enough enterprise to assure us that even in the secular context they are not wanting; enough affirmation in their writing to encourage us to keep reading; enough of the problematic to let us know that they live in a real world and that they share with all of us the "human condition."

—M.E.M. and D.G.P.

The Intellectual Crisis of British Christianity*

Ninian Smart

"My promotion of a little *odium theologicum* was meant to bring some illumination into an area where all is sweetness and light." So concluded Ninian Smart in a letter in the July 1965 issue of the Anglican monthly *Theology*,** replying to critics of his article which appeared in the January 1965 issue of that journal. The illumination afforded by Dr. Smart's article is, one must admit, accompanied by a bit of heat—but it is heat tempered by a wit seldom found in theological writing. Smart's thrusts are directed at what he sees as the subjectivism and reductionism of atheistic and "crypto-atheistic" theologians such as Paul van Buren and Ian T. Ramsey and the confused metaphysics of a thinker such as Paul Tillich (van Buren and Tillich both being names, incidentally, which indicate that the "crisis" Smart is dealing with is not confined to his native England). Both trends he describes as "lethal"— a term which some may be tempted to use to describe Smart's own essay! "Unless transcendence is taken seriously," he insists, "there can be no truth claim in Christianity." Dr. Smart is H. G. Wood Professor of Theology in the University of Birmingham.

* The present article generated some correspondence in the later issues of *Theology*, including replies by I. T. Ramsey (February, 1965), E. L. Mascall and John Kent (March, 1965), and a reply to replies by myself (July, 1965). Professor Mascall rightly complained that I had not been fair to Professor Ramsey, though he sympathized with my arguments. My remarks in the article should not be taken to mean that I consider that Ramsey is, or thinks himself, an atheist, and Mascall is correct in holding that Ramsey is defending theism. My question is rather this: need Ramsey's apparatus of "cosmic disclosures" be incompatible with the kind of this-worldly empiricism which lies behind Braithwaite and van Buren? Mr. Kent is baffled by my analysis of a passage from one of Tillich's books. My critique was more fully expressed in "Being and the Bible" in *The Review of Metaphysics*, Vol. IX, No. 4 (June, 1965). Readers might also consult Paul Edwards,

THE SITUATION is shocking and ludicrous. So I hope no one will mind if I am rude about it.

Christianity is in an intellectual crisis in Britain. This has to do, broadly, with philosophy. Why?

Christianity (I think) claims to be true. If so, what are the grounds on which it rests? We can avoid philosophizing directly about them by centering Barth-wise everything on revelation. Barth is, for that reason, respected by philosophers. He does not compromise, and he does not play around with dubitable metaphysics. He challenges precisely because he does not allow the question of natural theology to arise. We can, then, remove the intellectual crisis by following Barth. But a price has to be paid. The great Calvinist distance between heaven and earth can turn into a gap between the Church and "secular" society. And a man can feel spiritually crushed when he cannot discuss his faith with friends. When, too, they belong to another faith, there is stalemate. Nothing can be said: One can only go on talking. Barth is magnificent, but he is imprisoned. It may be that we should thus be prisoners of the Lord, but there must be those who doubt it. What alternative is open to them?

This is where the ludicrous and tragic nature of our present crisis becomes apparent. The fact is that most of the influential intellectual anodynes—Tillich, Ramsey, van Buren —are lethal.

After the last war, linguistic philosophy boomed, and religious intellectuals became sensitive. You didn't want so much to show that religion is true as that it is meaningful. This was a new version of the Ontological Argument. If "God" means something, all is well: It is but a small matter to go on to show that he exists. But the intellectuals were sensitive too about empiricism. So we had analyses (or supposed analyses) of religious language which made its meaning look strange. These unrealistic accounts of religious language have proved quite incapable of providing a secret defense of Christianity.

"Professor Tillich's Confusions," *Mind*, Vol. LXXIV, No. 294 (April, 1965).

  ** The S.P.C.K., Holy Trinity Church, Marylebone Rd., London N.W. 1.

Notoriously, R. B. Braithwaite's empiricist account was atheistic. R. M. Hare's account of the "blik" makes us ask whether truly God exists, or whether it is just a way we have of looking at the world. And what of the Marxist and Buddhist bliks? Marx would, no doubt like St. Thomas Aquinas, be shocked to have his doctrines thus watered down. Bliks may have nothing to do with truth. It is no wonder that the atheistic Paul van Buren finds so much in the blik concept. If Christianity becomes thus noncognitive, it becomes ineffective; for a man cannot rest his life on seeing elephants in the clouds. We can look on the clouds that way: They may look like elephants on a stormy afternoon. But we cannot expect the elephants to descend and haul logs for us.

Besides all which, the blik analysis does not chime in with the way folk use religious utterances. Folk make truth claims about the transcendent, as if it is a sort of fact that God exists, not unlike the fact that we exist.

Braithwaite and Hare seem to represent a modern trend toward formulating a nontheistic Christianity. A colleague of mine recently said to me: "My wife is an atheist, but she wants to be an Anglican as well. Is there anything she can read?" "My dear fellow," I replied, "we've got plenty of books showing how the trick can be done." (I reflected sadly that it was difficult to find books on how to be a *theist*.)

Such "empiricism" culminates in Paul van Buren. For him, a transcendent God is meaningless. The doctrine of creation boils down to an affirmative attitude to the world (in which case most of my atheistic friends believe in the doctrine). He has not yet written *The Secular Meaning of the Covenant*. No doubt it is this: The Jew has a perspective on the world centered on the historical events of the Exodus, and he is gripped by a contagious legalism. Nor has van Buren expounded the secular meaning of Jesus's own faith. There is no Father to forgive van Buren: He knows not what he does. I can't imagine Anthony Flew rushing into the Church from reading van Buren. He no doubt is chuckling: At last these Christians have realized that all this talk of God is empty. Well, if it is, let us abandon Christianity. A Christian atheism can be a new force in the world—except that some folk would not be self-sacrificing just on the grounds of a secular Gospel. In any event, candor is best. If we really are atheists, let us stop the clap-trap about worship and prayer.

Unfair to Paul van Buren? He means well, but he does not mean much. But it may be that there is more in him, for he leans too on Ian Ramsey, and it might seem a bit outrageous to say that Ramsey is an atheist. But let us look at his *Religious Language* more closely. It is a book with a wide circulation. If it is inadequate as an analysis or as an anodyne, it will confirm the fact that the intellectual basis of contemporary British Christianity is in a bad way.

The main function of religious language, for Ramsey, is to evoke a disclosure situation in which the universe comes alive in a personal way. Thus religious language has primarily an engineering function. It engineers insight: It engineers discernment. It whirs until the penny drops. It does this by massive negation (as in negative theology), or by using limiting concepts like "perfection," or by the use of models and qualifiers ("perfectly good," "first cause"). The language of religion is like the significant tautology "I'm I," which somehow shows the self to be more than observables. The objections to all this are manifold.

First, and perhaps less importantly, it is only an analysis of theistic language. That is not the only kind of religious language.

Secondly, if the function of religious language is one of evoking a discernment, there is no reason to suppose that it *describes* anything. Swearing, which is notoriously non-descriptive, evokes responses. But some religious language (not of course "Praise be to God" and the like) is seemingly descriptive. If we take the descriptions away, we take truth away. This is why Ramsey's position, though it so far need not entail atheism, is compatible with it.

Thirdly, Ramsey appears to concede (*op. cit.*, p. 74) that "God" becomes a word to talk about discernment situations. He writes: "What we posit is language which claims to talk about what is given and disclosed to us in a certain way." In short, "God" becomes a name for penny-dropping experiences. But experiences are not ontologically privileged.

If "God" is about items in the world, theology is only concerned with a small fragment of reality. It is as though someone were to say that "God" was the name for all patches of blue. Ramsey thus has really dispensed with transcendence. This must be fatal, if religion is to make truth claims, for claims not involving reference to the transcendent will always be claims about bits of the world. God becomes finite and of this world. This is equivalent to a superstitious atheism.

Fourthly, though the universe may come alive in a personal way, it may evoke other reactions, like Buddhist ones. Such different reactions, considered merely as experiences, and without reference to truth claims, are compatible. Thus if the Ramsey line were generalized by men of other faiths, including atheism, the way would be open to a new psychological syncretism.

Fifthly, as Frederick Ferré has pointed out,[1] Ramsey has not defended himself against the charge of mere subjectivity. It is not enough to reply, as he does, that religious experience is subject-object in form: so are experiences of pink rats. No criteria of objectivity, i.e. truth, are given, beyond the fact that if the religious man goes on talking long enough a penny will drop. Such "verification" cannot be enough, for, as we have seen, there are alternative ways of talking.

Sixthly, and connectedly, Ramsey's position means the death of argument. The Cosmological and Teleological Arguments come in through the back door, but by the time they reach the dining room they are served up as hash. (I confess to doing something like this in my *Reasons and Faiths*, but in this case curry was added.) But the "First Cause" penny can only genuinely drop if there are grounds for holding that the existence of the cosmos requires explanation. Otherwise, this sort of natural theology cannot be worked. There are even naughty Thomists who try to substitute intuition for argument in these matters—Dom Illtyd Trethowan for one. The trouble is that either you have an intuition or you don't, and that's that. Truth is different.

Seventhly, Ramsey's thesis about significant tautologies must be wrong. He counts "God is Love" as one such, like "I'm I." Tautologies are fine. They are virginally true: They cannot be violated. But they can have no offspring. They can tell us nothing about the world. The person who repeats "I'm I" is bombinating. It may be true that there is self-discernment, over and above particular items of consciousness. But if there is such a self, it is as good a claimant for eternal status as God. We end up with Vedānta. Shankara argued exactly in such terms, about the "self-luminous intuition of the Self." If the self is something (and I have my doubts), it is something tremendous. Ramsey's God is doubtful; and not everyone has a disclosure. But each man has a self, if anyone does.

For these various reasons, Ramsey's prescription on how we ought to look at religious language is not only compatible with atheism: It implies a kind of atheism, but a superstitious one, in which "God" is the name for bits of experience. Neither science nor true theology can be done by induction from experience. It is thus no coincidence that Paul van Buren, who has a confessedly noncognitive approach to religion, i.e. who is a crypto-atheist, should use Ramsey as one of the ingredients in his new recipe.

In a way, linguistic philosophy in these manifestations of it is close to Existentialism. There too the world is seen through man's reactions and commitments. This is as though God is waiting to be called into existence by my decisions. This is anthropocentric pride. Though Existentialism can give us insights into the meaning of authenticity and freedom, it cannot serve as the *basis* for theology, just as it cannot serve as the basis for a metaphysics. Truth may concern persons as well as things; but truth is objectivity. One needs a genuine ontology.

But Tillich's will not do, because it is itself a farrago of linguistic confusion. If there is one thing that has been learned from linguistic philosophy (and much too still has to be learned), it is that loose talk of "being" is not good enough. Consider a typical Tillich passage:[2]

In order to be able to ask for something, we must have it partially, otherwise it could not be the object of a question. He who asks both has and has not at the same time. If man is that being who asks the question of being, he has and has not the being for which he asks. He is separated from it while belonging to it. Certainly we belong to being

—its power is in us—otherwise we would not be. But we are also separated from it; we do not possess it fully. Our power of being is limited. We are a mixture of being and nonbeing.

The first sentence seems false: When I ask for an omelet I do not already have a partial omelet. Of course, an omelet has to be possible, or I am an ass to ask; but that is the most favorable interpretation to put on Tillich's words, and it is not good enough. So the second sentence seems false (though if someone says to me "Do you have or not have?" I should want a bit more specification of what it is I am supposed to be having or not having). The third sentence is obscure. Elsewhere, Tillich interprets the question of being as "Why does anything exist at all?" (p. 6, p. 9) and as the question of "what it means to *be*" (p. 6). On the first interpretation, the apodosis of the third sentence seems false. If I ask whether God created everything else, I do not *have* God. I might answer in the negative. Still my question would show *interest*. (Anthony Flew, for instance, is interested in whether God exists.) But that can be stated without bringing in the mumbo-jumbo. On the second interpretation, what man is is a linguistic philosopher. The answer as to how the verbs "to be" and "to exist" function is complex and need not detain us here. Or perhaps Tillich means that people ask about the meaning or purpose of life. In what sense does anyone at this stage both have and have not the purpose?

The fourth sentence need not delay us. The fifth sentence deserves scrutiny, however. So we wouldn't be if the power of being weren't in us? Obviously: "Snookfish eats" implies that Snookfish is capable of eating. But though the sentence incorporates this uninteresting logical point, it also suggests that being is a peculiar kind of activity. This, to say the least, needs some extended defense, in view of most of recent philosophy. And it would be tedious to go on. We conclude that we are a mixture of being and nonbeing, a way, no doubt, of saying that we can do some things and not others. Certainly there are some things Tillich can't do.

Why then is a man so capable of this obscure ineptitude widely respected? Partly because here and there he is psychologically perceptive. Volume Two of the *Systematic*

Theology has some insights. The first volume, though, to anyone with a respect for philosophy must seem to be rubbish. It is a tragedy that this useless nonsense has gained currency among theologians—a part result of the split of the academic world into departments and faculties. And there are few philosophers willing to take time off to go through the weary business of exposing Tillich's trivialities. Mr. Heywood Thomas, it is true, not so long ago published a book criticizing Tillich from a logical point of view: But unfortunately he was not incisive. The unfortunate impression has therefore been created that Tillich is a philosopher to take seriously.

It is a painful matter that professional philosophical competence—the kind of thing a good teacher wants to create in his students—should be flouted in this way by a supposedly distinguished theologian. But he has his excuses. Those who follow him in this country have little excuse. The crypto-atheists have at least paid some attention to clarity and coherence.

There are of course, a few good philosophers here who are Christians. But the trends described above are the most influential ones, and they are lethal.

All this means that the dialogue with the humanist is difficult to start. Atheistic Christianity is so like Professor Ronald Hepburn's project of a reconstruction of humanist theology that there can be no dialogue, because no difference. On the other hand, a dialogue cannot start on the basis of Tillich, because no self-respecting philosopher would bother to take such Christianity seriously.

There are two things which hold an intellectual from Christianity—moral disapproval of Christian prescriptions, and difficulties about belief in God. We are here concerned with the latter issue. The way forward in discussion is by reconstructing the concept of a transcendent (and immanent) being. There will still, of course, remain the historical questions and the claims of other faiths: But unless transcendence is taken seriously there can be no truth claim in Christianity. And a man is not to be split into compartments. Belief is a spring of action.

These points imply something too about theological education. Philosophy should become an integral part of it, where this is not already so. Even Barthianism ("philosophy is a waste of theological time") implies this, for one has to *see* that philosophy is a waste of time, and this is partly a philosophical insight. I am, of course, far from decrying revelation. Theology, obviously, cannot begin without it. It is given. But there are questions about it, especially today, and these need to be faced. Even the thesis that they do not have to be faced has to be faced.

Something also is implied by the present situation. Systematic theology is unavoidable.

When I was teaching at King's College, London, I came across certain practical hardships. Thus I would ask students about the Fall—how it was to be interpreted and whether the doctrine as interpreted was true. The trouble was that very few of the students had any view. They were concurrently having the Bible taken to bits, by the brilliant Professor Nineham and others. This was extremely good for them. But it induced skepticism about the possibility of systematic belief. One of them confessed to owning a grubby and intellectually rather disreputable textbook on doctrine. He didn't quite believe it, but it gave him theories. I am sure he was right in one respect. We need the theories. They may be false, but they focus inquiry. The same is true in science. Otherwise, we get into the stamp-collecting syndrome. In short, we need both Nineham and . . .

Exactly.

Biblical theology is obviously not the answer. The texts are just quoted in a less random way. But the point remains— a systematic error can be illuminating and interesting and can help men to crystallize their own system, or nonsystem. Propositions are indeed heaven-sent, though not in the way we once thought.

(I had one other practical difficulty in London. One of the students did not exist. He signed the register regularly, but by sleuthing I found that he was a fiction, even though he wrote entertaining essays. Evidently he did not have the courage to be.)

By consequence of all this the Humanist is liable to encounter a mushy faith, somewhere between Thomism and the Conservative Evangelicals. If this intermediate position is impossible, it is a poor show for ecumenism and, as I believe, for the faith.

The cause of the mushiness is the lack of philosophical competence and insight and the lack of Christian doctrinal coherence. I am not blaming anyone. I am just, as I think, telling the truth. The time has come for a new *Summa*, even a second-rate one.

Can we end with a short litany?

"From being, bliks, Braithwaite, and van Buren, good Lord deliver us.

"From 'I'm I,' alleged logical oddity and penny-dropping, good universe-coming-alive-in-a-personal-way deliver us.

"From looking on freedom as a mere contagion, good affirmative attitude deliver us."

("But, Lord, I am worried: These fellows are good, better than I am." Perhaps the answer is: "Men can have faith in me, even when they by implication do not believe that I exist. But I shall not tell you whether this is a point for or against Humanism.")

NOTES

1. *Language, Logic and God*, p. 141.
2. *Biblical Religion and the Search for Ultimate Reality*, p. 11.

The Secular City:
Toward a Theology of Secularity

Daniel Callahan

Appraising Harvey Cox's much-discussed book *The Secular City,* Daniel Callahan finds much to praise: Cox's biblically based affirmation of secularization and urbanization, his healthily pragmatic approach to the modern world, his repudiation of the debilitating sacred-secular dichotomy—these are accents the church sorely needs to heed if it is to serve the needs of man. But, Callahan queries, will sheer pragmatism suffice? Can man eschew metaphysics altogether? For "man does not live by social reconstruction alone," and "wretchedly ultimate" problems—such as the meaning of death—do persist. Nevertheless, if the contemporary Christian must choose between metaphysics and social planning (unfortunately, they seldom seem compatible), he should choose the latter—for man's sake. Author of *The Mind of the Catholic Layman* and *Honesty in the Church* and editor of *Generation of the Third Eye,* Dr. Callahan is Associate Editor of *The Commonweal.** This article originally appeared in the September 17, 1965, issue of that Roman Catholic lay-edited weekly journal of opinion.

ORDINARILY, THERE is nothing so hard for the religious man to cope with as social change. It sets him to twitching, worrying, and desperately attempting to squeeze from Scripture some measure of solace. Now and then he may try to find a way of turning the change to his advantage, or see some faintly redeeming possibilities in cultural earthquakes. But his more common response is denunciation of the new. He feels threatened, and his instant reaction is defensive and abusive. Historically, he has some reason to feel this way. Massive social change inevitably affects the religious life of a society. The shift from feudalism to capitalism in the West is as good an instance as any of what can happen. Entrepreneurs, not bishops, began to call the tune. Troubled believers felt they could only hum a dirge.

* 232 Madison Ave., New York, N.Y. 10016.

Of late there has been a shift in this pattern. During the past couple of decades one theologian after another has come forward to reluctantly bless scientific, technological, and economic advances. They have learned at least one lesson from their predecessors' mistakes: no amount of ecclesiastical railing can do much to stop social upheavals. The way to survive is to hang on for dear life, all the while looking for some way of legitimately baptizing the new tiger. The theologian may not always like what he has to do, but at least he does it. He smiles gravely and gets to work.

Harvey Cox is very much a part of this new mode, only he goes one step further, ecstatically hailing contemporary social change as the occasion for a revitalized Christianity. As much as anything, it is probably this fetching enthusiasm which accounts for the reception being given his book *The Secular City* (Macmillan, $1.45). Already into a third printing, eagerly passed from hand to hand, quickly adopted by a variety of study groups, it has all the earmarks of a religious *cause célèbre*. It must, then, be meeting some deep need: the longing for a persuasive and unembarrassed theology of secularity. Many attempts have been made in this direction, but almost all of them suffer from the debilitating drawback of treating secularity as a religious disaster—a redeemable disaster, but still a disaster. There is no hint of this in Cox's book.

The key to its power lies in his almost rapturous love for two characteristic features of our age: secularization and urbanization. This won't commend the book to some, but Cox starts from a premise hard to dismiss, *what is*. Far from running their course, secularity and the city are just beginning to take hold. There are always strategies available to evade the impact of historical trends: One can work for the return of a golden age, or fashion utopias, or just withdraw into private metaphysical enclosures, seeking an otherworldly transcendence. Cox will have none of this. His method is to look squarely in the eye that face of contemporary life which most offends the religious and cultural savants; and then to say: You are good, and if you are not we can make you so.

The much bemoaned anonymity of urban life, for instance, Cox hails. It provides the possibility of a historically unparalleled freedom from social convention and culturally enforced mores. Mobility and rootlessness provide like possibilities: a liberation from the smothering embrace of small-town provincialism. Another omnipresent bogeyman of the wise, the modern organization, is no less extolled. Better that structure of human relationships and purposes, with its flexibility, secularized goals, orientation toward the future and limited claims upon its members than a sacred order with its enslavement to the past and its deification of law and custom.

Cox's treatment of "secularization" is unflinching. Defining it as "the liberation of man from religious and metaphysical tutelage, the turning of his attention away from other worlds and toward this one," he defends its human values and claims that its roots are biblical. How is this possible? Cox's argument rests on three points. There is the disenchantment of nature stemming from the Hebraic conception of creation; the desacralization of politics arising from a separation of the political and religious order; and the deconsecration of values which issues from the Jewish relativizing of human values and their representations. Thus was the way opened for a "constructive relativism," which "allows secular man to note the transience and relativity of all cultural creations and of every value system without sinking into the abyss of nihilism." From these roots the technological-urban tree was able to spring.

Pragmatic and Profane

The cumulative result is a secular man who is pragmatic and profane: "Life for him is a set of problems, not an unfathomable mystery. He brackets off the things that cannot be dealt with and deals with those that can. He wastes little time thinking about 'ultimate' or 'religious' questions. And he can live with highly provisional solutions." Just the kind of man, in other words, who is the despair of Sunday preachers. Not so for Cox, whose book shows the decisive impact of Bonhoeffer. "The Gospel," he writes, "does not call man to return to a previous stage of his development. It does not summon man back to dependence, awe, and religiousness. Rather it is a call to imaginative urbanity and creative secularity." Just as the city has replaced the town, so also should the political replace the metaphysical as the context of human thought.

Are there any clouds on the horizon? Very many, but none which are incapable of human mastery given intelligence, planning, and the full freedom of the Gospel. The role of the Church is not to change the present historical direction of society but to exercise its power of cultural exorcism, its mission of reconciliation, its potentialities as an avant-garde for the Kingdom of God.

"God"? One might well inquire at this point just how God fits into this secularized world. Having dismissed metaphysics, Cox is not tempted to create a new natural theology. Instead he asserts that the word "God" has no meaning for secular man, and he implies that even the Christian is not very certain what it means. But shouldn't this at least be a source of discomfort, or even of those existential paroxysms which Cox deplores? Not at all, for God has often hidden Himself for a time, choosing to reveal His name only gradually "through the abrasive experiences of social change. . . . Perhaps, like Moses, we must simply take up the work of liberating the captives, confident that we will be granted a new name by the events of the future."

All of this is a rich pudding, especially from a Protestant minister and professor who in an earlier age would have been called a "divine." But it adds up to a coherent whole, however questionable many of the pieces. By and large, it makes considerably more sense than some of the speculation to be found in a recent volume of the *Concilium* series, *The Church and the World*, edited by Johannes B. Metz (Paulist Press, $4.50). This is painful to say, because the purpose of the volume is to chart the new frontiers of Catholic thought. The problem is not that the *Concilium* volume lacks boldness or even originality but that many of the authors are still too much caught up in metaphysical, existentialist, or personalist quandaries.

A reading of Cox's book has *almost* convinced me that

the day of such problems has passed. However pertinent for some aspects of human existence, a relentless concentration on them contributes very little to the creation of viable social structures and mastery of the material world. It is to continue, in other terms, the traditional quest for the absolute—whether that be construed as a grasp of the totality of being, the nature of existence, or the essence of persons. All too easily this plays into the hands of those who can't stand the problematical, the functional, the pragmatic, the experimental. They are essentially "religious" searches, at least if religion is understood as a hunt for the permanent in the face of the transitory, of ultimate meaning amidst uncertainty. Too often they are concerns which tend to keep alive some old and dangerous dualities, even if that is not their intention.

The persistence of dualism can be seen in a distinction Monsignor Gerard Philips commends in his essay in *The Church and the World*. "Catholics," he says, "are learning to make a clearer distinction between their strictly ecclesial mission and the mature program of action they have to realize now in the world." Heaven help us if they are. What Monsignor Philips does not seem to notice is that a sharp sundering of the spiritual and the temporal leads to an egregious type of Christian utilitarianism: Man should be served, not for his own sake, but for that of the Church. As he revealingly puts it, the Church "could not perform its primary mission if it did not rouse in its members, in behalf of all their human brethren, a spirit of disinterested mutual help." This kind of thinking has been the source of the Church's failure to demonstrate that it is fully able to help build a humane social order. It is nothing less than a gentle way of saying that the Church's ultimate interests lie elsewhere, thus forgetting that when man is slighted for the sake of God, God will soon be slighted also.

Equally mistaken, though less hazardous, is Hans Urs von Balthasar's assertion in the same volume that a "demythologized" and "dephilosophized" theology "would have nothing more to do with the totality of being." "Of necessity," he says, "it could only present itself as a solace for the anguished existential subject." I must confess I can't discover where this "necessity" lies. The whole point of trying to rid theology of dead myths and an excessive dependence upon philosophical modes of thought is to better grasp the essence of the biblical message in its own terms, and from there to learn something about man's condition. One major fruit of this effort has been the discovery that the Bible is far more than the husk of hidden eternal truths. It is a record of man's encounter with God: a God who reveals Himself in history rather than in the philosopher's study, a God who speaks through the language of events rather than that of timeless essences.

Put abstractly like this, there are probably few Catholic theologians who would sharply dissent. I am merely saying what it has now become fashionable to say. Yet if one looks to find evidence of a new creativity in dealing with man's historical and political life, one is most likely to discover only a new set of abstractions. One might expect, for instance, to find the Catholic sociologist or psychologist accorded a stature equal to that of the theologian. Or to find the natural and social sciences, which deal with matter and man in their empirical grittiness, dominating the advance guard of Catholic thought. This is not the case at all. Most of the great Catholic figures of our day—the Rahners, the Küngs, the Schillebeeckxs, the von Balthasars—are notably scant in references to economics, political science, urban planning, and even to the sociology and psychology of religion.

What they have done, and what the Church has honored them for, is to substitute new theologies for old theologies. That is a worthwhile project for those concerned with the intricacies of the Christian revelation, and some people should be. But it is also a graphic illustration of why even the freshest Catholic theology has the same mark of irrelevance as did its forerunners. It is essentially turned in upon itself, and nowhere more obviously than when it tries to talk about "the world" exclusively in the language of theology. The new realm of Catholic thought—of I-thou encounters, salvation history, omega points, Lonergan-like insight, *sein* and *dasein*, kerygma—is a delightful place for Catholics to live. It's just that we're the only ones who live there, along with a few scattered Protestants. The rest of the world lives somewhere else, and our new jargon is just as esoteric and beside the point outside the family circle as the old.

I say this out of a vast sense of frustration. Give or take a few setbacks, the recent progress of Catholic theological thought has been nothing less than spectacular. But I see little evidence that it will come to mean anything more to secular man than did the old scholastic panoply of clear and certain ideas. I am secular man, too, and my Catholic brothers are legion.

Sacred and Secular

In an otherwise excellent article in *America* recently on Christian secularity, Father Thomas E. Clarke, S.J., felt compelled to caution that "the distinction between *sacred* and *secular* is beyond question." There we have the central issue: Is this distinction actually beyond doubt? If it is, then it is almost certainly hopeless to expect that secular man will ever know what the Christian is talking about. Equally hopeless would be an expectation that the Christian secular man could come to know how to construct a coherent human life. As long as he feels that life for him necessarily entails walking some delicate tightrope between the sacred and secular, the natural and the supernatural, the redeemed and the unredeemed, he will always be dizzy. He won't and can't go off into the desert, but then he will always worry whether he can be as totally committed to man's life on earth as the most ardent atheist.

I don't think this is a fictitious or outdated problem. Some of the most disturbed Catholics I have run across recently are those who have heeded the Church's call to serve the world and then have found, once they started doing so, that their Christianity ceased to have much meaning for them. They discovered that the work of the world seems to carry its own intrinsic justification, requiring neither religious motives nor religious goals. A shock of this kind is only natural to those exhorted for years to maintain a balance between sacred and secular—and all the more so when they have been told that the secular world has no final meaning.

Far more illuminating is a perspective on God and man which sees man's temporal concerns and drives as one with his spiritual destiny. The central meaning of the Incarnation, I take it, is that Christ *has* redeemed man and matter. If this is so, then the sacred and the secular have entered into a relationship of unity; not a perfect or complete unity, but surely enough to render any talk of their radical difference highly misleading. Worse than that, a desire to maintain the distinction forces one to follow Monsignor Philips' route into the wilderness of primary and secondary ecclesial missions, of separating love of God from love of man. Once into that jungle there is no way out.

Yet Cox's stance has some equally imposing difficulties to overcome. Can secular man, after all, afford to ignore metaphysics? Can he really get away with a purely pragmatic solution to his socio-historical problems? Up to a point, I think the answer is yes to both questions. It has to be yes, because many men patently manage to live antimetaphysical, pragmatic lives and seem to be none the worse for it. The Christian may look at such a man with skepticism and incredulity, but there are many secular men who can confound his pessimistic expectations.

The question, then, is not whether such men can exist, and exist happily—they just do—but whether mankind as a whole can live this way either now or in the future. Let me say that I personally don't know; it would be silly to say anything else. At the same time, it also has to be said that decisions have consequences. The pragmatic decisions taken by this generation for the sake of its own life will inevitably affect, if not decisively shape, the life of future generations. The past has always imposed its relativities upon the future, and it is likely to continue doing so. The pragmatic man who does not recognize this will be a dangerous man. But as soon as he does see that his decisions will have consequences, and tries responsibly to take this fact into account, he will cease to be wholly pragmatic. He will have no other choice. One way or the other, he will have to dip his toe into the murky waters of metaphysics. He will have to fashion at least some tentative conclusions about what is good for man regardless of his specific historical situation. He will have to say what minimal conditions are necessary for human freedom, existence, and fulfillment.

Cox would have the Christian "unreservedly contextual" in his ethics and in his evangelism. Yet if the responsible secular man can't be all that contextual himself, it is difficult to see how the Christian can either. What Cox wants is a Christian who knows how to respond to his present age; how to unencumber himself of an anachronistic past; how to speak to the here and now; how to lay the ground for the future. These are fine goals, but each of them actually requires the ability to get out of one's context, at least some of the time. Cox himself does this when he speaks warmly of a "biblical perspective" on the world; or when he uses the imagery of the "kingdom of God." These are categories which cut across time and through history. They illuminate the contextual without themselves being wholly contextual.

Ironically, of course, once Cox begins using biblical language, he cuts himself off from secular man. Here, I think, Cox has to fish or cut bait. If secular man and his way of life are self-sufficient, any talk about taking a "biblical perspective" is beside the point. Who needs it, and so what, anyway? The only possible reason for bothering would be that even at its utopian best the world of secular man will have its nether regions. The *Playboy* bachelor can make the most of urban anonymity; not everyone else can. Mobility is grand if one has brains and a future; not everyone does. And so on. The urban-secular coin has two sides—and so does man.

Had Cox recognized this more clearly, he might well have been less cavalier toward those caught up in existential anguish. One reason for their plight is the often oppressive weight of the present. There are times when life is just awful: boring, stupid, brutal, or trivial. The promise of the future does not always, nor can it, drive out the pain of the present. Some people are going to die tomorrow. That is their context, and they want to know why. This is a very personal question, not something that history of sociology or politics can throw much light on. A question like this is wretchedly ultimate, direct, and noncontextual. It just won't go away.

An obvious conclusion at this point would be to say that the upshot is something of a draw. Those who would have men put aside metaphysics, existentialism, and the higher speculations of personalism in favor of politics, sociology, and history have the temper of modern man on their side. They are also in a better position to turn directly to immediate human needs, unencumbered by any pressing demand to work out final values and goals. On the other hand, man is not just a political and historical creature; he does not live by social reconstruction alone. Someone has to speak to the nonhistorical self, and never more so than when all of a man's plans and hopes come to nothing or when he looks death in the face. Thus can the ball be volleyed back and forth.

Still, I suspect that a choice has to be made. Ideally, it should be possible for humans to turn their attention simultaneously toward metaphysics and social planning. Psychologically, this is difficult to manage. Historically, the Christian's obsession with ultimacy has meant a debasement of the temporal. Even when he tried to take his present moment seriously, his theological concerns would not allow him to do so. His orientation toward an eternal future kept him in bondage to the historical past; the world was always outrunning him. Once again it is outrunning him. His only hope of catching up, I'm afraid, is to let go. To let go of his desire for immediate meaning. To let go of his wish for religious security. To let go of his need to see the hand of God. To let go of the quest for a new vision, or the revivification of the old one.

I suppose this is almost too much to ask of the Christian. But if the Christian cannot wait for God, if the Christian cannot make the course of history his own, if the Christian cannot give himself unreservedly to man and his temporal existence—then it is hard to see how he will ever live in the present, much less speak to it. There are many ways of gaining the whole world while losing one's soul. There are also many ways of gaining one's soul and losing the world. The world we stand to lose is the world Christ redeemed.

How Can We Think of God?

John Macquarrie

Year in, year out, John Macquarrie, Professor of Systematic Theology at Union Theological Seminary in New York, writes remarkably lucid prose; what's more, the substance is commensurate with the style. In an article from the July 1965 issue of *Theology Today,** Dr. Macquarrie acknowledges the inadequacy of older ways of speaking of God—such as the mythological and the metaphysical. He also expresses dissatisfaction with some of the more modern modes of "God-talk"—among them the "encounter" or "I-thou" mode, the "God is Christ" mode, and the mode which conceives of God as "supreme value." Macquarrie himself favors the Heidegger-influenced "God as being itself" approach—and tells why he thinks it succeeds in avoiding the pitfalls of traditional metaphysics. He also suggests why "the difference between the religious man or the believer in God and the humanist remains a perfectly clear and fundamental one." Books by Dr. Macquarrie include *The Scope of Demythologizing* and *Twentieth-Century Religious Thought.*

How CAN we think of God? How can we talk about him? There was a time when questions like these might have seemed absurd, for most people did talk about God and believed that they had a sufficiently clear conception of what they meant when they did talk about him. The idea of God was part of the apparatus in terms of which people thought about themselves and their world, and so the word "God" communicated when it was uttered. Communication depends on the sharing of basic ideas and presuppositions which allow one person's discourse to be intelligible to another person. But let us suppose that some of these presuppositions are gradually eroded away, and that new modes of thinking about ourselves and the world take their place. Then some words that once communicated may

* P.O. Box 29, Princeton, N.J.

not communicate any longer. We find that we cannot place them within the framework of our thinking. They become increasingly vague and indeterminate, and may end up without any assignable meaning at all. Something like this has happened to the word "God" in our own time, so that we are forced to ask the questions: "How can we think of God? How can we talk about him?"

I

The question has been sharpened above all by the school of analytic philosophy. This school takes as the primary task of philosophy the logical analysis of our language in all its many forms. What do we mean by the assertions that we make? What procedures are relevant either for verifying or falsifying these assertions? As soon as we begin to raise questions of this kind, we see how slippery and misleading an instrument language can be. What look at first sight like grand, sweeping, imposing assertions may turn out on investigation to be quite jejune, and indeed to have very little ascertainable meaning at all. This is especially the case with assertions about God. The background of contemporary analytical philosophy is empirical science, which has fairly well-established procedures of observation, experiment, and verification. But these procedures seem quite irrelevant to the kind of assertions about God that the religious man may make. Yet the religious man is probably also for at least six days of the week a man whose thinking is informed by the attitudes of empirical science. Where does his thinking about God tie in with his other thinking? Does he have to confess that there is no relation between the two, that his thinking about God is something altogether free-floating, vague, and problematical, and if asked the question, "What do you mean when you talk about God?" he has no coherent answer to give, and may have to acknowledge that such talk is just a survival that has come down to him from an earlier age and has no secure place any longer?

Of course, even in times when human thinking was informed by religious ideas, there were many ideas of God, and it never was possible to point to any single idea of God such as would have been acknowledged by everyone who talked about God. Some have thought in terms of one God, others in terms of a plurality of gods. Some have thought of God as having a nature that we can understand—very often indeed of God as a kind of magnified human being—while for others God has utterly transcended human understanding. Some have thought of God primarily as transcendent, remote from the world; while others have stressed his immanence, perhaps to the point of pantheism, where God and the world are hardly distinguishable. So it can hardly be claimed that there ever has been a clearly defined and universally accepted signification for the word "God," such as there is for the word "cat" and for a great many other words that we use.

The oldest ideas of God are mythological. In mythology, God himself can be an object of sense perception, and of course there are many elements of this mythological thinking in the Bible itself, both in the Old and New Testaments. God might actually be seen upon the earth. When the idea that God could be seen became intolerable, it was still believed that he might be heard, as in the voices from heaven reported in the New Testament accounts of the baptism and transfiguration of Christ. Alternatively, God might show himself indirectly in physical phenomena or in unusual events, signs, wonders, miracles. Gradually, however, these mythological ideas were left behind. The gods were no longer located in the sky or on mountaintops, nor was it any more believed that they could be seen or perceived by any of the senses.

Next came metaphysical ideas of God. He was no longer located in any particular place, though he was said to be metaphorically "above" or "beyond" or "outside" the world. He was conceived as a being who is personal, yet invisible, intangible, and in general, inaccessible to any kind of sensuous investigation. He was supposed to have created the world in the beginning, and to exercise a general government over it, perhaps intervening in its affairs from time to time in order to keep it on the right lines. But with the rise of modern science, with its increasing and apparently unlimited capacity for accounting for events within the world in terms of other events within the world, the need for positing such a God has gradually been eliminated. There is nothing left for him to do. At the best, he might remain as a kind of constitutional monarch, presiding as a figurehead with no real power in the world. But Occam's razor reminds us that superfluous causes are not to be entertained. So the God of metaphysical theism has suffered the same fate as the God of mythology, and fades out of the picture.

II

Does this mean the end of God? Is God dead, as Nietzsche proclaimed? Or does it mean that we have to think anew and more deeply on what this word "God" means, that we have to be prepared for just as revolutionary a change in our conception of God as took place when the old mythological idea of God gave place to the metaphysical idea? Let us see then whether it is possible to find a meaning for this word "God," and assign it a place in the framework of contemporary thinking.

At first sight, it might seem as if the word "God" is a proper name. It designates a person, just as the names Peter and Paul do. Many contemporary theologians do in fact seem to think of the word "God" in this way. It has its meaning, so we are told, in an encounter or meeting like the meeting of two persons. Such meetings belong to a different dimension of life from those experiences of the world of things, which it is the business of science to explicate. To use Buber's terminology, encounter belongs to the dimension of the "I-thou," whereas scientific knowledge belongs to the dimension of the "I-it." Now this is a very important distinction, and it may indeed help us to avoid some of the difficulties in which we find ourselves if we try to think of God in metaphysical terms. Here the word points not to some invisible, intangible being to be conceived as standing outside the world, but to a person who meets us in an encounter.

But the new way of thinking of God runs into its own difficulties, perhaps just as serious as those which it has tried to escape. In his book, *Individuals*, P. F. Strawson points out that we do in fact recognize two primary kinds of entities, things and persons; but he also points out that we do not think of persons as disembodied spirits, but as embodied persons. In the ordinary sense of the term, a "meeting" or "encounter" between persons always includes some kind of physical relationship between them. Most typically, this will take the form of words spoken and heard. In a face-to-face meeting, as we call it, part of the encounter may consist in the facial expressions of the interlocutors, or even in tactile sensations, such as a warm handclasp. Granted that a personal encounter is something of quite a different order from, let us say, the collision of two automobiles, nevertheless the personal encounter has its physical side, and this would seem to be the necessary bearer of whatever communication or even communion takes place on the intellectual or spiritual level. Now, we do not think of any corresponding physical events as taking place in the alleged encounter with God. At the most, therefore, to speak of a meeting or encounter with God is to use an analogy. It may be *like* a meeting between two persons, but it is not such a meeting *simpliciter*. The question then arises, "How like is it? Can the analogy stand up?" It must be confessed at once that there are many difficulties in seeing how it can. We have the difficulty first of conceiving a person who has no body, and then, further, of conceiving how there could be a meeting with such a person, in the absence of those physical contacts of hearing or speech or sight or touch that seem to be the universal conditions for a person-to-person encounter.

III

When faced with these problems, still another move is open to the Christian theologian. He points to the doctrine of the incarnation, that "the word was made flesh." Thus, it is possible to have a meeting with God "in the flesh" or "face-to-face," so to speak. This was possible in the first place for the contemporary disciples who conversed with Christ precisely as you and I might converse with each other, and it is still possible for us through the records of the New Testament or through the sacraments of the Church to have an encounter with Christ, in the same sense in which many historians would agree that we can have something like a personal encounter with notable figures of the past whose deeds or words or attitudes have been preserved.

A good illustration of this theological position is provided by the Ritschlian theologian, Wilhelm Herrmann. Philosophically, he was a positivist, and denied the possibility of metaphysics. To his philosophical positivism, he added a theological positivism. "God is Jesus" was his creed, and Jesus, or at any rate, what he called the "inner life" of Jesus, is accessible to us as a verifiable historical phenomenon. This is an extreme development of Christ's own saying: "He who has seen me has seen the Father"—though perhaps it is also an evasion of the words which Christ is reported to have uttered on the same occasion: "I am in the Father and the Father in me" (Jn. 14:9–10). A much more up-to-date statement of a similar theological positivism is found in Paul van Buren's book, *The Secular Meaning of the Gospel.* I have so much admiration for the honesty and courage of this book in facing the predicament of faith today that I regret very much to speak critically of it. But it seems to me that van Buren's attempt to assimilate all theology to christology suffers from the same errors as had already appeared in Herrmann.

In the first place, this point of view represents much too easy a capitulation to positivism and a premature despair of making sense of the word "God" in its own right. In the second place, it represents an arbitrary narrowing of the word "God" which is, after all, not a private possession of Christianity but a word with a much wider currency, used to designate One who has made himself known at many times and in many ways. In the third place, the simple identification of God with Jesus or Christ represents a very serious deviation from the traditional faith of the Christian Church—a deviation sometimes called a "unitarianism" of the Second Person. For while Christian faith has maintained that "Christ is God," this has never been regarded as a convertible proposition, that is to say, we cannot turn it around and say "God is Christ." God, in Christian teaching, is Father, Son, and Holy Spirit. The claim that Christ is God is not an assertion of identity, but a predication of Christ's Godhead. Finally, if we push Herrmann and van Buren to the conclusions that are already implicit in their assertions, what this amounts to is simply to claim that Jesus of Nazareth, idealized as the Christ, is the supreme standard of value to whom we owe allegiance. This kind of claim, so far as I can see, could as easily be made by a thoroughgoing humanist as by a Christian.

IV

This last remark brings us to consider another possible way of looking at the word "God." If it is not satisfactory to think of this word as a proper name, perhaps we should take it as meaning something like "supreme value," that to which we must pledge our uttermost allegiance. The word "God" is sometimes used in this way in ordinary speech. We are all familiar with such expressions as "He makes a god of money" or "The Nazis made the state their god." This is undoubtedly a strand of meaning that runs almost universally through the uses of the word "God." No religion teaches about the gods in a disinterested way, as though the purpose were just to give information about them. They urge their devotees to love God, to worship him, to serve him, to put their trust in him. "God" is not therefore a neutrally descriptive word. It is a word that evokes commitment, and this aspect of meaning is very well brought out in Paul Tillich's description of God as "ultimate concern."

It is for this reason that we find John Dewey, in his book *A Common Faith*, quite willing to reintroduce the word "God," provided it is stripped of all transcendent and metaphysical connotations, and made to stand simply for those human ideals and aspirations which command our ultimate devotion. I have some sympathy with those secularist and humanist followers of Dewey who felt that he had compromised their cause by reverting to what may be called "God-language." While it is indeed true that if one takes the word "God" in the sense that Dewey assigned to it, there is no departure at all from a strictly humanist point of view; nevertheless, this is so arbitrary a usage for the word and disregards so many of its universal connotations that it would be much better to drop the word completely and talk in a purely humanistic vocabulary. That the word "God" does include as a strand of its meaning the notion of supreme value, we have already seen to be the case; but to take this particular strand as exhausting the content of the word can be only misleading. Certainly, the Christian theologian, unless he is prepared to jettison not only the form but the very substance of his traditional faith, cannot remain satisfied with an interpretation of the word "God" in terms only of value.

V

This brings us to a further strand of meaning in the word "God," a strand which is just as fundamental as the notion of supreme value or ultimate concern. This further strand is the notion of reality, of being. One of the most ancient and hallowed of all revelations of God was the disclosure of his name to Moses—the name "I AM" (Ex. 3:14).

But this meaning of the word "God" may itself be interpreted in one or other of two ways. We may think of God as a particular being, the supreme being, the *ens realissimum*, in the traditional terminology. But this leads us back precisely to the discredited God of metaphysics. We have already seen that our modern scheme of thought affords no place for another being, however exalted, in addition to the beings that we encounter within the world. This supreme being who was supposed to operate behind the scenes, as it were, this *deus ex machina*, has become superfluous.

The alternative is to think of God as Being itself—Being which emerges and manifests itself in and with and through every particular being, but which is not itself another such being, which is nothing apart from particular beings, and yet which is more beingful than any particular being, since it is the condition that there should be any such beings whatsoever. To think of God in this way demands, of course, something like a revolution in theology. It is a revolution that is presently being carried out by such men as Paul Tillich and John A. T. Robinson, but for the clearest understanding of what is happening, we have to go to the philosopher Martin Heidegger. He has conceived it to be his philosophical mission to rekindle for our time the question of being. Our Western tradition, as he sees it, has forgotten Being in its exclusive preoccupation with particular beings. Even God himself was conceived as a particular being, and with his elimination, we have now entered on the final stage of the forgetting of being—the age of technology, when all our thinking is calculative thinking aimed at the mastery and exploitation of particular beings. In such an age, the question of Being may seem completely unreal. But it is Heidegger's merit that he has shown the empirical anchorage of this question in certain moods of our own human existence—moods that light up for us the wider Being within which we live and move and have our own being. "Each one of us," Heidegger claims, "is grazed at least once, perhaps more than once, by the hidden power" of the question of Being. This is not a question that can be easily answered, or even one that can be easily explicated and formulated, for it has to do with something quite *sui generis* and which our ordinary categories of thinking cannot contain. But it is so far from being an empty question that it is the most concrete of all. "Being can be compared with nothing else," but "the word 'being' cannot be empty. And in truth, it never is empty."[1]

VI

To conceive God as Being goes far toward solving some of the most intractable problems of traditional metaphysical theism, and opens up new possibilities for the interpretation of traditional theological doctrines in such fields as christology, the doctrine of the Trinity, the problem of evil, and so on. But someone may object that to identify God with Being escapes some of the problems of traditional theism simply by begging the question. It relieves us of the need of proving that there exists a particular being corresponding to our idea of God. In saying that God is identical with

Being itself, are we not simply engaging in a verbal trick, and begging the question of God?

This is a good criticism, but I think it neglects certain aspects of the case. What has been asserted is that the notion of Being constitutes an indispensable strand in the meaning of the word "God," but it has not been said that this strand of meaning is exhaustive of the content of the idea of God. Indeed, it is no more exhaustive of that content than was the other strand noted earlier, the idea of supreme value. "God" is a word of complex meaning, and it contains at least the two notions of value and being. As was stated earlier, "God" is not a neutrally descriptive term like "Being," but a term that already expresses an attitude toward whatever is designated "God"—the attitude of worship and commitment. Let us suppose, for instance, that Being turned out to be quite indifferent to whatever we set value upon. Then Being could not be designated "God," nor would it call forth any response of worship or devotion. On the other hand, a focus of value which laid its claim upon our allegiance could not properly be called "God" if it were merely an ideal focus, a product of the human spirit brought forth in alien surroundings. It is properly called "God" only if it is also believed to be rooted in the structure of Being as such. This lets us see very clearly the difference between the religious man and the humanist or atheist. Both are devoted to certain ends; both are ultimately concerned about what they take to possess the highest value. The religious man, however, believes that his pursuit of these ends is consonant with and supported by the structure of Being itself, whereas the other believes that he has no support or ground for hope outside of what men can accomplish of themselves.

A different kind of criticism has come from Alasdair MacIntyre in an article entitled "God and the Theologians."[2] He starts off by remarking that the most striking feature of Robinson's book, *Honest to God*, is that the author is an atheist. But as he sees this book as summing up the thought of many other Protestant theologians of our time, MacIntyre goes on to argue that most of them are in fact atheists, though they go on using a religious vocabulary. In Tillich's theology, for instance, it is claimed that "belief in God has been evacuated of its traditional content" so that "the substance of atheism has been conceded." The term "atheist" is, of course, always one with a meaning dependent on the context in which it is used. The early Christians were called "atheists" by some of their opponents, and so they were since they denied the gods of the classical world. Tillich presumably is an "atheist" if the term is used for someone who denies the traditional type of theism. But MacIntyre is scoring only a verbal point here, and one that is of no special importance. As I have already pointed out, the difference between the religious man or the believer in God and the humanist remains a perfectly clear and fundamental one. The former interprets his experience as showing that his aspirations for value have their support in Being itself, or, to put it otherwise, that Being has the character of grace. The latter conceives that man must pursue his ends entirely trusting in his own resources. This latter case is the true atheism, and the difference between the two cases is a real difference with important practical consequences.

If, however, the charge of atheism can easily be rebutted, one does not wish to minimize the revolution that takes place when one thinks of God as Being rather than as a being. It is quite clear, for example, that one cannot think of God as literally a person. Being, as incomparable, cannot fall under any of the categories that we apply to particular beings. On the other hand, if Being does manifest itself in particular beings and is indeed nothing apart from them, we can have some clues or pointers to Being. As Heidegger points out, the very fact that traditionally philosophy has distinguished between Being and becoming, or between Being and appearance, shows that Being has some determinate character. The mysterious complexity of Being can be best symbolized for us in terms of the particular beings which in the highest degree show us a unity in diversity, and since the complex phenomenon of personality does this more than any other phenomenon, personal language may be symbolically used of God. This is the justification for the traditional language of Scripture and liturgy.

It might be thought that the charge of pantheism is more plausible than the charge of atheism in criticism of the idea of God as Being. But this charge also fails. Pantheism, strictly speaking, would be the view that equates God with the sum, or rather, with the totality of all particular beings. But Being itself cannot be characterized as a sum or even as a totality. As an incomparable, a wholly other from any possible entity or sum of entities, it has the character of transcendence. On the other hand, as manifesting itself in and with and through every entity whatsoever, it has also the character of immanence. This way of thinking about God is neither deistic nor pantheistic, and is perhaps better able than traditional views of God to show how he can be at one and the same time transcendent and immanent. It calls us to see the world both of persons and of things "in depth," as it were; that is to say, as not just a collection of particular beings to which we ourselves belong as particular beings, but as particular beings who are at once transcended and indwelt by Being itself, at once judged and supported by Being. That this way of understanding our world is also determinative for one's behavior in the world is too obvious to need comment.

VII

Presumably we are standing only at the beginning of the revolution in the idea of God. Its full application to particular Christian doctrines is something that has still to be worked out. That it will prove to be a more mature and more satisfying way of thinking of God than the old way which regarded him as a "Louis XIV of the heavens," I cannot doubt. It has the merit that it can be developed in secular terms from the analysis of human experience itself, so providing our talk of God with that link with ordinary experience which was traditionally provided by the now outmoded natural theology of the metaphysical type. But while beginning from secular experience, it does not remain there but recalls us to forgotten dimensions of life. It tries in our technological age of calculative thinking to awaken again the kind of thinking that brings us into the dimension of the holy. So far is it from voiding the traditional idea of God of content that it rather complains that the traditional ideas have fallen far too short of the reality. It strives to open up for our time and culture new glimpses into that mystery, at once awesome and fascinating, which we falteringly designate by the word "God."

NOTES

1. *Introduction to Metaphysics*, pp. 1, 79.
2. *The Honest to God Debate*, eds. Robinson and Edwards, pp. 215–31.

Homo Religiosus and Historical Faith

Kenneth Hamilton

Opposed to the Barth-Bonhoeffer brand of theology, which views religion as distinct from—even the enemy of—Christian faith, is the position of Paul Tillich and Mircea Eliade, which views the decline of religion in the West as a woeful development indeed and which holds that a renewal of the spiritual outlook of *homo religiosus*—man living amidst manifestations of sacred realities, man "open to the cosmos"—is both possible and desirable. It is the assumptions and judgments of this latter approach that Kenneth Hamilton calls into question, and he does so in the context of a closely reasoned examination of Eliade's influential book *The Sacred and the Profane*. Without coming down firmly on the side of Barth and Bonhoeffer—whether there can be a wholly "religionless" Christianity remains to be seen—Hamilton concludes that the Tillich-Eliade school of thought does less than justice to historic Christianity and the ethic it entails. Dr. Hamilton, Assistant Professor of Systematic Theology at United College, Winnipeg, is author of *The Protestant Way, The System and the Gospel: A Critique of Paul Tillich*, and *Revolt Against Heaven*. His article is from the July 1965 issue of *The Journal of Bible and Religion*.*

THE DISTINCTION between Christian faith and religion, which was urged so strongly by Karl Barth in the second edition of his *Epistle to the Romans*,[1] has become almost a commonplace. From the 1930's through to the 1950's, the distinction was made the subject of formal theological investigation, and notably by Hendrik Kraemer.[2] And now in the 1960's it has found more popular expression through such books as John A. T. Robinson's *Honest to God*[3] and William Stringfellow's *A Private and Public Faith*.[4] Undoubtedly, though, the form in which this distinction is presently stated owes most to Dietrich Bonhoeffer, whose last jottings

* 1010 Arch St., Philadelphia, Pa. 19107.

on the possibility of a religionless Christianity have aroused the widest interest and debate.[5]

Bonhoeffer leaves us no more than a few hints and roughly worked suggestions about his positive program, yet he sets out his fundamental starting-point with complete clarity. He argues that twentieth-century man has outgrown religion. Whereas in former ages religion supplied the cosmological frame of reference within which mankind viewed the universe around him, science has since become the purveyor of the facts of life and guide to the secrets of nature. So *homo religiosus* has died, or else lives on as an anachronism. But Christians, says Bonhoeffer, should not regret this development. Rather, accepting the situation as God-given, they ought to restate their faith for a nonreligious generation. The disappearance of the gods desired by the human mind for its own purposes has opened the way for faith in the one true God. Only the fearful and the faithless, then, can wish to return to the conditions of past ages or to resurrect *homo religiosus* from the dead.

Against the Barth-Bonhoeffer argument, which welcomes in the name of Christianity the withering-away of religion, there stands a counter-argument. It begins from the thesis that the decay of religion in the modern world is the sign of a failure in the human consciousness, a failure caused by the one-sided development of culture in the West. Consequently, the human spirit is now suffering from religious malnutrition. A return from the artificial values of contemporary civilization to the deeper satisfactions experienced by earlier generations is thus quite imperative. For those satisfactions arose out of the unquestioned sway of religion over men's lives, and the passing of religious meaning from everyday experience has brought into existence a sick world. According to this argument, the fortunes of Christianity are bound to those of religion in general. Man, even when secularized, is *homo religiosus* still; and the condition of his becoming a satisfactory Christian is that he learn to allow his real nature to develop freely and reach a state of ripeness.

The argument for the basic, ineradicable hold of religion upon the human spirit has been advanced powerfully and continuously by Paul Tillich. Twenty years ago Bonhoeffer wrote: "Tillich set out to interpret the evolution of the world itself—against its will—in a religious sense, to give its whole shape through religion."[6] And these words are true not only of such an early work as *Die religiöse Lage der Gegenwart*[7] but also of the "core" work of his maturity, his *Systematic Theology.*[8] However, an even more direct exposition of the theme of *homo religiosus* has been undertaken by Mircea Eliade. Writing out of the perspective of a historian of religions, Eliade does not limit himself to descriptions of religious beliefs and customs; he goes on to draw conclusions concerning the value of religious consciousness as such, and to speculate on the subject of what religion is in itself.

I

The present essay attempts to look at Eliade's valuation of religion in his volume *The Sacred and the Profane: The Nature of Religion*[9] in order to investigate its relevance to the debate about religion and Christianity.

Eliade argues that a claim to define the nature of religion, and at the same time to uncover truths related to man's being, is one which makes large theological assumptions. And he suggests that other assumptions, equally plausible, would result in a very different picture of the religions of mankind.

The Sacred and the Profane, like Eliade's *Myths, Dreams and Mysteries*,[10] gives a fascinating account of the way of life of primitive man, bounded by myth and ritual, and it contrasts this way of life with the outlook of modern Occidental man. Today, the author urges, understanding of the sacred is gravely weakened if not destroyed; religious rituals linger on in degenerate, pallid forms; and myth lives mainly in the depths of the unconscious mind. Eliade's conclusion is that from the Christian point of view, contemporary non-religion is equivalent to a new Fall.[11]

This is a radical diagnosis of the spiritual history of the race. If the secularization of culture has indeed resulted in something so catastrophic that it can be likened only to a second Fall, then mankind has experienced much more than a revolutionary upheaval and a cultural transformation. Human history itself has been broken in two. Theologically speaking, man's predicament would seem to demand a new salvation. For, *sub*original sin now having made its appearance, the overcoming of original sin is no longer the prime necessity. Furthermore, we are faced with the odd and unprecedented experience of finding two types of humanity existing simultaneously on earth: the once-fallen and the twice-fallen. Communication between the two must be that of the higher type addressing the lower. And as it is in the Christianized West that secularization has proceeded most rapidly, we should expect the non-Christian religions to take the lead in halting—and perhaps in reversing—the second Fall. (In *Myths, Dreams and Mysteries* Eliade uses Indian philosophy to explain the European existentialists' fear of Nothingness.[12]) Should we also expect, from the same sources, a second savior?

However, even if we do not take altogether literally Eliade's image of a new Fall, his diagnosis remains radical enough. The world continues to be divided into two. On the one side lies the "metaphysical" comprehension of the universe as sacred, which was characteristic of archaic man universally and abides wherever secularism has not triumphed completely. On the other side lies the refusal to recognize transcendence and the attempt to live in a profane, desacralized universe, which is the choice of nonreligious man today (even though, to be sure, some vestiges of the behavior of *homo religiosus*, emptied of meaning, remain visible in secularized life). The *sacred* and the *profane* "are two modes of being in the world."[13] And they are in competition with each other.

Nonreligious man, says Eliade, "has been formed by opposing his predecessor, by attempting to 'empty' himself of all religion and all transhuman meaning."[14] While Eliade asserts also that his own role of historian of religions does not require him to pass judgment upon the situation, he nevertheless stresses what has been lost. Today "the cosmos has become opaque, inert, mute: It transmits no message, it holds no cipher."[15] Even Christianity has greatly changed since the Middle Ages, for "the religious sense of urban populations is gravely impoverished. . . . Their religious experience is no longer open to the cosmos."[16] In Eliade's view openness to the cosmos is the prime gift of religion and the essence of the sacred as a mode of being. Thus the weakening of man's religious sense wounds his humanity by depriving him of a living, creative relationship with his environment and by making him a creature of the moment, lost in an indifferent, meaningless world. This argument is crucial, and we must therefore look at it more closely.

Eliade tells us that the sacred is equivalent to a *power,* and in the last analysis to *reality.* Religious man deeply desires *to be,* to participate in *reality,* to be saturated with power. "The polarity sacred-profane is often expressed as an opposition between *real* and *unreal* or pseudoreal."[17] *Homo religiosus,* therefore, lives in the midst of hierophanies, or manifestations of sacred realities. By becoming aware of the sacred he becomes open to the cosmos, the ordered and meaningful world—this for the following reason: "When the sacred manifests itself in any hierophany, there is not only a break in the homogeneity of space; there is also revelation of an absolute reality, opposed to the nonreality of the vast surrounding expanse. The manifestation of the sacred ontologically founds the world. In the homogeneous and infinite expanse, in which no point of reference is possible and hence no *orientation* can be established, the hierophany reveals an absolute fixed point, a center."[18]

Here is set forth in brief the *Weltanschauung* of religious man. The sacred provides a center around which he can order his universe. Because this center is conceived to involve a sacred revelation it is believed to be beyond doubt, and so the believer is able to rest absolutely assured. He has found his Pole Star to steer by. For him, truth has emerged out of the unintelligible, the cosmos has emerged out of chaos. Henceforth, he is no longer an alien in a strange land. Now he is "open" to that world which, by disclosing to him part of the "mystery" of its own being, has made it possible for him to be at home there. Once the sacred has made itself felt and has established itself at one point, endless vistas of meaning open out. The "cosmic rhythms" have declared themselves to be an intelligible language, a kind of divine Morse Code, and "man need only decipher what the cosmos says in its many modes of being, and he will understand the mystery of life."[19]

It is important to note that Eliade's explanation of the sacred puts *sacred space* first. Such an explanation makes religion primarily the means which man uses to bind himself to his environment in an effort not to be overwhelmed by it. The manifestation of the holy founds the world; or, at least, it founds *a* world, a place in which man can live and feel at home. Then, along with his awareness of sacred space, *homo religiosus* becomes aware of *sacred time*. The gods act, or mythical heroes live, "in the beginning." Their exploits are repeated in the telling of myths and the performance of rituals, which make the sacred time appear again and again. For sacred time is not really temporal but only the manifestation in time of the eternally real and true. Time, it would seem, is actually spatialized. The divine time, the *time of origins,* comes again in that place where it is faithfully imitated—for instance, in the sacred festival. The festival "is not merely the commemoration of a mythical (and hence religious) event; it *reactualizes* the event."[20] In this way reality is guaranteed a place on earth continually. Life's meaning will not evaporate so long as the sacred remains *here,* in the midst. And *homo religiosus* will never be without a home so long as sacred space provides orientation for him in his universe.

II

The preceding summary is only a partial exposition of *The Sacred and the Profane,* and, of course, does not try to convey the richness of the material, which is itself a distillation of data worked over in previous books by the same author. Nevertheless, the summary may be of service in concentrating attention upon a pivotal point of the study. Eliade has drawn a brilliant picture of *homo religiosus.* Other specialists in the history of religions may wish to add to or to modify that picture. But, granted that Eliade's picture is substantially correct, there is room to take further the question which the author has himself raised concerning the relation between the religious and the profane—especially in the light of Christianity. There is room also to question the judgment that the so-called Fall from the sacred to the profane must be described in terms of impoverishment. The fact that the religious consciousness of modern Christians is no longer "open" to the cosmos as was the consciousness of medieval Christians or of archaic man may mean more gain than loss. Perhaps the assumption of *homo religiosus* that he need only decipher what the cosmos says in order to understand the mystery of life was an ill-founded assumption needing to be corrected by the counterthesis of nonreligious man that the cosmos holds no cipher.

At this point something must be said about the survival of mythical thinking in modern man's unconscious. Eliade makes several illuminating comments on the subject. No one will wish to dispute his conclusion, which is, in effect, that since we cannot simply divest ourselves of the past, conscious irreligion does not banish all religious behavior. In contemporary society there is plenty of evidence of nonreligious man's "camouflaged myths and degenerated rituals."[21] These are to be accounted for largely on the basis that the drives from the unconscious mind retain the pattern of archaic thinking, and so carry a religious "aura." The unconscious mind still thinks mythologically, using symbols to comprehend the universe. Thus the healing power of religion can continue to be made available to the modern psyche—although less thoroughly than if the whole being of an individual, and not merely his deeper self, were "open" to the cosmos. As matters stand, secularized man has "forgotten" the religious sense he possesses and, all unknowingly, continues to use in part.[22]

These facts are of great interest. Unfortunately, the way in which Eliade presents them gives the impression that Western man has sunk far below the level of archaic man, who allegedly lived in a golden age of the human spirit. For instance, Eliade speaks of how, by contemplating actual objects as religious symbols, "a man of the premodern societies can attain to the highest spirituality, for, by understanding the symbol, *he succeeds in living the universal.*" Modern nonreligious man, on the other hand, is not awakened in his total consciousness by any symbol, and so the symbol "has not yet raised him to spirituality—that is, it has not succeeded in revealing one of the structures of the real to him."[23] Here, the terms "highest spirituality," "the universal," and "the real" are misleading because they are set down without qualification. What Eliade shows unquestionably is that nonreligious man retains in his thinking traces of the symbolically orientated thinking of archaic man but does not allow this particular "spirituality" to dominate his total understanding of the universe. Similarly, nonreligious man does not "live the universal" as his forefathers did, because he is concerned with the world at more than the universal (mythical) level. Hence, he does not identify the "real" with the sacred, with transhuman meaning mediated through hierophanies. Yet it certainly does not follow that because he fails to attach himself to the mode of being characteristic of *homo religiosus* in premodern societies, he therefore has no comprehension of—or does not participate existentially in—spirituality, the universal, or the real. He has simply broken free from one particular way of conceiving these things.

The most evident characteristic of the mode of being which Eliade calls the sacred is a sense of cosmic coziness. The sacred is said to establish the world. But while this was no doubt true for archaic man, and no other way of beginning to map out a human universe was possible for him, such an "ontological" ordering of the cosmos is obtained at a large cost: that of writing off all nonsacred space as unreal, and of discounting all time which is more than a repetition of the mythical beginning. Within the sacral cosmos, values are secure and life has indubitable meaning. To go outside the sacred space, to leave the religious center—this is to risk encountering a chaos which will not necessarily be resolved into a meaningful cosmos. Having taken this course, modern man naturally enough looks back nostalgically to the golden age when (so it seems, at least, from this distance) life was successfully lived in the universal and there was, in consequence, a religious cure for all the disorders of existence. The historian of religions is likely to be struck particularly by the contrast of mental attitudes engendered by the sacred and the profane modes of being. Yet, without a decisive breaking out of the circle of cosmic coziness which sacral societies build around themselves, there could be none of the

possibilities of existence which we now take for granted—
including the possibility of there being historians of religions!
It belongs to human spirituality to "question" the universe as
well as to be "open" to it, and to live in the particular as well
as in the universal. *Homo religiosus,* by refusing to admit that
anything except sacred space is real or has being, limits his
experience. Thus does he prepare the way for his own
obsolescence.

Two realms of experience ignored by *homo religiosus* become especially prominent in human spiritual awakening:
history and morality. Eliade stresses archaic man's complete
indifference to history. Profane time is unreal, and society
continues simply by maintaining the sanctity of its world
through imitation of the gods and heroes of the "beginning."
When the historical dimension of existence gains recognition
this is an admission that man has meaning apart from the
gods—although not necessarily without them. And historical
existence is accompanied by moral existence. *Homo religiosus,*
deciphering what the cosmos says in its many modes of being,
finds that the gods engage in every kind of behavior from the
gentle to the ruthless. What the gods do, man must imitate.
One does not ask the question of right or wrong in the face of
the sacred; for, unless he maintains the sanctity of the world
by means of the appropriate rituals, his cosmos will disin-
tegrate into chaos. As Eliade points out, the sacrifice of
children to Moloch had "a profoundly religious meaning."[24]
And yet, once man's existence in time comes to be regarded
as significant in its own right, action in the profane world
becomes noteworthy. Therefore, his acts also become praise-
worthy or blameworthy. The demand for moral criticism of
the sacred itself appears next, showing that the sacred no
longer founds the cosmos. Human existence ceases to be
organized around a single center. Human initiative replaces
imitation of the gods. And the human mind finds new
universals by means of which to order the world.

All this results in an inevitable rivalry between the sacred
and the profane. If the reality of historical existence is admitted, the eternal being and power of the gods is not the
whole of knowledge. It follows, then, that the ideal of a
completely secularized society made up of men who, in

Eliade's phrase, have "killed the last god" becomes a live option. Nevertheless, even though the sacred and the profane when abstractly considered are opposites, it does not follow that they cannot coexist and interact. The existence of such "historical" religions as Christianity and Islam shows, indeed, that the contrary is true. The religion of archaic man is not the final word to be spoken about spirituality.

III

It is here that the schematization of the sacred and the profane as rival modes of being in the world breaks down. Eliade's approach illuminates brilliantly the mythical thinking of archaic man which lives on in modern man's unconscious zone, yet it fails to do justice to the conscious spiritual revolt against that way of thinking which has been of such incalculable importance in shaping the modern historically minded age. True, Eliade recognizes that Judaism's understanding of a revelation in historical time instead of in cosmic time "presents an innovation of the first importance."[25] He grants that Christianity goes even further than Judaism in positing "a *theology* of history."[26] He does not go on, however, to draw the clear conclusion which recognition of the "innovation" demands. In particular, he ignores the most prominent feature of historically oriented faith: its polemic against idolatry.

From Elijah's confrontation of the prophets of Baal on Mount Carmel to Isaiah's mockery of idol-worship the Old Testament presents an increasingly direct challenge to the mythical concept of the sacred. The Elijah story still assumes the world-view of *homo religiosus*. Yahweh is proved to be *the* God because his power is vindicated (I Kings 18:36–39). At the same time, Yahweh's will is elevated above the realm of the sacred as such. Israel has to do with a jealous God (Exod. 20:5; Deut. 4:24; etc.) who, as it were, absorbs the sacred into himself. Isaiah (44:6–20) actually denies the possibility of any "heathen" hierophany, on the grounds that the sole reality present in idolatrous worship is a natural object. Even apart from religious delusion, the "lie" would be evident to common-sense vision. Thus, a profane estimate of space is made with the deliberate purpose of discrediting the religious experience of those who claim to decipher what the cosmos says without acknowledging that the only true power is a power manifest in history (Isa. 45:14–17). The prophets of Israel addressed themselves to the task of turning their nation away from mythical patterns of belief and behavior towards ethical ones. Holiness became assimilated to righteousness. Revelation came in the form of the command: "I desire mercy and not sacrifice" (Hos. 6:6; Mic. 6:1–8)—an emphasis taken up with renewed force in the New Testament (Matt. 9:13, 12:7; Jas. 1:27). This meant that human effort was no longer to be directed to sanctifying the world through re-enacting myths and so preserving the cosmos.

The loss of the Jewish holy space of the Temple (the "center of the world") undoubtedly was a decisive factor in preparing for a new orientation of faith. Yahweh's people might be dispersed, yet his historical purpose is not thereby thwarted. Henceforth, obedience to his righteous will is to be the true sanctification of the profane (Jer. 7; 31:21–40). Christianity reaffirmed the historical destiny of Israel ("It is from the Jews that salvation comes," John 4:22), extending the saving mission of the holy nation to all who acknowledged the Man whom the God of Israel had chosen (Acts 17:31). This Christ was no mythical hero. Instead, he was a historical person initiating a new historical age (I John 1:1) that abolished the distinction between the sacred and the profane (Acts 11:1–17). The holy purpose of God was believed by Christians to have been disclosed in a new way. The Christian emphasis upon the revelation of *the new* (Matt. 9:17, and parallels; John 13:34; Gal. 6:15; Heb. 10:20; II Pet. 3:13) was a reverse of the attempt by *homo religiosus* to guarantee a place on earth where the real might be continually available. Sacred space no longer abolished historical time. In Christian symbolism the New Jerusalem (in which, conspicuously, there is no Temple) represents the fulfillment of the divine purpose, coming at the end of the historical process.

It would seem that Eliade is reluctant to admit the reforming thrust of Judeo-Christian faith at the point where this faith has sought to lead men away from "times of ignorance" (Acts 17:30), i.e., from the era of *homo religiosus*. He criticizes urbanized Christianity by contrasting it with the Christianity of rural Europe, because in the latter he finds elements of pre-Christian feeling for sacred space and of behavior based on continuing myths. And he complains that the religious experience of modern Christians has narrowed so as to become a private experience involving the individual, God, and history: "But in these man-God-history relationships there is no place for the cosmos. From this it would appear that, even for a genuine Christian, the world is no longer felt as the work of God."[27]

The judgment just cited is a theological one, and it is questionable on at least two counts. First, since Christianity spread originally as an alternative to, and *as a condemnation of,* religions "open" to the cosmos, it is hard to believe that the purest Christianity is that which has come to terms with the paganism it superseded. Already when Judaism denounced the "abominations" of Canaanite cults, it attacked not merely the forms of ritual but more especially the false worship celebrated in those cults. The "profoundly religious meaning" of child sacrifice to Moloch was repudiated no less than its barbarity. Second, a religion concerned with establishing sacred space in order to keep chaos at bay must always view the profane world as unreal. Thus, it is not a cosmically oriented but a historically oriented faith which is able to view the world as the work of God. Eliade's theological bias is seen in his appeal to primitive and Oriental cultures when he seeks to show the "poverty" of modern man's religious experience.[28] The basis of the Indian quest for Absolute Being, as he himself points out, is the recognition of historical existence as representative of our situation in *māyā* or cosmic illusion.[29] At best, the present world is the result of the play of the gods—which is not at all the same as the work of God. Unless the profane is admitted equally with the sacred, the term "creation" is necessarily a misnomer. A created world is one which, though wholly dependent upon its Creator, has been given reality in and for itself. Having been genuinely created as God's creature, man does not have to attain to reality by escaping from profane illusion. Christianity teaches this truth by insisting upon the Incarnation of the Son of God in place of a mere theophany. According to the historic creeds, Jesus was a real individual *and also* the incarnate Word. Both Docetism and Nestorianism were declared heretical because they maintained that the sacred and the profane, being opposites, could not co-exist but must remain aloof from each other.

For Eliade, every religion carries, implicitly or explicitly, an ontology. Primitive religions and the highly developed religions of the Orient are alike in their concern with Being. On this account, it is in them that Eliade finds the best illustrations of his concept of the sacred. It is interesting to find that the same territory is covered when an ontologist looks at religious cultures. In the third volume of his *Systematic Theology*, Paul Tillich, treating of human life in relation to Being, finds that life poised between the holy and the profane.[30] The revelation of the holy is not to be found in any particular faith but in "revelatory experiences" (i.e., Eliade's "hierophanies"), because every religion is tainted to some degree by the profane: ". . . no religion is revealed; religion is the creation and the distortion of revelation."[31] Life in the context of historical existence is called by Tillich "ambiguous." It partakes at once of the real and the unreal. This ambiguity is clearly very close indeed to the concept of *māyā*, where the factual seen through profane eyes is illusion, while to spiritual vision it is the vehicle of Absolute Reality. For Tillich, too, true spirituality means being "open" to the cosmos. *Homo religiosus,* says Eliade, lives as much as possible in a sacralized cosmos, since to participate in sacred reality is to be saturated with power.[32] Tillich's abstractly stated version of the same sentiment is "that nothing can be said about God theologically before the statement that he is the power of being in all being."[33] The goal of the spiritual life, it seems, is to be assured of the possession of ontological substance.[34]

What is important to grasp is that such a view of "spirituality" represents a particular theological outlook, and one based on the championing of *homo religiosus,* either in his primitive or in his sophisticated (ontologically oriented) form.

The establishing of sacred space is conceived to be the function of religion. On a lower level, religious theory and practice find expression in myth and ritual. On a higher level, religious reality is explored through analysis of the "structure of Being" and mystical experience. But the end result is the same: elevation of the religious man into the sacred sphere and the exclusion of the profane.[35] Historical existence must be transcended—and so the claims of historical faiths must be repudiated. Theophanies are valid. There may be Christs, or manifestations of the divine in the temporal, so long as each historical manifestation is separated carefully from the divine nontemporal reality which it declares. "Jesus as the Christ" is a meaningful form of words, so Tillich contends, while "Jesus Christ" is not.[36]

IV

Can the spiritual outlook of *homo religiosus* be revived in our modern, historically minded, antimetaphysical age? Eliade, Tillich, and others of like mind seem to believe that it can and should—or at least that the spiritual health of humanity depends upon its present renewal. The purpose of this article has been to query this last assumption. The larger issue of the spiritual needs of the contemporary world, together with the question of whether there can be a wholly "religionless" Christianity, clearly will not be decided without asking other questions and carrying the analysis of the difference between historical and nonhistorical religion much further than has been attempted here. Yet the objection raised by Bonhoeffer to Tillich's effort to interpret the world "in a religious sense" is, equally clearly, the place to begin any such analysis. By so doing we shall avoid, for example, the confusion introduced by Robinson's *Honest To God*, where Bonhoeffer's "Beyond in our midst" and Tillich's "Ground of all being" are grotesquely merged.

Among further questions to be asked are, especially, those concerning the implications of two central doctrines of Christianity as a historical faith: Creation and Revelation. Once the whole world is regarded as the divine handiwork, the belief that sacred space must be marked out from profane space cannot stand. Further, the concept of reading the ciphers of the cosmos is at odds with that of receiving the Word by faith. We are brought back to an old issue—one stated in Lessing's famous dictum that eternal truths can never be based upon "accidental" facts of history. Historical faith finds God precisely in those facts, which is why it is concerned to question the world view of *homo religiosus*. It rejects cosmic coziness for the sake of ethical strenuousness, for it does not agree that what is religious is necessarily either true or good. Thus, historical faith can hardly acquiesce in Eliade's belief that the passing of *homo religiosus* amounts to a second Fall. Even if the religionlessness of the modern world presents a problem in communication for Christianity, Bonhoeffer's thesis that the situation is to be welcomed remains a tenable one. Historical faith has never held that to be open to the cosmos is to be obedient to God.

NOTES

1. *Der Römerbrief*, 2nd ed. (Munich: Chr. Kaiser Verlag, 1921).

2. See his two books: *The Christian Message in a Non-Christian World* (New York: Kregel Publications, 1938), and *Religion and the Christian Faith* (Philadelphia: Westminster Press, 1957).

3. Philadelphia: Westminster Press, 1963.

4. Grand Rapids: Wm. B. Eerdmans, 1962.

5. Bonhoeffer's thoughts on religionless Christianity are given in *Letters and Papers from Prison* (New York: Macmillan Co., 1957); (London: SCM Press, 1956).

6. *Letters and Papers from Prison*, pp. 197–8.

7. Berlin: Ullstein, 1926. Eng. trans. by H. Richard Niebuhr, *The Religious Situation* (New York: Henry Holt, 1932).

8. Chicago: University of Chicago Press, Vol. I, 1951; Vol. II, 1957; Vol. III, 1963.

9. Trans. Willard R. Trask (New York: Harcourt, Brace, 1959). First published in German by Rowohlt Taschenbuch Verlag, 1957.

10. Trans. Philip Mairet (London: Harvill Press, 1960). First published in French by Gallimard, 1957.

11. *Op cit.*, p. 213. Cf. Eliade, *The Myth of the Eternal Return*, trans. Willard R. Trask (New York: Pantheon Books, 1949), p. 162. *The Myth of the Eternal Return* was reissued by Harper & Row in the Harper Torchbooks series in 1959, under the title

Cosmos and History: The Myth of the Eternal Return, with a new preface by the author.

12. *Op. cit.*, pp. 238 ff.

13. *The Sacred and the Profane*, p. 14.

14. *Ibid.*, p. 204.

15. *Ibid.*, p. 178.

16. *Ibid.*, pp. 178–79.

17. *Ibid.*, pp. 12–13.

18. *Ibid.*, p. 21.

19. *Ibid.*, p. 148.

20. *Ibid.*, p. 81.

21. *Ibid.*, pp. 204–5.

22. *Ibid.*, pp. 210–13.

23. *Ibid.*, p. 212; italics in the text.

24. *Myths, Dreams and Mysteries*, p. 142.

25. *The Sacred and the Profane*, p. 110. Cf. *The Myth of the Eternal Return*, pp. 102 ff., 159 ff., and Preface to the Torchbook Edition, vii–viii.

26. *Ibid.*, p. 112.

27. *Ibid.*, p. 179.

28. *Ibid.*, p. 178.

29. *Myths, Dreams and Mysteries*, pp. 239 ff.

30. Tillich, *Systematic Theology*, III, 98–102 and *passim*.

31. *Ibid.*, p. 104.

32. *The Sacred and the Profane*, p. 13.

33. *Systematic Theology*, III, 294; cf. I, 189.

34. "Creation is accomplished by a surplus of ontological substance" (*The Sacred and the Profane*, p. 97). Eliade explains that this is why myths "of the beginning" are ritually enacted, so that the powers of creation may be available to the participants in the ritual.

35. Tillich draws upon Schelling's concept of "essentialization" to explain how the ambiguities of history are to be transcended in eternity, with every negative element excluded. He adopts a Hegelian-type view of the real, in which the historical process is a necessary condition for the unfolding of the essential, freed from the distortions of existence. See *Systematic Theology*, III, 400–1.

36. *Systematic Theology*, II, 97–9, 118–21; I, 132–37. George H. Tavard's study of Tillich's Christology stresses Tillich's Christological "mistake" as being found in the following thesis: ". . . the Christ (a universal) cannot be directly apprehended as Jesus (a concrete man); the eternal cannot be the historical" (*Paul Tillich and the Christian Message* New York: Charles Scribner's Sons, 1962), p. 172. See also, Kenneth Hamilton, *The System and the Gospel: A Critique of Paul Tillich* (New York: Macmillan Co., 1963), pp. 170 ff.

Context Versus Principles:
A Misplaced Debate in Christian Ethics

James M. Gustafson

The "great debate" in the field of Christian ethics in recent
years has been between the proponents of the more traditional
approach focusing on formal prescriptive principles or norms
and the proponents of the newer "contextual" approach
stressing existential response to a particular situation. In the
opinion of James M. Gustafson, however, it is time to call
a halt to the debate, which he sees as the cause of an unfair
and false polarization. For there are wide differences within
each group; not all contextualists have the same starting point,
and the same is true of the defenders of principles. Moreover,
just as lines of division are to be discerned within the groups,
so are lines of rapprochement to be found across them. Dr.
Gustafson then proceeds to defend the thesis that "Christian
ethics can and does begin from at least four points, and no
matter which one is primary for a particular theologian, he
moves toward the other three as he extends his moral discourse within a Christian frame of reference." Dr. Gustafson,
author of the well-received book *Treasure in Earthen Vessels:
The Church as a Human Community*, is Professor of Christian Ethics at Yale Divinity School and Chairman of the
Department of Religious Studies at Yale University. His
article first appeared in the April 1965 *Harvard Theological
Review*.*

THE FIELD of Christian ethics has been the
location of a debate over the past decades between roughly
delineated parties representing an allegiance to the use of
formal prescriptive principles on the one hand, and those
representing the cause of the more existential response to a
particular situation on the other hand. The debate has taken

* Harvard University Divinity School, Cambridge, Mass. 02138.
Copyright © 1965 by the President and Fellows of Harvard
College.

place in Europe and the United States, it has taken place in Catholicism and in Protestantism. In European Protestant literature Karl Barth's *Church Dogmatics*, particularly Volume II/2, Bonhoeffer's *Ethics*, and Niels Søe's *Kristelig Etik*, have represented what has been called a "contextual" approach.[1] More traditional Lutheran theologians who stress the importance of ethics under the law have a larger place for traditional ethical principles. Werner Elert and Walter Künneth would be representative of this group.[2] In Catholic literature there was a movement in the early years after World War II that came to be called "situational morality." A critic has typified it in the following terms: "The ultimate differences between this new morality and traditional morality come down then to this: In an objective system of ethics the moral judgment is submitted to an extrinsic norm, an ontological norm founded on the principles of being. In situational ethics the moral judgment is measured only by the subjective, immanent light of the individual in question."[3] In contrast to the situational emphasis is the whole tradition of natural law ethics and moral theology as this developed in Roman Catholicism. It should be noted that some of the recent Catholic ethics continues to be influenced by a situational approach, though not in the extreme way of earlier materials.[4]

In American Protestant ethics, a number of writers have been called "contextual," or "situational" ethicists. Among them are Paul Lehmann, Alexander Miller, Joseph Sittler, H. R. Niebuhr, Albert Rasmussen, Joseph Fletcher, Gordon Kaufman, Charles C. West, and the author.[5]

Writings have been published in criticism of the contextual viewpoint by John C. Bennett, Paul Ramsey, Alvin Pitcher, Clinton Gardiner, Robert Fitch, and Edward L. Long.[6]

The purpose of this study is to show that the debate is no longer a fruitful one. The umbrella named "contextualism" has become so large that it now covers persons whose views are as significantly different from each other as they are different from some of the defenders of "principles." The defenders of the ethics of principles make their cases on different grounds and use moral principles in different ways.

Finally, I will argue that there have been, and legitimately can be, four different base points for Christian moral discourse, and that no matter which point a writer selects to start from, he moves into considerations that are dominant in the other three if he seeks to develop a complete Christian ethics.

Before engaging in a development of the major theses, however, it is important to notice that the debate has located the problem of Christian ethics at a particular point, namely the question, "How does the Christian community or any of its conscientious members go about making a particular moral judgment or decision?" This question to a great extent determines the levels of discourse in the argument. Henry David Aiken, in an essay that ought to have great importance in theological ethics, has distinguished four levels of moral discourse, of which the answer to this question is only one. He has called them the "expressive-evocative" level, the "moral" level, the "ethical" level, and the "post-ethical" level. The first is almost ejaculatory in character; it is characterized by an unreflective moral comment that expresses feelings of indignation or of approval. At the moral level, the reflective question begins to emerge, for there men are asking, "What ought I to do in this situation?" "Is that which I admire so much really good?" Reasons are given for the choices that men make; rules are turned to in order to justify moral judgments. The discourse is essentially practical, in a sense that does not derogate "practicality" to expediency. The third, or ethical level, is the one on which questions are raised about the rules or considerations that justify a particular moral judgment. "Can the rules or the reasons by which I have justified a particular decision *really* be defended?" At this level men seek to give reasons for those other reasons that more immediately determine moral conduct. For example, if the answer to the question, "What ought I to do?" is decided in terms "I ought to do what the Christian community has long expected men to do in comparable situations," the ethical question becomes, "On what grounds are the expectations of the Christian community accepted as normative?" The post-ethical level raises the question, "Why be moral?" At this point perhaps the offering of "good reasons" finds its limits, and an element of commitment made in freedom enters in.[7]

Aiken's pattern has been introduced here in order to indicate that the context vs. principles debate has emerged on the second level of discourse, the moral level. It has come about in an effort to clarify an essentially practical question of morality: What ought I to do? In the polarization of the discussion, some have said, "Immerse yourself in the situation in which you live, and in which God is acting, and then do what appears to be the right thing in faith." Others have said, "Look to the objective morality of the Christian and Western tradition, for there are principles of conduct that have been derived from nature and revelation that will show you what you ought to do." Obviously the discussion moves rather quickly from this "moral" level to the "ethical" level, and the defense of each side takes place in the effort to say why the contextualist or the principled approach is the right approach. Presumably, for Christian moralists, the answer to the post-ethical question is the same, namely, "One ought to be moral because it is part of one's faith in Jesus Christ to conduct one's life in a way that is good for man." Within this general answer, however, there are very different accent marks, and these in turn affect the way that discourse goes on at other levels. The concerns of this essay begin with the moral level, and move to the ethical level, although some references are necessary to the post-ethical level as well. This is so because the debate with which we are dealing itself begins with the practical moral question.[8]

The Contextualist Umbrella

Any discussion that men force into a debate inevitably polarizes opinion, partly for the sake of clarifying the fundamental issues that divide, but partially for the sake of the convenience of lecturers in survey courses. Such has occurred in the current discussion in theological ethics in the United States. The contextualist pole has been covered by an umbrella that is so large that it begins to collapse. Men of quite different persuasions are placed under it. Men who might finally argue that assessment of the context is a matter of the first order of importance in moral decisions make that particular case for very different reasons. Writers have different contexts in view. Thus I shall show that the label itself is no longer very useful, since the differences of opinion among those so called are very great indeed.

For what reasons are men called "contextualists?" There are almost as many reasons as there are contextualists. In the area of social ethics there has been a growing concern over the past few decades for accurate analysis of what is actually taking place in the world in which Christians act so that their moral conduct can be more realistic and responsible. The realism that is sought is not at this point a critical assessment of the limitations of man's capacities to know and do the good by virtue of the limitations of his finitude and sin. It is a realism about what is actually occurring, and thus about where the pliable points, the interstices in human society, are in which Christians can act, and from which can come some of the desired effects or consequences. The responsibility that is sought at this point is in relation to spheres of activity already existing. Put simply, some contextualists are saying, if you wish to act out of moral intentions in the political sphere of life, you must know the context of politics with as much accuracy and insight as is humanly possible. This means, then, that the study of politics and of the scientific interpreters of political activity is essential for Christian moral action. If you wish to act with moral intentions in the economic sphere of life, you must have a disciplined knowledge of the economic context of moral intentions and actions. If you wish to affect the social morality of a local community, you must know that social context, its power structure, its mores, its institutional arrangements, its population movements, and so forth. Thus this particular contextual intention leads to the use of technical social analysis in the moral decision making of the Christian community. It sometimes leads to primary research by the ethically motivated Christian scholar, in order to understand what forces are actually shaping events in a society.

An example of contextual analysis of this sort, motivated by this particular reason for being a "contextualist," is

Kenneth Underwood's *Protestant and Catholic*. In this widely known study, Underwood's intentions are basically ethical. He analyzed the staggering weakness of the Protestant moral community in Holyoke, Massachusetts, when it faced the question, "What ought we to do?" in a particular situation. The situation was an invitation extended to Margaret Sanger to lecture on planned parenthood in a dominantly Roman Catholic city in the 1940's. Underwood put detailed sociological research to the service of a moral intention. In order to understand what the Protestants did do and did not do in those circumstances he made a detailed study of the city of Holyoke and its churches. He did a comparative analysis of the authority of Protestant and Catholic religious leadership, of the beliefs of Protestants and Catholics on religious and civil questions, of the class structure of the churches, of the relation of the churches to the labor movement, to business, and to politics, and he studied the history of Protestant involvement in politics in the city. Underwood's conclusions are in effect these: Protestants were socially ineffective partly because they failed to understand the community situation in which they lived; they were unrealistic about the social context of which they were a part. If Protestants wish to affect comparable situations in other urban centers, they ought to take the social context—its political, religious, and economic aspects—more seriously than they normally do.[9]

A similar pattern of contextualism occurs in other areas of Christian ethics. In the ethics of medical care, for example, there is a constant reference to the particular circumstances of the patient. One might bring moral generalizations to bear on the question of abortion in general, for example, but physicians will often modify the implications of such generalizations with particular reference to the situation of the pregnant woman. This became a matter of international attention in the recent Finkbine case. The possibility of malformation of the child due to the drugs that were used during the pregnancy was the most important datum used in the decision of the parents to seek abortion. Under these particular circumstances, it was argued, abortion is morally responsible. The "context" was determinative of the decision.

The importance of knowing the actual social or personal situation is obviously not the only reason for being a "contextualist." Some writers propound the point of view in the first instance for theological reasons. This is the case for Karl Barth, as every reader of the Church Dogmatics, II/2, knows. Christians are to be obedient to the command of God. But the command of God is not given in formal, general ethics; it is not given in traditional rules of conduct. It is given by the living God in the concrete situation. It is a particular command addressed to a particular person in a particular sphere of activity, in a particular time and place. "The command of God as it is given to us at each moment is always and only one possibility in every conceivable particularity of its inner and outer modality."

> It is always a single decision. . . . We encounter it in such a way that absolutely nothing either outward or inward, either in the relative secret of our intention or in the unambiguously observable fulfillment of our actions, is left to chance or to ourselves, or rather in such a way that even in every visible or invisible detail He wills us precisely the one thing and nothing else, and measures and judges us precisely by whether we do or do not do with the same precision the one thing that He so precisely wills. Our responsibility is a responsibility to the command as it is given us in this way.[10]

Clearly Barth is not arguing for a "contextualism" on the grounds of a social realism that exists in the case of Underwood. Behind this particular quotation there is a whole doctrine of God who is for man in Jesus Christ, who is free, who is living and present to men in faith in the world. The fact that the ethics is expounded in terms of the particularity of God's command is more the function of Barth's doctrine of God than it is the function of a theory of human moral responsibility for a particular occasion. Theological conviction is the primary criterion by which an interpretation of the moral life is to be judged for its validity. This is clear from Barth's own extended discourse on the question, "What are we to do?" The answers are given primarily in theological and religious terms, not in ethical terms. "We are to respond to the existence of Jesus Christ and His people. With our action we are to render an account to this grace."[11] "We are to accept as right, and live as those who accept as right the fact that they do not belong to themselves, that they therefore do not have their life in their own hands and at their own disposal, that they are made a divine possession in Jesus Christ."[12] "We are to accept it as right that God never meets us except compassionately, except as the One who comes to the help of our misery, except apart from and against our deserts, except in such a way as to disclose that what we have deserved is death."[13] "We are to accept it as right that God is our righteousness."[14] Further discussion of the question "What ought we to do?" adds little of moral particularity to the answer. We approach God as those who are ignorant and stand in need of divine instruction and conversion. We are to have complete openness, bracketing and holding in reserve what we know about the rightness and goodness of past decisions. We are to obey the command of God joyfully. We are to accept responsibility personally.[15]

Barth's ethics is called contextual or situational because certain basic theological affirmations permit only an ethics that is open to the present and the future, that is radically concrete in its commands. God's freedom to be for man in his grace, God's lordship over all things through his creation, redemption, and reconciliation of all things, God's present activity and direct speech to man, God's calling each man to responsibility to him in the particular sphere of his life: These affirmations permit no general or formal ethics but only an ethics of obedience in the particular time and place. Among American theologians, Joseph Sittler and Paul Lehmann also come to a contextual or relational ethic out of doctrinal affirmations, rather than from independent ethical grounds.

Joseph Sittler states that the Christian moral life is the actualization of man's justification in Christ. In man's organic relationship to God's work and presence, and to other men, the will of God is met as both known and unknown. "It is known in Christ who is the incarnate concretion of God's ultimate and relentless will-to-restoration; service of this will is presented to the believer not as a general program given in advance but as an ever-changing and fluctuant obligation to the neighbor in the midst of history's life."[16] The Christian perceives the neighbor's good and acts in continuity with his life in Christ and the ever-changing and fluctuant situation of the other person. Echoing Luther, Sittler says that the Christian moral life is "faith-doing." It is not a programmatic set of ideals, or a pattern of predefined obligations and duties. The authorization of this point of view is biblical.

The language of Christian ethics is in accord with the language of revelation, and the language of revelation is in accord with the nature of God's relationships to men and the world. This language or speech is organic, and not propositional. Just as the Bible does not define the nature of God, or prove his existence, or elaborate his attributes in rational categories, so in the area of ethics the Bible does not give abstract counsels, duties, obligations, or ideals. Just as "God simply *is* what God manifestly *does*," so there is an "inner logic of the living, the organic, the destiny-bound," that is expressed in "time terms," which is appropriate to the Christian moral life, and thus to ethics.[17] Biblical speech about God, the Church, and man is all characterized by the language of organic relatedness.

Thus the Christian is organically related to his neighbors, and to the events and occasions of his historical life. He is also organically related to Christ; at least there is a continuity between the Christian and Christ that is best depicted in relational language. Thus "the Christian life is here understood as a re-enactment from below on the part of men of the shape of the revelatory drama of God's holy will in Jesus Christ. . . . Suffering, death, burial, resurrection, a new life— these are actualities which plot out the arc of God's self-giving deed in Christ's descent and death and ascension; and precisely *this same shape of grace* in its recapitulation within the life of the believer and the faithful community, is the nuclear matrix which grounds and unfolds the Christian life."[18] Out of this matrix comes faith-doing in the "ever-changing and fluctuant obligation to the neighbor in the midst of history's life."[19] Christian ethics has to be in accord with these prior theological affirmations, which in turn are consonant with the character of the relations of God to man and man to other men. Thus there is an immediacy to the commands in the Christian life that is "not communicable in the causalities of propositional speech."

Paul Lehmann is the one author who extensively uses the particular term "contextual." As with Barth and Sittler, his primary intention is to delineate a position in Christian ethics that is not alien to the fundamental dogmatic statements of the Christian Church. He seeks to shape an ethics that is in accord with God's revelation in Jesus Christ, particularly with an interpretation of that revelation that stresses God's freedom in his humanizing work for man. He seeks an ethics that takes the Christian community seriously as the matrix of the Christian conscience, rather than as a prescriber of Christian moral propositions. Such an ethics then is one that delineates the Christian's participation in the world as one which coincides with what God is doing for man in a very particular set of events. The Christian is to have a theonomous conscience, a conscience "immediately sensitive to the freedom of God to do in the always changing human situation what his humanizing aims and purposes require. The theonomous conscience is governed and directed by the freedom of God alone." "Christian ethics in the tradition of the Reformation seeks to provide an analysis of the environment of decision in which the principal foundations and preceptual directives of behavior are displaced by *contextual foundations and parabolic directives*. In a word, the environment of decision is the context for the ethical reality of conscience."[20]

Such an ethics is grounded in the divine indicative rather than the divine imperative. "The primary question is not, 'What does God command?' The primary question is, 'What does God do?' "[21] Christian ethics analyzes what God is doing as its first order of business, not what the churches have said God has ordered men to do. It is the theological discipline that reflects on the question, and its answer, "What am I, as a believer in Jesus Christ and as a member of his church, to do?"[22] The answer is that I am to do what my theonomous conscience says I should do as it is immediately sensitive to what God in his freedom is doing.

There are three contexts out of which Christian behavior

comes for Lehmann. The largest and most determinative is the theological one, namely the context of what God is doing. This is known in faith in Jesus Christ. Thus he develops a Christological statement that undergirds the assertion that God is doing "political activity," or "humanizing work." "A theology of messianism [Lehmann's characterization of his Christological theology] is theology with the accent upon the politics of God, that is, upon what God has done and is doing in the world to keep human life human. For such a theology, three Christological affirmations acquire particular significance. They are the doctrines of the Trinity, of the threefold office of Christ, and of the Second Adam and the Second Advent."[23]

The second context is that of the Christian community. Jesus is really present in history among the true people of God. "It is this reality of the *koinonia* . . . which denotes the concrete result of God's specifically purposed activity in the world in Jesus Christ. We might, therefore, say that Christian ethics is *koinonia* ethics. This means that it is from, and in, the *koinonia* that we get the answer to the question: What am I, as a believer in Jesus Christ and as a member of his church to do?"[24]

The third context is the particular situation in the world in which God is acting, and in which the Christian acts. In his affirmation of the importance of the concrete place of Christian activity, Lehmann executes his sharp critique of those who would view Christian ethics in more rationalistic terms, stressing basic moral propositions from the Christian tradition, and seeking to deduce the ways in which these can be applied to particular situations. Lehmann, on theological grounds (not on ethical grounds, that is, not on the basis of an argument about the futility of imposing rationally derived propositions onto the dynamics of human history), bypasses this more rationally reflective procedure in favor of one that perceives, apprehends, or is sensitive to what God is doing. The stress is on other aspects of the self than the purely cognitive or intellectual aspects. He finds in the *koinonia* a coinciding of the response of Christians to what the community knows God has done and is doing. This leads relentlessly to highly particularized responses and actions, always sensitive to the historical present, rather than to generalizations about what ought to be.

For Lehmann, as for Barth and Sittler, a Christian ethics that stresses the importance of the particular situation and the immediacy of involvement and response in that situation is legitimated on theological grounds. A quarrel with these men about the issue of contextualism must properly be a theological discussion. It necessarily involves the large and important question of the relation of ethics to dogmatics, and also the more particular questions about whether these men have properly appropriated the fundamental theological affirmations of the faith. The question of independent moral responsibility, or moral realism, in itself is not an appropriate question. There is a highly concrete sense of the place of responsibility and of the character of personal responsibility in this ethics, but it is theologically authorized. Contextual ethics are sound because they are consonant with what the Christian community knows God to be saying and doing, as this is made known in Scripture.

There is yet a third reason for contextualism in Christian ethics, namely an understanding of the nature of human selfhood, of existence. Ethics is contextual because persons live in a pattern of human relations which inevitably make more responsibility a particular response to persons or events. A social theory of the self requires a relational or situational ethic. Social views of the self, however, are not the only anthropology that brings contextualism into Christian ethics; a more individualistic existentialism does so as well. Ethics is contextual because men are free to shape their own existences in faith by their responsible and creative decisions in the world. A view of social selfhood is to be found in the writings of H. Richard Niebuhr; a more individual approach can be found in the ethics of Rudolf Bultmann and others. In either case the anthropology is also authorized by an interpretation of theology; it is not absolutely independent. But each has a degree of autonomy that is notable, and on this ground can be dealt with in a way different from Barth, Sittler, and Lehmann. For purposes of brevity only Niebuhr's discussion will be used to make the point.[25]

For H. Richard Niebuhr, the notion of moral responsibility is so closely related to the idea of man as the responder that each necessarily implies the other. "What is implicit in the idea of responsibility is the image of man-the-answerer, man engaged in dialogue, man acting in response to action upon him."[26] He distinguishes this view of man, and consequently of ethics, from those that used the image of man-the-maker and thus worked with basically teleological images, and man-the-citizen and thus worked basically with legal images and with a sense of duty or obligation. The case for the view of man-the-answerer is not derived in the first instance from particular Christian doctrines; it was built upon "common experience." Thus there is a phenomenology of moral experience that is common to all men that makes the relational view of ethics appropriate, whether in Christian ethics or some other view that has a different center of loyalty. When one observes moral action, he observes persons responding to the actions of other persons or to events that have effects upon him. This is to be distinguished from those views that would affirm that men live and think morally first of all with reference to rules of conduct, or to ideas of what the future state of affairs ought to be. "All action . . . is response to action upon us."[27] "In our responsibility we attempt to answer the question: 'What shall I do?' by raising as the prior question: 'What is going on?' or 'What is being done to me?' rather than 'What is my end?' or 'What is my ultimate law?' "[28]

The effect of this understanding of selfhood is the delineation of an ethics that seeks to define and do what is fitting and appropriate in the particular relationships of the self. For Christians the interpretation of the situation involves an understanding of what God is saying and doing there. "Responsibility affirms—God is acting in all actions upon you. So respond to all actions upon you as to respond to his action."[29] The Christian community acts not only in response to the natural and historical context of its life, but in the light of a particular interpretation and understanding of that very particular context, namely what God is saying and doing there. Thus Niebuhr moves with ease between a view of the nature of man's moral existence to a view of the nature of God's being and presence as an active one. The two are coherent and congenial with each other, but Niebuhr does not seek to derive his anthropology from his doctrine of God. He is perfectly willing to find it in the common human experience as this was reconstructed in quite secular thinkers such as G. H. Mead, C. H. Cooley, Josiah Royce, and others, as well as theologians such as Buber. Finally, Niebuhr would say that a contextual ethics (though he fervently disliked the adjective) is necessary because of the nature of man.[30]

The fact that Christian moralists are contextualists in tendency for quite different reasons does not in and of itself imply that there is not enough common to all of them to make the use of the umbrella term appropriate. Obviously all have a special concern that the place of moral responsibility be understood to be highly specific and concrete, and that Christian ethics attend more to acting responsibly in a given place than it has done in those times and persons that seem satisfied with broad moral generalizations. There is a kind of personalism common to all of them, though it would be interpreted differently by various of them. But the main point to be noted for purposes of this essay is that men come to contextualism from different fundamental starting or base points, and the place from which they start sets the pattern for what considerations are most important in the delineation of Christian ethics. I shall return to this in a subsequent section of this study. It needs to be noted also that within a general common ground of concern for the particularities of time and place there are differences of opinion about the place and use of moral generalizations. Lehmann, for example, eschews them with a vengeance; he keeps his elaboration of the meaning of "humanizing" to a minimum. Barth, in *Church Dogmatics*, III/4, avoids formal principles, but is willing to accept the idea that for Christians certain forms of behavior are usually appropriate. Normally Christians do not take life, for example. H. Richard Niebuhr has a large place for the principles by which human action and divine action are interpreted, though he does not stipulate a series of rules of conduct.

Finally, it needs to be noted that no serious Christian

moralist who champions the place of principles avoids the issues involved in their appropriation and application within unique situations. The defenders of principles seek to move from the general to the particular in a disciplined way. These observations are the occasion for the assertion that the term contextualism has been used to cover too many theological heads, and that the debate is misplaced as it has often been specified. The defenders of principles are equally hard to lump together, and to a demonstration of this I now turn.

The Authority and Use of Principles

Three of the ablest and most influential American writers in Christian ethics have defended the significance of Christian moral principles either in a self-conscious methodological way, or simply by effective use of Christian moral norms. They are Reinhold Niebuhr, John C. Bennett, and Paul Ramsey. The inclusion of the three together immediately suggests to the reader of their works that they use principles in different ways in Christian moral discourse. Niebuhr and Bennett are concerned with the use of moral generalizations to give direction to the consequences and effects of moral action; Ramsey very deliberately stresses the use of principles for the determination of the right means of conduct. To make this differentiation is not to say that Bennett and Niebuhr are unconcerned about the proper means to be used to establish a state of affairs that approximates a Christian norm, nor that Ramsey is unacquainted with the idea that right means of conduct have to be appropriate to the right ends of conduct. But the difference of concern is notable enough to indicate that the purposes for which principles are used are different, and thus these writers cannot easily be lumped together.

Reinhold Niebuhr's love-justice dialectic is widely known and thus does not require detailed exposition. In *An Interpretation of Christian Ethics*, he derives the distinctive significance of Christian ethics largely from the teachings of Jesus, in intellectual continuity with the theology of the social gospel. The problem of the Christian practical reason is then set by the discrepancy that exists between a moral ideal that is impossible of historical realization, a law of love that cannot be easily applied on the one hand, and the condition of man the sinner and the complexity of moral dilemmas on the other hand. His polemic had a particular historical reference, namely "all those forms of naturalism, liberalism, and radicalism which generate utopian illusions and regard the love commandment as ultimately realizable because history knows no limits of its progressive approximatiòns."[31] Niebuhr's argument was not against an ethics of impossible ideals or unrealizable laws of love, but against those who too simply believed that history could be shaped by them. Thus he developed a procedure of reflection in which some approximation of the ideals could occur through the idea of justice and its ramifications for balances of power, and greater equality in the distribution of the means of power in human social affairs. Love remained the moral ideal and the moral law; indeed "the law of love is involved in all approximations of justice, not only as the source of the norms of justice, but as an ultimate perspective by which their limitations are discovered."[32] The action which seeks to achieve moral ends in the human community is always to be guided and judged by the "impossible ethical ideal" that is given in the gospel.

This basic pattern of moral reflection continued in Niebuhr's writings, though the statement of the authority of the norm and some of the concepts and their uses were slightly altered. In *The Nature and Destiny of Man* the self-sacrifice of Jesus on the cross becomes the central point for understanding the meaning of heedless *agape*, rather than the teachings of Jesus; and the dialectic is refined and complicated by the introduction of the idea of mutuality.[33] The fact that Niebuhr had an acute "contextual awareness" needs to be noted, for in the dialectic of Christian ethical thought and life it is necessary to have an understanding of what actually is going on in the realms of politics and economics, of international relations and war. Indeed, this is one pole of the dialectic. But Christian faith in effect provides a revelation of moral norms which always judges and guides the more pragmatic responses to the fluctuations of human history. The norms derived from revelation are authorized by God's deed and by Scripture, but they were also supported by their basically ethical significance as well. For example, Niebuhr argues for their significance in terms of the potential perversions and distortions of justice, if justice is not judged and tempered by a higher norm of self-sacrificial love.

John C. Bennett, like Niebuhr and many persons called contextualists, seeks to avoid utopianism and the lack of realism in Christian moral reflection and action. His concern also is to be significantly related to what is actually going on in human history and society. He also shares Niebuhr's view that there are norms given in the Christian revelation that can give guidance to the involvement of Christians in social change. His procedures are also well known to students of Christian ethics, particularly in the version of them he gave in *Christian Ethics and Social Policy*, where he shares J. H. Oldham's conception of "middle axioms" that stand between the transcendence of the Christian ethic on the one hand, and the situation of human sin and "technical autonomy" on the other hand. These middle axioms are goal oriented, and not means oriented. "The Christian ethic guides us in determining the goals which represent the purpose of God for our time."[34] Thus the church is to provide guidelines or provisional definitions of goals that will help Christians relate the transcendent Christian ethics to given times and places. In writings subsequent to the book of 1946, Bennett has continued to indicate the necessity for more fixed principles as anchors and compasses (the words are mine, not his) for Christian ethics. Like Niebuhr, his concern is twofold; he does not wish to compromise the absoluteness of the demand of Christian ethics for indiscriminate love by some theological argument that mitigates their starkness, and yet he accepts a Christian sense of responsibility for the moral character of what is going on in human society. It is through the statement of fundamental principles and more particular derivative directives that Bennett keeps both poles in proper tension.

Paul Ramsey's polemic is both against what he deems to be the "wastelands of relativism" that are the effect of contextualism, and against those who use moral principles more for the purpose of prediction and governing of consequences than for the determination of the proper means of conduct. "*How* we do *what* we do is as important as our goals." Ramsey, like Niebuhr and Bennett, takes love to be the central point of reference for Christian ethics, although he also suggests in various writings that he wishes to resuscitate a modified version of natural law in Protestant ethics as well. "Love posits or takes form in principles of right conduct which express the difference it discerns between permitted and prohibited action, and these are not wholly derived from reflection upon consequences."[35] Ramsey's accent on the ethics of right conduct does not mean that he ignores prudential consideration of consequences, but that he wishes to make a corrective stance against a Christian ethics that seems to be exclusively governed by such calculation. He works this methodological position out with reference to the situation of the Christian community in the nuclear weapons age, largely by a contemporary formulation of the just war theory. These principles of the right conduct of war are authorized by the Christian theological and ethical tradition, as it has sought to find the "in-principled" forms of love that enable conduct to be guided during conflict, and by the biblical revelation of love made known in the faith that Christ died for all men. They are worked out in relation to the possible use of nuclear weapons, as the writers on military strategy have considered the potential function of these weapons in an open international conflict. Ramsey's procedures, as he does this, are much more akin to the rational procedures of the moral theology tradition of the Roman Catholic Church than they are to most of the work of his fellow Protestant theologians. This makes him the most audible and visible defender of "principle ethics," as Lehmann's use of the notion of contextualism makes him the most audible and visible critic of such ethics.

In this brief analysis of these writers, it becomes clear that principles are used in different ways by different writers, and have different degrees of authority. In the case of Reinhold Niebuhr, love and justice are norms that are given a minimum of definition, and certainly are not spelled out into a series of moral propositions given for the guidance of conduct. The weight of his work is so heavily upon the assessment of what is going on in society, and the pragmatic judgments made (to be sure, under the judgment and guidance of the ideas of love and justice), that he could easily be located on the contextual side of the debate. John C. Bennett's statements of middle axioms are deliberately relativized as being the creatures of ethical reflection under very specific circumstances and thus open to revision as circumstances change. Paul Ramsey's delineation of principles of right conduct are weighted with more authority, for he has a confidence in the tradition that makes him take its distillations of the bases of judgment very seriously in their own right, apart from the contemporary occasions in which they are to be applied. If our discussion were extended to include Roman Catholic ethics, an even greater certitude about certain traditional moral propositions would be disclosed. Niebuhr and Bennett tend to use principles for the determination of a better state of affairs, or for the delineation of proper goals; Ramsey stresses right conduct and means as well as calculation of ends, and in this sense shares the ethos of Catholic moral theology. Apart from such a refinement of what is involved in the ethic of moral principles, the lumping of these writers together is a serious oversimplification.

In an earlier essay, I suggested a distinction between the prescriptive use of principles and the illuminative use of principles.[36] The distinction is introduced here to indicate some of the difficulties inherent in the polarization of the current debate. For Paul Ramsey, traditional Christian moral principles have such authority that they in effect prescribe the right conduct of Christians. Another moralist can read Ramsey's arguments, take them with great seriousness as an illustration of how a thoughtful Christian ethicist reflects upon a current moral situation, and find the principles to illuminate his own judgment without being determined by the authority of the principles or the argument. He can find other statements of principles and other arguments equally illuminating, and equally important for his own decision. If the moralist stresses the openness of the present situation, the responsibility of the person in it to make his own decision, and the power of affections, dispositions, and perceptiveness also to give guidance to behavior, he need not necessarily ignore traditional moral principles. Rather, they are a significant part, though only a part, of what goes into his own moral reflection. Principles enable him to *interpret* what is morally wrong and morally right about a particular occasion; to interpret what direction subsequent events ought to take in order to maintain the existence of the good and preserve it from disaster; and to interpret what patterns and means of action are more appropriate morally as he participates in events. But they are not prescriptive in the sense that the principles and arguments made concerning their application are the most important or sole authority for the governing of action. Thus casuistic arguments can be read with a great deal of serious interest without being determinative of conduct. In the illuminative use of principles the center of gravity is on the newness, the openness, the freedom that is present, in which the conscientious man seeks to achieve the good and do the right. In the prescriptive use of principles the center of gravity is on the reliability of traditional moral propositions and their reasonable application in a relatively open contemporary situation.

On the basis of this distinction, it is possible for persons who appear to be contextualists actually to be very serious students of moral principles and of the science of casuistry. The function that this study has, however, is different from what it appears to have for Paul Ramsey and for traditional Catholic moral theologians. But its function can be important enough to raise a serious question about the easy identification of theological moralists into two camps. Karl Barth, for example, in *Church Dogmatics*, III/4, discusses particular instances of moral decision with some care and precision as a way for the reader to become sensitive to what God might be commanding him to be and to do in an analogous situation. Even Paul Lehmann introduces the notion that God's activity is "political" and "humanizing," terms which are susceptible to more extensive exposition than he gives them, but which nevertheless function as points of illumination for the actual conduct of the Christian man.

The debate between context and principles, then, forces an unfair polarization upon a diversity of opinion that makes it both academically unjust and increasingly morally fruitless. Persons assigned to either pole are there for very different reasons, and work under the respective umbrellas in very different ways. It also becomes clear that contextualists find some moral principles or generalizations that give guidance to existential decisions, and that the defenders of principles find some ways to proceed from generalizations to particular situations. This assertion points to the theme of the remainder of the paper, namely, that Christian ethics can and does begin from at least four base points, and no matter which one is primary for a particular theologian, he moves toward the other three as he extends his moral discourse within a Christian frame of reference.

Four Base Points for Christian Moral Discourse

The four base points have already been introduced, though one not as directly as the others. There are moralists who begin with as accurate and perceptive social or situational analysis as possible. Others begin with fundamental theological affirmations. Still others locate moral principles as the center point for discussion. In addition to these three a fourth can be discerned, namely the nature of the Christian's life in Christ and its proper expressions in moral conduct. To be related to Jesus Christ in faith is to have a certain manner or quality of life which in turn has its appropriate moral expressions in intentions and actions. I shall indicate by use of examples the way in which moral reflection beginning from each of these points moves to a consideration of the other points as it engages in moral discourse.

It is appropriate to begin with the two base points that have already received most attention, namely with moral principles and with theological affirmations. Ramsey seeks to think about the use of modern weapons within the tradition of just war principles, and particularly the principle of noncombatant immunity. Noncombatants are not to be directly and intentionally killed in warfare. This is a moral proposition that is to be applied to the conduct of war in every time and place; it is as valid for the twentieth century as it was for the fifth century. Obviously Ramsey cannot and does not wish to remain at the level of reiteration of an honored principle. He necessarily moves toward the particular context of warfare in the twentieth century, because the conduct of warfare and even of the testing of weapons for warfare is different by virtue of the state of technology than it was when the principle was first formulated. When a large part of the economy of a nation is marshaled for the productive effort needed to conduct modern warfare, are the producers in factories combatants or noncombatants? When the scale of destruction by weapons is so great that a precise demolition of military installations is made difficult, is it meaningful to counsel noncombatant immunity? Ramsey takes the technological situation into view when he proceeds to ask these questions that any critical person would. He indicates in a number of his writings that he has read such authors as Oskar Morgenstern and Herman Kahn as carefully and seriously as any Christian moralist has done, writers who discuss the problems involved in the use of weapons and the potential effects of their use in terms of the contemporary international situation. The point is a simple one: Ramsey moves from a basic moral principle to the problems that exist in and for its application under very particular conditions of the technology of welfare. He is cautious to keep his argument on the moral level; what makes the conduct of war right according to the just war principles is not derived from analysis of weapons, nor merely from the potential consequences of the use of weapons now being made, but from the fact that in-principled love requires guards against indiscriminate killing. But he cannot avoid dealing with what now potentially exists in the state of contemporary technology.

Ramsey also moves from a particular principle to some theological justification for the principle. He believes that the just war principles are authorized in at least a twofold manner. When reasonable men think reasonably about the conduct of war, they will make the means used in war proportionate to the ends to be sought, and the ends to be sought will also be reasonable. In this sense there is an appeal made to human reason, or to the natural law as a ground for the principles. When Christians in the history of the Church's involvement in Western history have sought to understand what their central theological and moral point of reference—love—implies for the restraint of evil within social responsibility, they have worked this out in terms of just war principles. Thus there is also an appeal to the particular touchstone of Christian ethics. St. Augustine, St. Thomas, and other theologians have put the principles into love so that they can give direction to human activity. There is congruity between the particularized principles such as noncombatant immunity, and the affirmation that Christ, in love, died for all men. Thus in moving from the moral level of discourse to the authorization of moral rules Ramsey turns to philosophical and theological affirmations.

In yet another way Ramsey moves toward theological affirmations. He opens the way for a revision of ethical principles when certain theological realities take over. The principles are to be used as a service, and not as a reliance; "these rules are opened for review and radical revision in the instant that *agape* controls." In indicating where he differentiates his work from certain Catholic moralists, he suggests that "in the view here proposed, charity enters into a fresh determination of what is right in the given concrete context, and it is not wholly in bondage to natural-law determination of permitted or prohibited means."[37] Love is not only the basis for moral principles, it is an active reality that makes the moral person open to revision of the principles derived from it and enables him freshly to determine what is right in a particular context. God's love, then, is free to alter the rules that men normally live by, though normally they ought to live by the rules derived from knowledge of God's love. A contrast with Karl Barth's procedure is instructive. Barth seems to say, God in his freedom commands man in his situation ever anew. Since he is not capricious, he is likely to command similar things, indeed the same thing over and over again. But one is not to make a moral principle out of the consistencies of God's speech. Ramsey seems to say that Christian love usually acts within the law and lays down rules or principles. Thus we normally act according to these rules. But, since Jesus Christ is Lord, there can always be a "fresh determination of what should be done in situations not rightly covered by the law, by natural justice, or even by its [Christian love's] own former articulation in principle."[38] Thus in moving from principles to Christian love, presumably to God's active love, one finds the source not only of principles, but of the fresh determinations of what should be done. What is Barth's first declaration comes in as a qualification of Ramsey's ethical style, though as a theological moralist he necessarily takes account of it.

Ramsey says little about the freedom of the Christian in faith and love to apprehend freshly what he ought to do and to be, though perhaps such a view is implicit in his understanding of the moment that *agape* controls. If he were to be more completely systematic than he has been, it would be necessary for him to develop an understanding of the Christian man in faith, who is open to the love of God both in its form of rules and its freer form. He would answer questions pertaining to the nature and authority of the Christian conscience to determine what is morally right. Thus he would move not only from principles toward the historical situation and the theological affirmations, as he does, but also to a view of human moral life in faith.

The theological moralist whose apparent base point is certain theological affirmations about the nature and activity of God necessarily moves toward the other base points as his reflection becomes systematic. I have indicated how Paul Lehmann, like Barth, develops a view of Christian ethics that is coherent with his understanding of God's work made known in and through Jesus Christ. It is also clear from our previous exposition that Lehmann's conception of God's activity in the events in which men participate requires an acute sensitivity to what is really going on in the particular personal and social context of behavior.[39]

Although Lehmann's view of conscience has been alluded to, it is worth further elaboration here, for the possibility of the kind of contextual ethics he expounds depends in large part on the viability of his view of the nature of the Christian moral self. Certain accents are distinctive and important. Lehmann pays more attention to the role of sensitivity, imagination, and perceptiveness than do many writers in the field of ethics. In his description of the theonomous conscience we have already seen this: it is "immediately sensitive to the freedom of God to do . . . what his humanizing aims and purposes require." Immediate sensitivity to what God is doing in his freedom apparently is not something that comes from a more rationalistic ethical discourse. It assumes a transformation of the self in faith. The church is the matrix of this transformation. "The reality of the church is an ethical reality because what God is doing in the world becomes concrete in the transformation of human motivation and the structures of human relatedness which are the stuff of human fulfillment."[40] An ethics that is as free of rational calculation as Lehmann's is logically has to have a view of the self that accomplishes what precise rational discourse does for a writer such as Paul Ramsey. The activity of God, Lehmann asserts, "is brought directly to bear upon the life of the believer by means of a functional Christological content and connection . . . It is also a way of giving to the believer a clear understanding of the environment and direction of what he is to do and thus a firm foundation for behavior. The difference [between believers and unbelievers] is defined by imaginative and behavioral sensitivity to what God is doing in the world to make and keep human life human, to achieve the maturity of men, that is, the new humanity."[41] Lehmann's emphasis on transformation of motivation, on a clear understanding that is relatively unaided by moral or sociological principles, on imaginative and behavioral sensitivity, locates the personal nexus between God's activity and human action. Whether it stands up under various forms of criticism is not the concern of this essay. Lehmann does move to the outlines of a view of Christian moral life in faith that is consistent with the other bases of his ethics. Indeed, Christian ethics aims at a quality of life of which morality is the by-product. "*Christian ethics aims, not at morality, but at maturity*. The *mature* life is the fruit of Christian faith. Morality is a by-product of maturity."[42]

Lehmann eschews moral principles, and seems to assert that any use of them falls into a false abstraction, separating morality from life.[43] Consistent with this is his emphasis on the freedom of God, about which he says much more than he does about the love of God or the ordering work of God. Yet there is a consistency to God's activity, so that Lehmann reiterates that it is a "humanizing" or "maturing" activity. He desists from extensive exposition of what these terms mean. Maturity, he says, "*is* the integrity in and through interrelatedness which makes it possible for each individual member of an organic whole to be himself in togetherness, and in togetherness each to be himself." "For Christianity, what is fundamentally human in human nature is the gift to man of the power to be and to fulfill himself in and through a relationship of dependence and self-giving toward God and toward his fellow man. Thus, maturity is *self-acceptance through self-giving*. . . . In the fully developed Christian sense, 'maturity' and 'the new humanity' are identical."[44] In spite of the severe economy of exposition, Lehmann does have a particular content in view when he uses these key terms. The effect is that these notions become principles of illumination for sensitive Christians in discerning what God is doing. They are not to be used as the first principles in the resolution of a problem in the manner of the science of casuistry. But they provide meaningful points of reference for moral judgment. Where humanizing work is going on, God is active, and where Christians perceive this they are to act so that their behavior coincides with what God is doing.

Thus Lehmann moves from his prime base of theological affirmation to a consideration of the other three bases for Christian moral discourse. His reluctance to denote in greater detail what principles function for illumination and judgment is consistent with his starting point and the way in which he defines it, but clearly Christians are not to be immature, nor are they to engage in anything that is inhuman, or dehumanizing in its effects.

If the ethicist begins with disciplined social analysis, he has to move to other points in order to clarify the moral judgments that he makes about what he finds to be the case. Often there is a division of labor between the social analyst and the moralist, though it is quite typical for the moralist to make a judgment on the information he perceives to be important or adequate pertaining to a particular instance, whether this information is derived in a disciplined way or by impressions. It is also the case that social analysis is often freighted with moral judgments. If Kenneth Underwood's study is taken as a case of social analysis done from ethical intention, the need for movement between principles or bases of moral judgment and empirical analysis can be seen. If the weakness in thought and deed of the Protestant churches in Holyoke is bad, as Underwood clearly indicates he believes, it is judged bad on the basis of moral and theological convictions, not sociological evidence. One can extrapolate from the analysis he makes to indicate what some of the bases of judgment are. Presumably the churches were not acting out a theologically defined conception of their mission; they were not being responsible to the God they confessed in worship. Presumably also they lacked the ethical clarity to order the various activities in which they ought to be engaged, and thus were institutionally subject to social pressures. Underwood does not draw out these things, for he is particularly seeking to show how moral communities must understand their social contexts through a process of social analysis. He does not claim that the book has Christian ethics as its primary subject matter. But a more extensive ethical treatise would require movement in the directions of the other bases. There is something theologically awry with the actual situation, there is something morally weak about it, and the religious leaders and laity lack some qualities of Christian existence which prohibit them from becoming more active in accord with professed convictions.

The fourth base, that of a conception of Christian existence, has not been clearly represented in our previous analysis. In the case of H. R. Niebuhr, an interpretation of moral existence is clearly a major starting point for ethical and moral reflection, but in *The Responsible Self* he is not concerned to suggest the particular qualities that the religious life in faith brings into being. Further exploration of Bultmann's ethics would be one way of making the point. Man in faith has a radical freedom to be himself, to be obedient to the command of God. The moral life is to some extent then a situational expression of that faith, that freedom, and that obedience.

The interrelation between base points, with a particular prime focus on the state of the life of faith, can best be illustrated by Luther's essay "On the Liberty of the Christian Man." In this work, Luther describes the Christian life in the famous aphorisms, "A Christian man is a perfectly free Lord of all, subject to none. A Christian man is a perfectly dutiful servant of all, subject to all."[45] He goes on to describe the nature of this Christian liberty and righteousness, which cannot be produced by work or by any external influence, but only by the Word of God received in faith. Thus, in the very description of the righteousness of the Christian, Luther immediately turns to the theological source and foundation of it, that is, God's gift of his Son, which is the act of God's justification of man. The concern for which Luther is most widely known even outside the Christian community enters in here, namely that law and works are unnecessary for any man's righteousness (in the sense of the gift of God's righteousness) and salvation. God counts men righteous, and in the faith of man gives the gift of liberty and righteousness. He unites the believer with Christ as the bride is united with the bridegroom. "Therefore, faith alone is the righteousness of a Christian man and the fulfilling of all the commandments."[46] Thus Luther describes the "inward man" with immediate reference to God's work for man in Jesus Christ.

This inward man, while never perfectly spiritual and holy in this life, nevertheless gives to the "outward man" certain characteristics. The works of the outward man never justify him before God, but they do express the desire born in faith to reduce the body to subjection and to purify its evil lusts. They are directed toward the neighbor in love. The attention given to the self in faith and the idea that the external actions are expressions of that faith can be seen when Luther writes, "These two sayings, therefore, are true: 'Good works do not make a good man, but a good man does good works; evil works do not make a wicked man, but a wicked man does evil works'; so that it is always necessary that the 'substance' or person itself be good before there can be any good works, and that good works follow and proceed from the good person, as Christ also says, 'A corrupt tree does not bring forth good fruit, a good tree does not bring forth evil fruit.' "[47] Faith, then, brings with it the gifts of righteousness and liberty, which are effectual through love. Faith "issues in works of the freest service cheerfully and lovingly done, with which a man willingly serves another without hope or reward."[48]

Luther does not digress from his primary attention to give illustrations of what the neighbor's needs are; he does not describe the kinds of personal and social contexts in which the works of love are to be effectual. But obviously he assumes that they are particular and concrete. Nor does he spell out some principles of Christian love that enter into the guidance of the action directed by love to the neighbor. He does have, however, the figure of the work of Jesus Christ in view, as that which gives something of the shape of the Christian's intentions and actions toward others. The full work of Christ presents a pattern for the relation to others. "Just as our neighbor is in need and lacks that in which we abound, so we also have been in need before God and have lacked His mercy. Hence, as our heavenly Father has in Christ freely come to our help, we also ought freely to help our neighbor through our body and its works, and each should become as it were a Christ to the other, that we may be Christs to one another and Christ may be the same in all; that is, that we may be truly Christians."[49] The work of Christ, received by Christians in faith, both empowers and shapes the arc of their relation to the neighbor, and in this sense functions as a broad but delineated pattern for the Christian moral life.

Thus Luther touches upon the four bases that have been indicated to be necessary for a systematic Christian ethic. His primary concern in the essay on liberty is to describe the Christian life, but he cannot do this without attending to the theological sources of that existence, and to both those persons toward whom it is expressed in love, and the shape of the life that properly expresses it.

The intention of this section has now been executed, namely to show that authors of important works in and for Christian ethics tend to focus on one base point in their exposition, and even to declare that a certain base point is the proper point for beginning Christian moral reflection, and that they necessarily move toward some consideration of the other base points. This is sometimes done with great self-consciousness so that the way in which they deal with them is consistent with their starting point, or it is only indicated in a cursory fashion that cries out for further exploration. The debate over context and principles is oversimplified if it does not take into account these base points and the way in which they are related to the discussions of context and the use and authority of principles.

For Clarification of Discussion

The way in which the debate has attended to the moral level of discourse without sufficiently moving to other levels is in part responsible for its being misplaced. It has tended to assume that the matter of how moral decisions are made could be separated from other considerations. I hope it is now clear that if one chooses to argue against "contextualism" one has to direct his arguments to the theological and ethical reasons given for the stress on context. Thus against Barth, Lehmann, and Sittler, one's argument ought primarily to be a theological argument. It is because these men have a certain view of God and his activity that they find contextualism congenial as an approach to ethics. None of them is fixed upon the question, "How do men decide what to do?" as if this ethical question were capable of abstraction from fundamental *theo*logical convictions in the strict sense. If one chooses to argue against H. R. Niebuhr, one would have to argue not only on theological grounds (not explicated in this essay), but also on the grounds of a moral anthropology. Is man to be understood as responder and answerer, or is he better understood as maker and citizen? If one chooses to argue against the demand for refined social analysis of the context of action, the character of one's concerns might be directed to whether that context is properly understood through the means of social research, and whether such a proposal does not carry with it unexplicated ethical and theological assumptions.

Similarly, if one argues against principles, one has to be particular about certain questions. From what sources are the principles derived? From nature, or from biblical revelation, or from the ethos of the Christian community? How are principles used? For giving direction to goals, or for the determination of right conduct? As prescriptive principles, or as analytical and illuminating principles?

If one persists in choosing sides in a misplaced debate, there are still questions that have to be dealt with. How does one move between moral principles and theological affirmations? Do certain defenses of principles assume certain views about God that are not necessarily consistent with such ethics? What is assumed about the nature of the moral self in various uses of principles? About the amenability of the social and personal world to subjection to principles, and actions governed quite exclusively by principles? How does one move between theological affirmations, moral principles, and moral judgments? Through a view of sensitivity and imagination? Through rational calculation?

Further elaboration of these questions is not necessary. One larger one still looms, namely, is there one normative starting point, or base point, for work in Christian ethics around which other discussion ought to cohere? On this question the author has convictions, but their exposition lies outside the scope of this methodological analysis.

NOTES

1. See, Barth, *Church Dogmatics*, Eng. ed. (Edinburgh: T. & T. Clark, 1957), II/2 especially pp. 631–701; see also *Against the Stream* (London: SCM Press, 1954), especially pp. 53–124, and *How to Serve God in a Marxist Land* (New York: Association Press, 1959), pp. 45–80. Dietrich Bonhoeffer, *Ethics* (London: SCM Press, 1955), especially pp. 17–25, 55–72, and 194–222. Søe, *Kristelig Etik*, 5th ed. (Copenhagen: C.E.C. Gads Forlag, 1962), pp. 11–234, especially pp. 108–70 (the second edition of this book was translated into German, *Christliche Ethik* [Munich: Chr. Kaiser Verlag, 1949], pp. 4–187, especially pp. 83–132). The Christian ethics of Bultmann also belong in this general camp; for a discussion see Thomas Oden, *Radical Obedience: The Ethics of R. Bultmann* (Philadelphia: Westminster, 1964). Currently the most significant ethics text that has come from the more radical Christian existentialist group is Knud Løgstrup, *Den Etiske Fordring*, 4th ed. (Copenhagen: Scandinavian University Books, 1958; German ed., *Die Ethische Forderung*, Tüebingen: H. Laupp, 1959). Obviously there are severe differences of opinion among these theologians, which point already to the mistake of trying to include too many writers under one rubric as is required in a debate formula.

2. See Elert, *The Christian Ethos* (Philadelphia: Muhlenberg Press, 1957); this is generally regarded to be a poor translation, and Künneth, *Politik zwischen Dämon und Gott* (Berlin: Lutherisches Verlagshaus, 1954).

3. Robert Gleason, S.J., "Situational Morality," *Thought*, (1957), XXXII, 555. The general movement was condemned by

Pope Pius XII in 1952. For a readily available example of this point of view, see Walter Dirks, "How Can I Know God's Will for Me?" *Cross Currents*, (1955), V, 77–92. For other discussions, see Karl Rahner, *Nature and Grace* (London: Sheed and Ward, 1963), pp. 84–111; Josef Fuchs, *Situation und Entscheidung* (Frankfurt: Verlag Josef Knecht, 1952); and John C. Ford and Gerald Kelly, *Contemporary Moral Theology I* (Westminster, Md.: The Newman Press, 1958), pp. 42–140.

4. See, for example, Bernard Häring, *The Law of Christ* (Westminster, Md.: The Newman Press, 1961), I, especially 35ff., and Josef Pieper, *Prudence* (New York: Pantheon, 1959).

5. See Lehmann, "The Foundation and Pattern of Christian Behavior," in John A. Hutchison, ed., *Christian Faith and Social Action* (New York: Charles Scribner's Sons, 1953), pp. 93–116, and *Ethics in a Christian Context* (New York: Harper & Row, 1963), Alexander Miller, *The Renewal of Man* (New York: Doubleday, 1955). Joseph Sittler, *The Structure of Christian Ethics* (Baton Rouge: Louisiana State University Press, 1958). H. R. Niebuhr, *The Responsible Self* (New York: Harper & Row, 1963). Albert Rasmussen, *Christian Social Ethics* (Englewood Cliffs, N.J.: Prentice-Hall, 1956). Joseph Fletcher, "A New Look in Christian Ethics," *Harvard Divinity School Bulletin*, (1959), XXIV 7–18. Gordon Kaufman, *The Context of Decision* (New York: Abingdon Press, 1961). Charles C. West, *Communism and the Theologians* (Philadelphia: Westminster, 1958). James Gustafson, "Christian Ethics and Social Policy," in Paul Ramsey, ed., *Faith and Ethics* (New York: Harper, 1957), pp. 119–39.

6. For a discussion of an unpublished paper by Bennett, see Lehmann, *Ethics in a Christian Context*, pp. 148–54. Paul Ramsey, *War and the Christian Conscience* (Durham, N.C.: Duke University Press, 1961), pp. 3–14, and various occasional writings. Alvin Pitcher, "A New Era in Protestant Social Ethics?" Chicago Theological Seminary *Register*, (1958), XLVIII, 8–14. Clinton Gardiner, "The Role of Law and Moral Principles in Christian Ethics," *Religion in Life*, (1959), XXVIII, 236–47. A running discussion of the issues can be found in the following references to *Christianity and Crisis*: Robert Fitch, "The Obsolescence of Ethics," Nov. 16, 1959; Alexander Miller, "Unprincipled Living: The Ethics of Obligation," Mar. 21, 1960; Paul Ramsey, "Faith Effective Through In-Principled Love," May 30, 1960. See also Edward L. Long, *Conscience and Compromise* (Philadelphia: Westminster, 1954). Attention should be called to Father Edward Duff's discussion in *The Social Thought of the World Council of Churches* (New York: Association Press, 1956), pp. 93ff.

7. H. D. Aiken, "Levels of Moral Discourse," in *Reason and Conduct* (New York: Knopf, 1962), pp. 65–87. The essay was previously published in *Ethics*, (1952), LXII, 235–46.

8. The movement from one level to another in theological ethics has been very confused. Indeed, the logic of theological ethical

discourse has not been very clear precisely at this point, sometimes as a matter of conscious commitment. A great deal of work could be done in the analysis of written materials on the nest of issues opened up by Aiken's essay.

9. Kenneth Underwood, *Protestant and Catholic* (Boston: Beacon Press, 1957). A more recent study partially in this mode of contextualism is Denis Munby, *God and the Rich Society* (London: Oxford Univ. Press, 1961). Other examples could be cited as well.

10. Barth, *Church Dogmatics*, II/2, 663–64.

11. *Ibid.*, p. 576.

12. *Ibid.*, p. 580.

13. *Ibid.*, p. 581.

14. *Ibid.*, p. 582.

15. *Ibid.*, p. 645–661.

16. Sittler, *The Structure of Christian Ethics*, p. 73.

17. *Ibid.*, ch. I, "The Confusion in Contemporary Ethical Speech."

18. *Ibid.*, p. 36.

19. I read Sittler's book as a contemporary statement of the basic character of Luther's ethics under the gospel. Christ is the shaper of the Christian life in the participation of the believer in faith in him. Christ is also the shaper of the Christian life that is active in love to the neighbor in his particular need. In this manner Sittler is close to the theme of the best known of Luther's writings in Christian ethics, "On the Liberty of the Christian Man." See discussion of this document below.

20. Lehmann, *Ethics in a Christian Context*, pp. 358–59, 347.

21. Lehmann, "The Foundation and Pattern of Christian Behavior," p. 100.

22. *Op. cit.*, p. 25. Note that the particular question of Christian ethics is on the "moral" level of discourse. Note also that Lehmann asks it in terms of "what *am* I to do," and not "what *ought* I to do." In this way he very self-consciously reduces the imperative tone in favor of a more indicative one.

23. *Ibid.*, p. 105.

24. *Ibid.*, p. 47.

25. For a discussion of Bultmann's ethics, see Thomas Oden, *op. cit.* Barth also has an anthropology that stresses the immediacy of responsibility given to the particular person, and softens any lines of continuity between the person and his community, or the person and his ethos. I shall not discuss Barth here, though it would be fruitful to do so.

26. Niebuhr, *The Responsible Self*, p. 56.

27. *Ibid.*, p. 61.

28. *Ibid.*, p. 63.

29. *Ibid.*, p. 126.

30. A similar view of man is penetrating Roman Catholic philosophy and ethics. See, for example, Albert Dondeyne, *Faith*

and the World (Pittsburgh: Duquesne University Press, 1963), pp. 145ff., and Bernard Häring, *The Law of Christ* (Westminster, Md.: The Newman Press, 1963), pp. 35ff.

31. *An Interpretation of Christian Ethics* (New York: Harper & Row, 1935), p. 117.

32. *Ibid.*, p. 140.

33. *The Nature and Destiny of Man* (New York: Charles Scribner's Sons, 1943), II, especially chs. 9 and 10.

34. *Christian Ethics and Social Policy* (New York: Charles Scribner's Sons, 1946), p. 76. Oldham's suggestions are found in Visser 't Hooft and Oldham, *The Church and its Function in Society* (London: G. Allen and Unwin, 1937), pp. 209ff.

35. *War and the Christian Conscience*, pp. 6, 4.

36. "Christian Ethics and Social Policy," in Paul Ramsey, ed., *Faith and Ethics* (New York: Harper & Row, 1957), pp. 126–29.

37. Ramsey, *op. cit.*, p. 179.

38. *Ibid.*, p. 190.

39. See, for example, his discussion of sexuality, *op. cit.*, pp. 133–40.

40. *Ibid.*, p. 72.

41. *Ibid.*, pp. 116, 117.

42. *Ibid.*, p. 54.

43. *Ibid.*, pp. 148ff., and particularly p. 152. "For a *koinonia* ethic the clarification of ethical principles and their application to concrete situations is ethically unreal because such clarification is a logical enterprise and there is no way in logic of closing the gap between the abstract and the concrete." I regard this assertion to be the slaying of a straw man, for no serious moralist has believed that logic alone closed that gap. Roman Catholic moral theology, which is most susceptible to the criticism, never assumes that logic alone is the path from principle to concrete action, and always has a place for the person, with his natural and theological virtues, who acts responsibly. See, for example, Josef Pieper's *Prudence*, which admittedly makes the most of the person who is the juncture between principles and actions.

44. *Ibid.*, pp. 55, 16–17.

45. Citations here are to the edition, *Three Treatises* (Philadelphia: Muhlenberg Press, 1943), p. 251.

46. *Ibid.*, p. 262.

47. *Ibid.*, p. 271.

48. *Ibid.*, p. 276.

49. *Ibid.*, p. 279.

New Ethical Possibility:
The Task of "Post-Christendom" Ethics

Paul Peachey

Far from bemoaning the fact that "history has disowned the expectation that world society would be made in the image of Christendom," Paul Peachey finds it a largely salutary development, affording the church an opportunity to unload some unbiblical baggage it has long been burdened with. For there is much in Christendom which partakes more of "Constantinian" than of essential Christianity. The conversion of the emperor Constantine in the fourth century A.D. and the eventual rise of the church to hegemony in the West were accompanied by an inevitable diminution of internal discipline in the community of grace; the church, now socially oriented, found itself looking upon such institutions as war and slavery as political matters, and whether it sanctioned or opposed them, it tended either to take its cue from the political order or to demand actions of the secular authorities which it was not itself willing or able to undertake. Now, says Peachey, the church has a chance to break decisively with the Constantinian world view. As Executive Secretary of the Church Peace Mission, Washington, D.C., Dr. Peachey has impeccable credentials for discussing the topic of which he writes. His article is from the January 1965 issue of *Interpretation: A Journal of Bible and Theology*.* Dr. Peachey is author of *The Church in the City* and editor of *Biblical Realism Confronts the Nation*.

I

THE DEVELOPMENT of nuclear weapons has accentuated immeasurably the already deepening crisis in Western Christian morality. Not only have events far outstripped the instruments we possess to manage them, but they

* Published by Union Theological Seminary in Virginia, 3401 Brook Rd., Richmond, Va. 23227.

move in a course that is deeply at variance with the sense of direction implicit in our traditional morality. We are left, as it were, without either rudder or compass.

Traditionally, and as the etymology of the word suggests, morality may be viewed simply as the cumulative values and wisdom emerging from historical experience. New historical facts emerge ceaselessly from the bosom of history, as products of the past, and from the reservoir of morality we extrapolate ceaselessly the formulas which these facts require. Thus by definition (whatever else may be involved), the *ought* in the life of society, the imperative, arises from what *is*. Characteristically, therefore, one of the criteria employed by the Kennedy administration during the Cuba crisis of October 1962 was that the policies chosen had to be in keeping with "the American character."

Within the framework of this morality, war may be viewed as a structural component in the architecture of Western history. In the words of the classical theorist, Karl von Clausewitz, war is "nothing but a continuation of political intercourse, with a mixture of other means. . . ." Though various factors are determinative in the total power of a nation, power depends, according to this view, at any certain point on the possibility of military sanctions. Moreover, "a nation can hope to have a strong position in the political world only if its character and practice in actual war support each other in constant reciprocal action." Thus, in von Clausewitz' more widely quoted words, "war is a mere continuation of policy by other means."[1]

This morality of war was codified in the doctrine of the "just war." While in a formal or technical sense this doctrine is essentially medieval and Catholic, in more loose and diffuse terms it remains to this day the dominant military ethos of the Western world. The doctrine simply assumes that war *at some junctures* is inevitable. The existence of men as social beings in self-determining "systems of action" results in an uneasy and ever-shifting equilibrium among them. Real conflicts of interest occur, and where other means are exhausted, redress may be sought by military means commensurate to that end. The true thrust of morality then would be to contain war and not to eliminate it totally.

From recent discussions concerning nuclear war the word has frequently come that the doctrine of the "just war" is now obsolete. But such an assertion, as it turns out, is ambiguous and susceptible to several interpretations. 1) It may suggest a change in the character of warfare itself, so that, when measured by the traditional criteria, war can no longer be viewed as just. 2) It may mean, on the other hand, that the doctrine is obsolete, and that it must be updated if it is to guide military policy in the nuclear age. The consequences flowing from this declaration of obsolescence are also ambiguous. In the first instance it may mean, precisely because the doctrine is perennially valid, that war is now outlawed. Or it may mean, in the latter instance, that the institution of war must stay, but that it must now be surrounded with new restraints and criteria—in sum, that the doctrine must be extended. The former conclusion is generally known under the label of "nuclear pacifism." The latter conclusion is illustrated, though not primarily motivated, by the upgrading and updating of conventional armaments during the last several years.

The basic question in this debate pertains to the nature of nuclear weapons. Do they constitute a *qualitative* leap in weapons development, so that the destructive potential war eclipses any possible gains from it? Or is the change, in the end, a merely *quantitative* one, another link in a long chain of social and technological evolution? To this day the debate remains inconclusive. For even if the case can be proven that the change is qualitative, the facts of power as such are not thereby necessarily altered. Nothing "eschatological" transpired at Hiroshima, if a theological term is permitted, to eliminate conflict from international discourse. If war now, contrary to all earlier times, can no longer serve as an instrument of policy, other means for handling conflicts heretofore solved in such fashion will have to be hammered out on the anvil of history.

Accepting for the moment this latter line of reasoning, we ask immediately what the prospects may be. Is the substitution of other means of conflict-resolution a live option? The current signs, however slight, of accommodation between the two nuclear giants, their halting steps toward policies of co-existence, reflect in part the impact of this logic, namely, that new ways of handling international conflict must be found. If war as such cannot be renounced, at least all-out nuclear war can never be a matter of deliberate policy. And time may reveal that this "softening" of positions must be viewed as part of the de-romanticizing of war which began in the trenches of World War I. For if that war was a climax in the crusading romanticism of war, it was also a turning point. The Allies fought World War II in more grim and pragmatic terms. Nor are these mere attitudinal changes. From the League of Nations to our present United Nations there have been forward strides in the development of the instruments of internationalism. Man's outlook and his institutions change correlatively.

Distressingly enough, however, our time displays also quite contrary trends. Military logic and power have come to permeate and dominate our life, and hence also our impact upon the rest of the world, to unprecedented degrees. The disillusionment brought by the collapse of the dream that the world had outgrown war at the beginning of this century has left a legacy of cynicism which throttles the daring for which our time calls. The threat of a new counterplan for world organization (international communism), inimical to the scheme molded by our own interests, strikes terror in the American heart. And, as if all this were not enough, a generation of newly independent and volatile nations will mean an uneasy international equilibrium for decades to come. Between the fear of nuclear destruction on the one hand and of communist expansion on the other, Americans for the most part stand transfixed in terror, frozen by the frightful dilemma. These opposites resemble, as it were, the hackneyed imaginary situation in which the irresistible force confronts the immovable object. It is from the stuff of this dilemma, rather than from any coherent rationale—for a "just war" doctrine or any other—that our present military policy is fashioned. The majority of the American people undoubtedly deplore the "necessity" of this policy and recognize that it provides no permanent solution. They handle the resultant guilt and anxiety, one may surmise, either by looking the other way or by resorting to the scapegoating of radical political movements.

Perhaps at this point we can only admit that as men we lack the overview and the prescience which would enable us to discern the emerging contours of the future. Will the impulses which make for war somehow be contained or sublimated? Do the growth of international institutions and the slow accommodations of hostile political systems constitute the early stages of a more stable world order? Or do dark countertrends constitute the real movement of our time, the preliminaries of a new Armageddon? In any event, it is difficult to see how we can draw further guidance from traditional "just war" canons. But if, as habitually has been done, we equate these canons with the "Judeo-Christian" heritage, we must really face the question as to the further relevance of that heritage as such.

II

There is a far more basic historical question, however, which, to my knowledge, is seldom faced in our present context. The issue is not merely whether military policies in the nuclear age meet the test of a just-war doctrine, or whether they can be modified to do so. The issue is really the reverse: Does the just-war doctrine itself pass the test of history or, more particularly, the test of a Christian view of history? Far more is at stake here than a rhetorical reversal of the question. For the doctrine of the just war, whatever its theological force, is itself a historical construct, a historical product. As such it presupposes certain historical facts as well as a certain world view whereby those facts were comprehended. We must be prepared to grant, on the other hand, particularly within a faith which takes history seriously, that the just-war doctrine may be the expression of a timeless truth, that today as always our task is to contain and to harness warfare, and that today as always efforts to eliminate it will result in Utopian mischief. But the opposite possibility must also be visualized with like seriousness—and this, precisely, has not been done. Events today, however, have caught up with us and demand imperiously that we face this question now.

To restrict ourselves for the moment to the historical

question: What if the doctrine of the just war were really
time-bound, normatively irrelevant to historical situations
other than the matrix which shaped it? What if, in the larger
perspectives of the divine purpose in human history, the
synthesis of Christendom together with its doctrine of the
just war were merely episodic in nature and therefore heretical
and sectarian in meaning when applied normatively beyond
its own boundaries in time and place?

It will be countered at once, and rightly so, that a sort of
process of self-repudiation of Christendom has been under
way for several centuries. The Renaissance, the Reformation,
the triumph of national autonomy, the industrial and the
scientific revolutions—all these and many other forces have
long since shattered the classic forms of Christendom. In fact,
American independence and the genius developed subse-
quently in American history represent the deliberate repudiation of the salient features of medieval Christendom. As our
legal tender proclaims, America is indeed "a new era."

But when we probe the deeper currents of ethical thought, it
is the *continuities* of Christendom, even in American life,
rather than the *discontinuities* which strike us. For while some
of the forces which shattered the synthesis were frankly
secular, the real shifts which have transpired represent an
internal reordering or new divisions of labor, as it were,
within the *corpus christianum* rather than a repudiation of
the system itself. Not the notion of civilization as "Christian"
was called into question, but the abuses—as they were viewed
—within that civilization. Not the settlements of Constantine
or Theodosius, nor the unity of civilization and Christianity
against barbarianism wrought out in the Donatist controversy
and the Gothic invasions, but corruption and perversions
within that scheme were the subject of the protest of the
Protestant centuries. This the pages of early American Puritan
history, for example, make eloquently clear. According to the
informal Puritan creed it was to be the historic mission of this
new nation, America, to purify the civilization of Christendom.
This inner reordering since the Reformation has been aptly
described by John Baillie as the rise of "an open as contrasted
with a compulsive Christian civilization."[2]

The vision of a Christian civilization as the destiny of mankind survived all the turbulences of the emerging "modern" era and persisted well into the twentieth century. The great missionary movements of modern times, though the fruit of heroic vision and faith, were sustained by the expectation that our Christian civilization was the destiny of mankind and the goal of history within history. Alexander J. Schem, writing in the M'Clintock-Strong Cyclopedia of 1868, hailed "the territorial extension" of "Christendom . . . almost without interruption from the beginning. . . . Thus the time seems near when the extent of Christendom will coincide with the extent of the earth." When the Edinburgh missionary conference raised the curtain on the present ecumenical movement in 1910, it appeared that, to use the words of W. A. Visser 't Hooft, "the stream of world history" was flowing "in the same direction as the stream of the history of the Kingdom of God." Missionary protagonists actually looked forward to the "mutual interpenetration of Church and Society" on a worldwide scale.[3] To note another example: Charles Clayton Morrison, first editor of the second of three journals launched during this century under the title *Christendom*, wrote in his initial editorial in 1935, that he regarded the new journal

> . . . as an expression of the new creative era in world culture into which, despite powerful counter currents, the broad stream of human life is moving. It believes that art and science and all social institutions are undergoing radical reorientation, and that the Christian Church is on the point of coming alive once more to the supreme responsibility of Christianity in civilization. And the goal of civilization can be nothing less than literally, a Christendom.[4]

In yet another context, as recently as 1953 Stewart W. Hermann could describe the same vision in these words: "The church is defined [in Sweden] as the state performing its religious functions. The definition is reversible: The state in the performance of its religious functions is the church."[5]

It may be that World War II and its aftermath have dealt the final fatal blow to this kind of thinking. As Visser 't Hooft pointed out in 1959 in the same lecture, "There is not the slightest chance to expect what so many expected in 1910, that within the foreseeable future anything like a Christendom civilization will spread to all parts of the world. The 'Great Society' which penetrates all continents is something very different from 'Christendom.' It is a technical civilization, which may have borrowed some notions from Christian civilization, but which is essentially this-worldly and man-centered." Even in the West, where churches long thought of themselves as national, embracing entire populations, they now find themselves in a position in which "they have become minority churches in an environment of secularism or religious indifference."[6] In sum, thus, history has disowned the expectation that world society would be made in the image of Christendom. The "world has come of age," to use a current cliché. It no longer awaits nor accepts the tutelage of the church. The church, therefore, can cut no more pitiable figure than to continue to issue interdicts, even in modern guise, in medieval, business-as-usual fashion.

While we—as men of all ages have been—are too close to our own time to judge its full significance, the arrest of this forward flow of Christendom is plain for all to see. The term "post-Christendom" is thus more precise than the more common expression, "post-Christian." This is not the place to resolve the conceptual and terminological problems which we here encounter. But for the moment we shall follow the distinctions made by William Temple that ". . . Christendom . . . is not identical with the Christian church, for that existed before there was anything that corresponds to the name of Christendom, and exists now far beyond the limits of Christendom. Christendom is the fellowship of professedly Christian nations considered as a unity."[7] That is, "post-Christendom" connotes the passing of a particular historical form, whereas "post-Christian" could suggest the passing of the Christian "religion" as such, which would be an obvious fallacy.

If the end of colonialism—what K. M. Panikkar calls the *Vasco da Gama period*[8]—and of the hegemony of the church in the West marks indeed the end of Christendom, our century, as a turning point, eclipses by far that from which most of us draw our orientation, namely, the Protestant Reformation. The real march of modern history entails not a mere internal reordering but the disbanding of the system itself. Here and there, of course, perceptive souls have long seen this. Thus Walter Hobhouse wrote, in the year of the Edinburgh Conference:

> Long ago I came to believe that the great change in the relation between Church and the World which began with the conversion of Constantine is not only the decisive turning point in Church History, but is also the key to many of the practical difficulties of the present day; and the Church of the future is destined more and more to return to a condition of things somewhat like that which prevailed in the Ante-Nicene Church; that is to say, that instead of pretending to be co-extensive with the world, it will accept a position involving a more conscious antagonism with the world, and will, in return, regain in some measure its former coherence.[9]

But for the most part we have barely begun to comprehend what this revolution entails. And even where we have grasped it intellectually, our older reflexes persist. Nowhere is the crisis more acute than in social ethics.

III

Even a superficial glance at the emergence and the further development of the ethical enterprise in Christendom reveals, once the major physiognomy had been sketched, that the tasks of ethical inquiry were determined largely by the constant undulation of the equilibrium within the system. Again, to return to the etymology of morals or ethics (closer definitions or distinctions lie beyond our present purpose), this appears to be precisely the function of ethics. But if only this was required in the past—and it is not ours here to judge— something other now confronts us. If history has repudiated our model, which itself had been a historical product, we must begin anew, and *radically* so. And this, for all the iconoclasm that has marked the field of ethics in recent years, has yet to be undertaken. That is to say, the Constantinian settlement, to employ a shorthand formula for a phenomenon vastly greater and more complex than this single event, entailed a sort of "faulting" in the strata of the faith (to use a geological figure) which remained permanently embedded in the life of the church. And this shift affected not, as it might seem, merely peripheral or developmental matters but the center of the faith. Central tenets such as Christology, soteriology, ecclesiology, and eschatology were fundamentally and permanently altered and, from here, the whole of Christian ethics.

In the present context we must content ourselves with a mere summary statement of what this development meant. Recognizing the over-simplifications of any summary, we shall venture to suggest nonetheless that the ethical consequence of the Constantinian shift was the transfer of the framework of Christian ethical thought from the community of grace, the new people of God, to the larger domain of the natural community, so that the church now looked to society for levels of ethical performance, which, paradoxically, she could not postulate for her own members. Changes in public morality at the points which matter were now to become the *condition* for changes within the Christian community and not their *consequence*. Or, to use the recent words of Donald B. Meyer with reference to certain liberal American churchmen during the interwar period, they "found themselves claiming something of theological significance about American life, which they could not claim for the Protestant congregations and churches themselves."[10] This means that the framework of ethical discourse came to be no longer the new possibilities of grace but the *value* dialogue of the civilization.[11] To quote Meyer again, this time with reference to Reinhold Niebuhr (who in this regard was indeed neo-*orthodox*), grace was not "a resource that, supplementing the virtue and intelligence of men, guaranteed the Kingdom": It was "a resource that consoled men for the fact that the Kingdom was an impossibility in history."[12]

To approach the ethical consequences from another angle, the Constantinian settlements transposed the watershed of human destiny from the biblical frontiers between faith and unfaith to the frontiers between "Hellenism" and "barbarianism," to use the words of Crane Brinton,[13] or between "christendom" and "hethenesse," to use the terms of a fourteenth-century English writer.[14] Therefore, an established church, which could lambaste the "sectarians" for pretending to distinguish believers and nonbelievers in the church, did not hesitate to invoke the far more drastic discipline, namely ultimate sanctions, at the now transposed frontiers of Christendom. Thus from the coerced settlement of the Donatist controversy there runs a clear stream in Christian history through the sumptuary laws of Puritan governments to the current campaign of the American churches for civil rights legislation. It is not that churches should not have opposed marauding in North Africa, drunkenness in Geneva, or cattle prods in Albany, Georgia. The error is, rather, that while failing in their internal ethical discourse, they enlisted the legislative and police power of civil government to demand of the whole society levels of performance not yet implicit in their own life.

Let us note two specific examples close to our present situation. Dwight Lowell Dumond, writing on practices among churches with reference to slaveholding, shows how, after having sought to restrain the practice, they finally "threw in the glove" about the turn of the nineteenth century and turned to legislative efforts. But "circulating petitions to legislatures," he says, "was nothing more and nothing less than abandonment of the power and duty of the church to direct the moral reformation of slaveholders by condemning slave-holding as a sin. This was no mere academic question. It was fatal to the church and a death blow to democracy. Henceforth the church considered slavery a political question. . . ." Between the "Quaker practice of individual repentance, manumission, and retributive justice on the one hand, and emancipation by political action on the other," there is a gulf as wide as the ocean. "The failure of the churches at this point in our history forced the country to turn to political action against slavery, and political action destroyed slavery as system but left the hearts of the slaveholders unregenerate and left oppression of the free Negro little less of an evil than slavery had been."[15]

The other example of error is the attitude of the churches toward war. Here, too, there is long-standing concern and action. But, characteristically, the effort is directed toward national goals and policies which are deemed desirable. The question is posed in terms of what can be done to limit or to prevent war—in terms of what Christians are called to do in a world that, in its fallenness, is already alienated and "at war." Thus the most recent attempt to deal with the question in the ecumenical framework was a study undertaken by the study department of the World Council of Churches under the title of "The Prevention of War in a Nuclear Age"—a study which even in this innocuous form, it might be added, proved embarrassing to the action department of the Council, namely, the Commission of the Churches on International Affairs.[16] The prevention of war, indeed, is a matter of Christian concern, and one can only deplore the lack of Christian initiative at this point. But stating the problem thus is to treat the matter only penultimately.

In effect, as Martin Buber points out in an incisive word, the churches summon the nations to assume risks that they themselves have not yet taken. When asked why the appeals of the churches for peace remain ineffectual, he replied, "They [those making the appeals] were not committed; they only said what *other* people—those in governments and the General Staff of armies—ought to do. They never stated what the authors of these appeals would do *themselves,* nor to what they committed themselves. . . . And it is only when a man commits himself that others really listen to him."[17]

IV

Having thus pressed the point we must now move on to recognize the fact that, on levels of analysis and of theological discourse, various aspects of these problems have come to increasing focus during recent decades. A striking example is the prophetic word of the 1937 Oxford Conference:

The first duty of the Church, and its greatest service to the world, is that it be in very deed the Church—confessing the true faith, committed to the fulfillment of the will of Christ, its only Lord, and united in Him in a fellowship of love and service.[18]

Or we may take a random example from assessments of the missionary experiences of Christendom: Thomas Ohm, a Catholic former missionary to China, concludes in his reflections on what we called, above, the *Vasco da Gama period*, and in contrast to it:

> It is part of the essence of the true Church to be in a minority and to be despised and oppressed by the world. Where Christianity is not judged in the light of grace, misunderstandings are inevitable.[19]

More on the theological side is this statement of H. D. Wendland, written in 1953:

> Thirty years ago, if someone had asked what the relevance of eschatology was for social ethics he would have received a rather knowing smile and the retort that Christianity had fortunately gone *beyond* eschatology *into* the field of social ethics. Christians had ceased to wait for the Kingdom of God and were concerned for improving the world and human society. . . . Today we need to move in the opposite direction, away from a social ethic which had its root in a secular, autonomous, idealistic or humanistic outlook, away even from a "Christian sociology" back into the realm of eschatology.[20]

Paul Minear, commenting on a study published by Olaf Linton in 1932, notes that since World War I, in studies of the early church, there has been a

> . . . steady turning away from the questions of organization to those of ultimate significance of the Church as a divine-human reality. . . . Theological categories have more and more displaced sociological and historical categories, for the Church is seen as the realm for the operation of the Holy Spirit.[21]

This list might, and indeed must, be extended to include developments such as the recovery in biblical theology in recent decades, the rediscovery of the church in settings of suffering, and the awareness of the perils of culture religion in our own land. To be sure, by now a rigorous skepticism is in order toward all vaunted "break-throughs." The theological enterprise reminds one of the amateur tire-changer who succeeds in getting the bead under the rim on one side only to see it snap out again on the other. Thus Luther claimed with pride (and somewhat in his steps much later, Emil Brunner) that he had finally resolved the old problem of dualism which has always plagued the church, only to have it emerge in a new

form in the "two-kingdom" theory. Thus, amid the undula-
tions of theological currents, perhaps the fact had better be
faced. The problem defies a systematic or permanent solution.
Somehow we must work with Christ's own formula—"Who-
soever shall do the will of my Father which is in heaven, the
same is my brother, and sister, and mother." From this duality
of "nature" and "grace" there is no escape.

But have we found our bearings? Do we know the direction and the form of Christian obedience in a pluralistic world,
a world of autonomous spheres of culture and society—
autonomous because no longer amenable to churchly proctor-
ing? The question of war, indeed of ethics as such, is but part
of the larger crisis of Christian meaning in our time. But the
relationship of faith and ethics is reciprocal. The one problem
cannot be resolved without the other. Thus we must ask more
earnestly than hitherto: May the recurrent crisis in modern
faith and theology perhaps derive in the end from the theological faulting of the Constantinian millennium?

To pose this question is not to deny some extraordinary
achievements of Christendom, nor is it to fall victim to the
illusion of primitivism, to the dream of a recaptured pristine
purity, as though nineteen centuries of history had not transpired. Theologically speaking, however, there is a sense in
which we can break out of the Constantinian, or "Christendom," circle only at the point of entry. Or, to state the matter
somewhat otherwise, if the perimeter of the vision of Christendom was quite rightly that whole world which God loves, its
axis, the moral dialogue of a fallen world, was false. Without
prejudice to the catholicity of the vision, it is the task of post-
Christendom ethics to restore as axis in Christian moral decision the discourse of the obedient congregation, where the
Risen Lord empowers us to bind and to loose. The Good
News is not merely a forensic proclamation to those trapped
in the fatalities of history; it is also the enactment of a new
ethical possibility. When once more she becomes vibrant with
that possibility, the church will be heard precisely in a world
that has "come of age."

NOTES

1. Joseph I. Green, *The Living Thoughts of Clausewitz* (Philadelphia: David McKay, 1943), pp. 12, 150.

2. Baillie, *What is a Christian Civilisation?* (Oxford: Oxford University Press, 1945), p. 44.

3. Visser 't Hooft, "The Asian Churches in the Ecumenical Movement," in *A Decisive Hour for the Christian Mission* (London: Student Christian Movement Press, 1960), p. 53.

4. Morrison, *Christendom: A Quarterly Review*, Vol. I (1935).

5. Hermann, *Report from Christian Europe* (New York: Friendship Press, 1953), p. 218.

6. Visser 't Hooft, *loc. cit.*

7. Temple, "The Restoration of Christendom," *Christendom, op. cit.*, p. 17. On the distinction between "post-Christian" and what we here call "post-Christendom," cf. David Danzig (*Commentary* [1961], p. 50): "We are on the threshold of, if not already in the "post-Christian" era—though not in the sense of a dying Christianity (which is how the term was first used), but rather as signifying the obsolescence of Christian ethnocentrism and the emergence of a religiously pluralistic world." Cf. also Baillie, *op. cit.*

8. Panikkar, *Asia and Western Dominance: A Survey of the Vasco da Gama Epoch of Asian History, 1498–1945* (London: Allen & Unwin, 1953).

9. Hobhouse, *The Church and the World in Idea and History* (London: Macmillan & Co., 1910), pp. ix f.

10. Meyer, *The Protestant Search for Political Realism, 1919–1941* (Berkeley: University of California Press, 1960), pp. 325 f.

11. When viewed from this perspective, Kant's "categorical imperative" could be regarded as the fullest flowering of the Christian ethic!

12. Meyer, *op. cit.*, p. 239.

13. Brinton, *A History of Western Morals* (New York: Harcourt, Brace, 1959), p. 17.

14. Quoted in *The Oxford English Dictionary* (Oxford: The Clarendon Press, 1933), II, 389.

15. Dumond, *Anti-Slavery: The Crusade for Freedom in America* (Ann Arbor: University of Michigan Press, 1961), p. 343 f.

16. Thomas Taylor and Robert Bilheimer, *Christians and the Prevention of War in an Atomic Age* (London: SCM Press, 1961).

17. Quoted by Helmut Gollwitzer, *Therefore Choose Life*, Gollwitzer *et alii*, (Nyack, N.Y.: International Fellowship of Reconciliation, 1961).

18. *The Churches Survey Their Task: The Report of the Conference at Oxford . . .* (London: Allen & Unwin, 1937), p. 57.

19. Ohm, *Asia Looks at Western Christianity* (London: Thomas Nelson & Sons, 1959), p. 217.

20. Wendland, "The Relevance of Eschatology for Social Ethics," *Ecumenical Review*, (1953), V, 367 f.

21. Minear, *Images of the Church in the New Testament* (Philadelphia: The Westminster Press, 1960), pp. 255 f.

Sexuality and Jesus

Tom F. Driver

Since the days of St. Augustine the church, reflecting an attitude more Platonist than biblical, has often undervalued and at times even disparaged man's sexual nature. Recent Christian thinkers, seeking to rectify this distortion, have affirmed sexuality as a God-created good. Even so, contends Tom F. Driver, their remarks on the subject tend to turn quickly to the "safe" subjects of love and responsibility— and they will continue to fail to deal with sexuality *per se* as long as they fail to deal with the question of the sexual nature of the God-Man Jesus Christ. Pursuing the logical if disquieting thesis that if Jesus was fully man as well as fully God, he could not have been a stranger to sexual desire, Dr. Driver comes to the conclusion that the Gospels are silent about Jesus' sexuality because Christ is himself the "great neutralizer" of the religious meaning of sex, seeing it as a fact of life rather than either a mystical or a demonic force. Dr. Driver's article originally appeared in the March 1965 issue of the *Union Seminary Quarterly Review*,* a publication of the New York seminary where he is Associate Professor of Christian Theology. A notably versatile man, Dr. Driver, having served as drama critic of *The Reporter* and *The Christian Century*, is at home no less in theatrical than in theological circles. A salient example of his critical acumen is his book *The Sense of History in Greek and Shakespearean Drama*.

NOTHING, IT has been said, frightens the Church as much as sex.

We might be inclined, in this day of frankness, to doubt the truth of such an observation and to point, by way of proof, to the spate of Christian literature in recent years that

* 3041 Broadway, New York, N.Y. 10027. Copyright © 1965 by Union Theological Seminary in the City of New York. Reprinted by permission of the author and his agent, James Brown Associates, Inc.

has addressed itself to sexual ethics in a positive frame of mind. Examination of the literature, however, reveals a curious fact. In almost every case sexuality is linked, by one argument or another, with love. Then, implicitly or explicitly, the two are equated, and the discussion of sexual ethics turns into a discussion of the ethics of love. This persistent tendency among Christian writers cannot but leave the impression that Christianity shies from sex as a horse will shy at danger. The argument turns aside into a "safer" subject, leaving the impression that sexuality is to be redeemed by love.

In one sense, of course, love *does* redeem sexuality, but this is the same sense in which it redeems *all* human activity. Hence, to speak of love as the fulfillment of sex, however true, is not to say anything unique or informative about sex itself. It is of no more help than to say that love redeems politics.

The situation is not improved very much if, in addition to love, the author speaks also of "responsibility." To urge that the sexual life be made responsible or that responsibility be the criterion of its rightness is at once to say too much and too little. It is counsel of perfection. The more seriously one takes it, the more likely is he to delude himself. To tell a person to be responsible is like telling a clown to be funny. He knows that's his business, but he may not know how to go about it, and he may think he's most funny when he's really boring us with his self-regard.

The accent is placed so strongly on love and responsibility in Christian writing about sex because the mood of the times is so strongly antilegalistic. The Protestant theologian who concerns himself with the law nowadays is a rare bird. As long as this is the case, the Church will not be able to shed much light on the subject of sexual ethics.

However, the question of law and gospel is one I shall not open at present. I shall merely observe that law is never taken seriously where the given phenomena of life are slighted, where there is a disposition to subordinate pragmatic decisions to general statements of value. As long as we prefer to speak of love and responsibility rather than of sexual acts and desires we shall not understand the wisdom of societies that have dealt with sexuality by confronting it with rules that are, or appear to be, partly arbitrary. Sex is a force, and like all other forces it dissipates itself unless it is, by some extraneous power, contained.

To see this, however, requires that sexuality be accepted and examined in its own right without being transmuted into a mere instance of an absolute value such as love. We must therefore ask why the Church refuses to do this in its present state of mind. I suggest it is because there is a very touchy spot in what might be called the "sexual imagination" of the Church. This spot appears in its thinking about Jesus and sexuality. It is there I shall probe to see if a pocket of infection may not be lanced.

Modern Sexuality

It was a matter of some disappointment to D. H. Lawrence that the Gospels say nothing about the sex-life of Jesus. Lawrence was more than disappointed by this silence: He was outraged, and I suppose that many Christians will in their turn be outraged if I choose to speak of that whereof the Gospels are mute. Nevertheless I do it, not only because others have preceded me but also because the Church's doctrine of the humanity of Christ is at stake. This doctrine, which might seem the least problematic of all Christian assertions—that Jesus was a human being—has actually proved to be one of the most troublesome. Almost every age has its own kind of Docetism, which is the theological name for a view of Christ that makes him no real man of flesh and blood but instead a being who appears human but is in fact something else. Docetism was early condemned as a heresy, but it has never disappeared. In our day it may be suggested that a Docetism lingers with regard to Jesus' sexuality. This means, if it is true, that Christians are not sure about the humanity of Him whom they call True Man. And this uncertainty results in a confusion about what it means for *us* to be human. One of the signs of this confusion is the chaos in sexual mores at the present time, which the Church has not been able to overcome and which it has actually helped to bring about because it had no adequate teaching with regard to the relation between sex and humanity.

D. H. Lawrence's dissatisfaction with the Gospels' picture of Jesus was most boldly stated in the famous short story, "The Man Who Died."[1] In it, Jesus' resurrection is pictured as an awakening to sensual love. The resurrection from the tomb is treated by Lawrence as a curse for Jesus until it is eventually followed by an awakening to the desires and consummations of the flesh. Lawrence equates Jesus' true resurrection with erection:

> He crouched to her, and he felt the blaze of his manhood and his power rise up in his loins, magnificent.
> "I am risen!"[2]

"The Man Who Died" has been regarded as blasphemous because Lawrence suggested that Jesus had, or should have had, sexual feelings and because Lawrence punned with holy phrases. The story, however, is less blasphemous than heretical, and this for the reason that Lawrence took it upon himself to reinterpret the total meaning of the Resurrection. He reduced the full mystery of God's victory over death to the age-old, pagan view that the victory of the gods is nothing but a transcendent version of the fertility principle. Thus Lawrence would have returned Christianity to a pre-Christian state in which natural sexuality is elevated into a religious and sacramental act. But sexuality will not bear this burden. Whenever it has been forced to carry it, a reaction has followed in which sexuality, and then all human relatedness, has been drained of meaning. That is the circumstance now. Our post-Lawrentian generation lives on an empty plain of sexual license and the collapse of human meanings. It is the opposite of what Lawrence intended, but he is in large part responsible for it. Yet Christianity is also responsible, because its inadequate teaching helped to call forth the equally inadequate teaching of Lawrence. In some quarters, the Church turns completely around and identifies its own message with what Lawrence was trying to say.

Lawrence was a sort of prophet *manqué*, and the prophet in him deserves to be taken by us more seriously, if less flamboyantly, than he took it himself. Underneath the Lawrentian manner there lies a genuine, although distorted, impulse. It is the urge to declare that sexuality belongs to the goodness of man's created nature and that if it does not find suitable expression and release, it turns man into something not more but less than human.

For Lawrence, modern rationalism and industrialism are both false at the core because they exclude on principle the formative power of the sexual drive. Rationalism does so because it regards sexuality as irrational—necessary perhaps, but ever to be regarded as an enemy of reason. One could say that rationalism assigns to sexuality only a "secondary citizenship" in the mind-body kingdom. Industrialism is also antisexual because its methods are determined by the machine, and its methods shape its values. Hence industrialism gives rise to a way of life that is ruthlessly unorganic. In industrial Nottinghamshire where he grew up, Lawrence observed the enervating effects that industrialism had upon sexuality as well as upon the spirits of men.

That an age of rationalism and industrialism is also an age of sexual license does not destroy Lawrence's point; it corroborates it. Under the sway of rationalism, sex becomes a subject of dispassionate study by the specialist and a topic of conversation in the parlor. People get what Lawrence called "sex in the head." If we sometimes feel that Lawrence himself had more than a touch of this disease, at least it is to his everlasting credit that he preferred and advocated sex in the loins.

As rationalism tends to put sex in the head, industrialism tends to turn sex into a machine. A manufacturing and commercial society deliberately amplifies sexual desire, then distributes and sells at a profit the gratifications for it. In industrial societies man lives amid huckstered and huckstering sex.

What Lawrence wanted was to combat sexiness with sexuality. He intended to be a champion of what we nowadays call "the whole man." He saw standing squarely in his way not only rationalism and industrialism but also a religious tradition that seemed to give aid and comfort to those twin perverters of human nature. For Christianity itself seemed to have said that sex was best managed by denying it. "Christian man" seemed to be something other than sexual man. Therefore Christianity led to a double standard and to an artificial sex life.

During the past fifty years, a number of Christian spokesmen have been very busy trying to repair the damage done by Victorian hypocrisy and, more serious, the damage done by Platonic elements in the Christian view of man. Biblical scholars have shown that Paul's word "flesh," which for Paul is the domain of sin, does not mean the sexual desires of the body, or at least not these alone. They have shown that the Bible does not, in the main, teach that the soul can be saved while the body belongs to the Devil. They have shown that marital sex is a positive good in both the Old and New Testaments. Karl Barth has even suggested that the best clue to the meaning of the *imago Dei* in man is to be found in the man-woman relationship. Christian ethicists have insisted that there is to be no condemnation of sex as such. Certainly the climate has begun to change.

Lawrence, however, saw with a clear instinct where the problem lay, as far as Christianity is concerned. Though he did not solve the problem well, he did locate it precisely. The problem lies in the New Testament picture of Jesus.

The Sexuality of Jesus

Exegesis might go on forever proving that sex is not necessarily sin. Ethics might echo the tune. But if The Man for Men was conceived to be without sexuality—was never, unlike the saints, even tempted by sex—then all would labor in vain who strove to prove that the Christian God looks favorably upon the sexual life of humanity. Hunger Jesus knew, and thirst. Death He endured. Pride, sloth, envy, desire for power, idolatry—all came close to Him and were overcome in favor of the virtues of which they are the perversions. But where do we find Jesus taking our sexuality upon Him? Human love, yes. Love extended liberally even to those who, in a sexual way, have "loved much." But never, so far as we are told, a man stirred in himself by that desire which for the rest of us is part of our created nature.

To put it bluntly, a sexless Jesus can hardly be conceived to be fully human. As long as Jesus is somehow above masculinity or femininity, the drift toward a Docetic Christ is inevitable. I do not know why this has not been more often observed. Lacking such a pervasively human element, the humanity of Christ tends to become a mere affirmation, a matter of pure dogma. Jesus is then man in principle but not in fact. If to this is added the belief that He was conceived in the womb of a virgin, His separation from our sexuality becomes complete. "Veiled in flesh," He is not flesh. He has the appearance of humanity but not its limiting substance, however much might be said in the abstract about "finitude." It is an inherent part of my finitude, and yours, that our lives are shaped in many decisive ways by our sexual histories.

Anti-docetism has become a recurring motif in modern imaginative literature about the Christ. Its presence should cause some theological reflection. It provides the motivation for Lawrence's story. We may object that Lawrence is "dragging Christ down" to our level, but there remains the biblical testimony that He *was* on our level, save only indulging in our sin. If sex is not inherently sinful, did He not share our sexuality also? Thus we find Nikos Kazantzakis representing Jesus as one whose spiritual struggle was in large part defined by His desire for woman, embodied in Mary Magdalene.[3] G. Wilson Knight, in *The Christian Renaissance*,[4] pictures Christ as androgynous, filled with both masculinity and femininity, thus "transcending" our sexuality while he yet shares it. Ronald Duncan, in his poem *Judas*,[5] pictures Jesus in an encounter with a prostitute:

> Remembering the brothel we'd passed outside the city
> Where an old whore had lifted her skirts in the doorway
> And challenged Jesus to prove He was a man
> And how He had surprised us by going up to the woman
> And had drawn the sore from her lips, the years from her
>   eyes
>   and—it was this that shocked Peter—
> How He had then kissed her, and pulled her hair in a tease
>   as she repeated her challenge
> Not realizing that He had proved much more.

If we try to reach some understanding of Jesus' sexuality and ours, we must be careful to avoid both the whore's challenge and also the too-facile resolution in the last line quoted from Ronald Duncan. The mistake of the whore's challenge lies in the opinion that "unproven" sex is not sex. Its taunt is, "Prove to *me* that you are a man," which is not only self-regarding but is also a temptation to what we would today call "inauthentic existence," since it requires to deliver over to another person the power to judge one's own nature. He who yields to this temptation enters that Hell that Sartre has described in *No Exit*, wherein all suffer because none has the courage to be his own judge. Jesus' refusal to "prove himself a man"—taken in both the colloquial and the generalized senses of the word "man"—is but the other side of the coin of His refusal to offer on demand proofs of His divinity. He will not be authenticated by "signs," and this is a strong reason to believe in His authenticity.

Here we touch upon what is the actual offense created by literature that attempts to "prove" the humanity of Jesus. It is not shocking, to me at least, to imagine Jesus moved to love according to the flesh. I cannot imagine a *human* tenderness, which the Gospels show to be characteristic of Jesus, that is not fed in some degree by the springs of passion. The human alternative to sexual tenderness is not asexual tenderness but sexual fear. Jesus lived in His body, as other men do. But as He is The Authentic Man, we are not to be shown a proof of this, neither by Him on our demand nor by a writer on his behalf.

Proofs of manhood never prove anything except that we desire proof. In this respect, stories written about the sexuality of Jesus are on the same footing as those popular novels (of Lloyd C. Douglas, for instance) that go out of their way to convince us that Jesus ate and breathed like other people. Such essays in this humanizing of Jesus have interest only insofar as their readers are already Docetists at heart and therefore want reassurance that The Man was man. That which is already human has no need of being humanized. I am always offended by a writer, be it Lawrence, Lloyd Douglas, or Dorothy Sayers, who urges me to believe what I never doubted—that Jesus was of my own race. Methinks the writer doth protest too much.

Ronald Duncan's Judas says that although the whore was disappointed that Jesus did not prove His manhood to her, actually "He had proved much more." One feels as he reads this line that the whore's question has received a rhetorical answer. I would prefer Duncan to say that it was precisely His manhood that Jesus had proved or, better, that He had denied her the inauthentic sign she had demanded. For it is not good theology to suppose that the question of Jesus' manhood can be answered by an appeal to His divinity. This can no more be the case than that the question of His divinity could be answered by an appeal to His manhood. Christian orthodoxy has always steered clear of making either affirmation dependent upon the other. That is why the Church has never enunciated the doctrine of the two natures with satisfactory logic. Logic demands that a relation of dependency be established, so that either the divinity follows upon the perfect manhood or else the perfect manhood is called forth by the divinity. Orthodoxy, to the chagrin of all theologians, has eschewed both these formulations, rendering the Incarnation, as Paul Tillich says, the only absolute paradox in Christian faith. Jesus was not man because He is God, neither is He God because He was man. But doctrine holds that He is both, an assertion that cannot be proved since it cannot even be explained.

We cannot, then, render Jesus more adequate as man by rendering Him the redemptive Son of God. That is why the line of Ronald Duncan I have cited falls short of its mark. In fairness to Duncan I should add that the main burden of his remarkable poem seems to me to lie in quite the other direction. It is about the too-late awakening of a very religious Judas to the fact that Jesus was very human.

Similarly, we cannot render Jesus more clearly or decisively Son of God by rendering Him more fully human. That is why stories about His alleged sexual encounters miss their mark. As proofs of humanity, they are superfluous and out of line with that authenticity that cannot be subjected to proof. As concerns His divinity, they neither add nor subtract, unless of course we take the *a priori* position that all sex is sin.

The Significance of the Gospels' Silence

I mentioned earlier the curious silence of the Gospels regarding the sexuality of Jesus. Let us now ask what bearing that phenomenon has upon the New Testament picture of Jesus as the Christ.

There are only three conceivable ways of dealing with the Gospels' silence on this matter. The first is easily disposed of. We may quickly rule out the possibility that the silence about Jesus' sexuality is due merely to the historical situation in which Jesus lived and in which the Gospels were written. On that ground we can plausibly explain silences about many things, such as the relation of faith to science or the evils of slavery, since the human mind and conscience were not sensitized to these problems until later periods. But sexuality as a matter of conscience and as a reality of importance to the gods is as old as religion, is basic to the natural man's conception of himself, and is therefore in another class. A different reason must be sought for the Gospels' failure to speak of Jesus' sexuality.[6]

The traditional explanation is that since Jesus was without sin, it follows that He did not engage in any sexual activity. A sinless man who loved sexually would, in this view, be a contradiction in terms, since sex belongs only to fallen man. Merely to think of Jesus as having sexual desire is to offend against His purity.

The first objection to this view, however much it be supported by traditions of theology and piety, is that it does not account for the fact that Jesus in the Gospels is specifically tempted by other sins, which He resists, but seems to have been spared this particular temptation. I submit that not to engage in sexual activity is one thing but that to be without temptation to do so is quite another. The significant fact is that the Gospels are silent on both counts.

The traditional view can therefore be maintained only if sex itself is held to be no part of the original goodness of created man, if it is made to be the very sign and seal of the Fall, so that the Sinless One is He who does not encounter it even as temptation. Sexuality, however, is so pervasive a reality in organic nature that one cannot assign it *in toto* to the Fall without coming eventually to Manichaeism: that is, absolving the Lord and Father of Jesus Christ of responsibility for the created structures of living things. For sexuality is not only, or even primarily, a human phenomenon but belongs to the created structure of all animal life.

If historic Christianity has failed in its dealings with sexuality, which is not far from the truth, a principal reason may be that its equation of sex and the Fall has fostered a Manichaeism that now informs the view of sex held by the majority of people in the "Christian" world. The equation, however, is not Biblical. It is to be found in the early Church Fathers, but it is never clearly stated in Scripture.

In Protestant theology any "necessary" link between sex and sin has been broken in modern times. This has been due to the Biblical research fostered by Protestantism in the last two centuries. It is no longer held (outside Fundamentalism, and not always inside it) that Adam's sin was sexual desire. The prevailing view is that sex is part of man's created goodness and therefore participates in sin only when man lives in disobedience to God and in lack of faith. It would appear that theology, guided by Biblical exegesis, has now gone so far in this direction that it cannot turn back, for to do so would undercut not only the results of Biblical study but also that entire effort so valiantly and wisely made to bring the life of "the whole man" under the Lordship of Christ.

If one moves in the prevailing direction, however, a consequence must be faced: namely, that the traditional view of the Gospel's silence about sexuality in Jesus himself must be abandoned and a new interpretation put on the facts. What may be the outline of such an interpretation be?

If we take it that the Gospels do not intend to present a Docetic Christ, if this may be true even of the Fourth Gospel, which in any case speaks most about Jesus' love for particular individuals, then the absence of all comment in them about Jesus' sexuality cannot be taken to imply that He had no sexual feelings. That would land us back into the traditional view, according to which the Christ redeems us *from* sexuality, it being the part of our nature He did not share. If the Christian, who is a member of the Body of Christ, is to grow up into a psychologically healthy and morally right sexual life, then the God-Man cannot be totally apart from the sexual realm.

Let us go a step further. If the Gospels do not speak of

Jesus' sexuality, this silence may occur for a positive reason.

Few characteristics of the Gospels separate them more sharply from the literature of other savior figures and religious heroes than their abstention from representing their protagonist *either* as a champion of sexual renewal *or* as a warrior against the "demonic" sexual force. This is astonishing. Almost all religions make sexuality a principal concern. Either they regard it as a sign of power that must be replenished from on high, or they regard it as a pollution of which man must be purged. From the point of view of comparative religion, it is not surprising at all that Christianity as a religion brought forth monasticism, made a cult of virginity, and elevated its God-man above all sexual feeling. What is surprising is that the Gospels show in Jesus himself no sufficient basis for these attitudes.

It is true that the Gospels include a few very sharp statements from the "teachings" of Jesus that are apparently negative about sex. The most severe of these is Matthew 5:27–28:

> You have heard that it was said, "You shall not commit adultery." But I say to you that every one who looks at a woman lustfully has already committed adultery with her in his heart.

This verse is peculiar to Matthew. Luke and Mark do not have it. The next two verses seem to take on an antisexual meaning when read in this context:

> If your right eye causes you to sin, pluck it out and throw it away; it is better that you lose one of your members than that your whole body be thrown into hell. And if your right hand causes you to sin, cut it off and throw it away; it is better that you lose one of your members than that your whole body go into hell.

However, the words may not be in their proper context here. With slight variation they turn up again in Matthew 18:8–9 in a very different context, at which point they are paralleled by Mark.

Matthew 5:31–32 goes on to the absolute proscription of divorce, and *that* passage not only appears also in Mark and Luke but is repeated later in all three synoptics. We are also told that "in the resurrection they neither marry nor are given in marriage" (Matthew 22:30, cf. Mark 12:25 and Luke 20:35) and so on in a few other passages.

It is not my purpose here to examine these passages in detail. It is sufficient to point out that the ascetic passages all come from the so-called "teachings," that they are not nearly as strong in the canonical Gospels as in the apocryphal, and that there is *no* passage that speaks one way or the other about any sexuality of Jesus, not even in the temptations.

The Religious Neutrality of Sex

Over against the pagan gods and the pagan religions we may say that Jesus appears as the great neutralizer of the religious meaning of sex. He does not, it is clear, regard sexuality as a mystical force emanating from the God-head. Jesus is no Dionysus. But contrary to what many Christians have assumed, the Jesus of the Gospels is not plainly "anti-Dionysian" either. That is, he does not, as far as we can tell, regard sexuality as a force emanating from Satan. This opinion was left to the Gnostics to develop, who found some remarks of St. Paul's to encourage them, and who have had a profound influence on the history of Christianity. Our modern ambivalence about sex, according to which it is either the best or the worst of all things, is Gnostic in origin and Manichaean in character.[7]

Most of so-called Christendom, not to mention other parts of the world, still labors under the assumption that, for a Christian, sexuality stands as a barrier in the way of salvation. Nowadays we meet this mainly in its inverted (actually its older) form: namely, the exaltation of sex into a *condition* of spiritual blessedness. D. H. Lawrence would blast Jesus out of His neutrality regarding sex. He would make Jesus a sensual lover in order to make Him a savior. Norman Mailer and others make the quest for the "good orgasm" into a religious quest. William Inge, like Hollywood in its hey-day, makes the reconciliations of the bed the end-all in human relationships. Aphrodite and Priapus have as many worshippers among us as ever they did at Corinth and Rome.

In combating these apostasies, the task is not to show that Aphrodite and Priapus are forms of the Devil. To do so would only ratify their religious power. The task is rather to proclaim what the Gospels show—that as far as Jesus is concerned these gods have lost their power. They are facts dressed up as numinous beings.

The reader will not assume that I am making any case for unbridled license in sexual behavior. Man may sin with sex, as he may with money or in politics. But if so, it is *man* who sins; it is not an exterior force sinning in him. Man is a debtor to Original Sin not because of his physical nature but because of the proclivities of his total self acting in his total world. He is the more prone to sin when he absolutizes (even in a negative way) any one part of himself and any one part of his world.

It may be thought that the position I urge puts too much emphasis on the Gospels, to the neglect of the Old Testament and the rest of the New. That may be so, but in any search for a Christian opinion, we should start in the Gospels, however much we may yet have to learn from the rest of Scripture. I am simply urging that we see the Jesus of the Gospels not as isolated from sexuality, even in His own person, but as refusing to sanction its religious status.

It may also be thought that I make too much of an "argument from silence" in the Gospels. Perhaps, but there is support for my view in the Gospels' accounts of Jesus' dealings with persons whose sexual life is "impure." Their "impurity" seems never to have been what concerned Him.

Finally, I have not attempted to frame, even in outline, a sexual ethic. My reflections belong only among the prolegomena to such ethics. I believe that the construction of a Christian ethic of sex cannot be properly attempted as long as one retains the mythology of sex that grew up in the ancient religions, is perpetuated in new ones, and from which Jesus as the Christ would liberate us.

I am arguing, then, for the demythologization of sex. Contrary to what some recent theologians seem to think, Christianity itself cannot be demythologized. But the world of our everyday experience can be. The task of theology is not to demythologize the Christ, but to share in His work of demythologizing the world. This is a labor that helps to realize "the glorious liberty of the Sons of God."

NOTES

1. *Christian Faith and the Contemporary Arts*, ed. Finley (New York: Vintage Books, 1959).

2. *Ibid.*, p. 207.

3. *The Last Temptation of Christ*, trans. P. A. Bien (New York: Simon & Schuster, 1960). Departing from the Gospels' accounts of the temptations (cf. Mt. 4:1–11 and Luke 4:1–13), Kazantzakis depicts one of the temptations as that of carnal love and marriage. Indeed, the fight between a spiritual vocation and a life of domestic love is the central motif of this book, and Kazantzakis apparently intended to say that this is not only Jesus' choice but that of every man. In this respect he takes an opposite stance from that of Lawrence, one more in keeping with Catholic and Orthodox traditions. But the anti-docetic intention is clear and results in numerous descriptions of Jesus' amorous stirrings.

4. Macmillan Co., New York, 1933. Reprinted by W. W. Norton, New York, 1962.

5. Anthony Blond, Ltd., 1960.

6. My reasoning throughout this section omits one further possibility: that the sexuality of Jesus is not mentioned by the Gospel writers because the early Church's selective memory of Him screened it out, and this because its consciousness was shaped by Judaic traditions of the time rather than, as I suggest, by confrontation with other Near Eastern religious attitudes. Lacking sufficient knowledge of first-century Judaism, I cannot evaluate this possibility. Even if true, it would seem to me a factor contributory to the reason I shall state below as the decisive one.

7. Cf. Denis de Rougemont, *Love in the Western World* (rev. ed.; New York: Pantheon Books, 1956).

The Uses of Agnosticism:
Secularism in Modern Literature

John Killinger

An ardent advocate of dialogic encounter between Christian theology and the arts, John Killinger argues persuasively for the view that Christians can learn even from a post-Christian literature that takes for granted the death—or at least the truancy—of God. For the contemporary writer's penetrating works of "negative witness" are helping make it possible for Christianity to be more incarnate in the phenomenal world; too tough-minded to settle for easy affirmations, the writer starts "where the incarnation began, in this miserable hellhole of mortal existence"—which is precisely where the church must start if it is to renew itself, if it is to count for anything in our fragmented, crisis-ridden time. Pertinent to Dr. Killinger's article—from the Summer 1965 issue of *Religion in Life**—are two of his books: *Hemingway and the Dead Gods: A Study in Existentialism* and *The Failure of Theology in Modern Literature*. Dr. Killinger, formerly Dean of Kentucky Southern College, is now Associate Professor of Preaching at Vanderbilt Divinity School, Nashville, Tennessee.

IT RECENTLY occurred to me, when I was asked to define the word "secularism" as I had used it in a lecture, that it is one of those words like "classicism" and "romanticism" which we frequently use without establishing their precise meaning. I take it that we are talking here about secularism as the final effect of the desacralization process, by which in turn we mean the transference of culture from a base in the holy to a base in the profane. And when we apply this to literature, we are reflecting on how thoroughly modern

* 201 Eighth Ave. South, Nashville, Tenn. 37203. Copyright © 1965 by Abingdon Press.

133

letters have abandoned an interest in the Christian faith except as that faith represents part of the over-all picture of the times. In other words, we are enjoining again the conversation about "the death of God," especially as the conversation is mirrored in or contributed to by well-known literary works.

Secularism *qua* secularism, it seems to me, implies a totally casual attitude toward the spiritual side of life—a kind of un-reflectiveness about God, as though it did not matter whether he existed. If this is true, then we have not yet reached the final stages of secularism in literature. Too many authors are still God-haunted. They do not tend to be particularly ortho-dox in their doctrines, but they often express inchoate and even wildly forceful statements of belief. I think of the out-croppings of spiritual presence, of the noumenal, in such places as the sunlit dells of D. H. Lawrence, the yelping jungles of Conrad, the bullrings of Hemingway, the honey-suckled porches of Faulkner, or the deserted-hotel universe of Kafka. These writers are not mere pantheists—they do not find a god in every bush and brook. It is not that at all. It is rather that they have somehow discerned what Otto and others have called the *mysterium tremendum*, the brooding some-thing-or-other, the ontological depth, that is present in the universe without being the universe, that is really, in a Barthian sense, over against the world. They exhibit in com-mon with the true Christian what Robert Penn Warren has called "an unscared reverence for the shockingness of inner truth."[1] And they walk much more reverently in the world than many an orthodox person who thinks he has solved the problem of the nature of God.

But this cannot blind us to the fact that a major geological shift has taken place in literature as well as in other ex-pressions of human life in our century, and that while the secularization process is not complete, it is by now a historical fact. The God we meet in contemporary literature no longer bears the shape he bore, say, in the literature of the first half of the nineteenth century. Now he is much more subtly and indefinably drawn. We do not know, in *Waiting for Godot* for example, whether we have really seen him or not. It has be-come pretty much a matter of the measure we bring to the reading. If we come to a play or a novel with Christian presuppositions, and listen or watch with a great deal of sensitivity, then we are liable to think we have really uncovered the *deus incognitus*; but others can come without these presuppositions and be equally happy at discovering none of the references to God and Christ and the church which once were obtruded upon the sensibilities of all.

Most writers today have matured beyond the kind of jejune antitheism expressed by characters in the writings of Melville and Dostoevski and Schreiner and Hardy. This could not have been said twenty years ago. The protests of writers such as Fitzgerald and Wolfe and Gide and Sartre were still echoing in most of the younger writers. Camus was in the earlier phase of his brilliant career. But now the pendulum appears to have swung full stroke, and not to have entirely toppled the idea of God. Robert Lowell and John Updike and Saul Bellow, each of whom has published a significant volume within the last two years, are not at all abashed to talk about him. They do not preach, but neither do they find him unfashionable.

The church, though, has not fared well. For the most part it seems to be regarded as a piece of medieval machinery which ought to be abandoned. Philip Larkin's poem "Church Going" is one of the milder expressions of post-Christian feeling. The author has been cycling through the countryside, and stops to enter a vacant church building. His eye roams over the seats, the little books, the stone floor, the bunch of withered flowers on the altar. Hatless, but wishing to show some sign of reverence, he removes his cycle-clips, and walks to the front of the church. When he returns he drops an offering in the box and wonders

> When churches fall completely out of use
> What we shall turn them into, if we shall keep
> A few cathedrals chronically on show,
> Their parchment, plate, and pyx in locked cases,
> And let the rest rent-free to rain and sheep.[2]

Will they become centers of superstition and witchcraft, with mothers stealing in at night to make their children touch a particular stone? Will superstition itself die out at last, leaving only

A shape less recognizable each week,
A purpose more obscure?[3]

For the most part, writers who have grown up in urban surroundings do not regard the church with so much nostalgia. What they think of instead is its failure to meet social issues, its want of courage, its neutrality in the time when modern life is being formed. They regard its ministry as both incompetent and undedicated. The preacher is often pictured these days as a man who has had second thoughts but is too far committed to a way of life to get out of it, so that he stays in his job as an agnostic and refuses to look in the mirror when he shaves. He is not usually so smug as the young liberal in Peter de Vries' *Mackerel Plaza*, who is pleased at being told he is the "Hemingway of the pulpit," but tends to be like Jack Eccles in Updike's *Rabbit, Run*, the uncertain rector whose days are sometimes "bothered by God." In short, he is an ineffectual, whose profoundest conviction is that he is a mere caudal appendage, albeit in clerical garb, on a world largely unaware of him. And if he lacks this conviction, he is a stuffed shirt who is all the easier to dislike or ignore.

The equivalent of saying "post-Christian," when we are talking about literature, is perhaps to say "Kafkan" or "post-Kafkan." For Kafka, more than any other writer of the century, concentrated our spiritual dilemma into fictional form. His chief genre, whether in the short story or in the novel, was the parable, which is the most dangerous kind of literature to read; as W. H. Auden has noted, we cannot read it without surrendering our objectivity and identifying with it completely; we cannot read it and remain neutral.[4] This accounts in part for the tremendous influence Kafka has had on the writers of nearly every Western country. He has been their reticent oracle, their retiring or introverted prophet. In a quiet and indirect way—he was as much the master of understatement and circumlocution as Henry James—he has convinced them that an enormous change has taken place in the milieu in which the writer does his work.

His novel *The Castle*, for example, begins somewhat like a story by Thomas Hardy, with the main character, who is simply designated as "K," arriving after a journey at the castle of Count Westwest. The reader is not swept up into the plot at this point, however, as he might be in a Hardy novel. Instead, he follows laboriously and meticulously the investigations and inquiries—adventures of an *interior* sort—which K makes about the Count, who is never seen. What K finally establishes is that the Count, whom by this time we may with some risk take to be God, is really no longer alive, although the entire populace continues to act and talk as if he were. K is thus the prototype of that lonely, isolated figure so popular in modern fiction who sees what the public does not see or is not willing to admit that it has seen—that the old order of things has collapsed and that no new order has obtained, that men are really between orders, in the chaotic and painful moment of passage.

One of the main traits of Kafka's work is its ambiguity. His sympathies seem almost always to lie with the theistic approach to life, and yet the world he describes seems more often than not a world without God, perhaps even a world convulsed by the absence of God. I suspect that the ambiguity accounts in part for the Kafkan vogue. Like Clamence's use of the subjunctive form in Camus' novella *The Fall*, it is a sign of the ultra-sophistication of the times, of our hesitation between the poles of thought, our uncertainty among alternate possibilities. It is much more modern to shrug the shoulders at the idea of God—or even to pine in despair—than it is to play the rebel urging men to defection.

In speaking of a Kafkan vogue, I have in mind especially the kind of theater being created by Beckett and Ionesco. The whole pattern of bleak setting, interiorized dialogue, and inaction under pressure that characterizes the Theater of the Absurd owes much to Kafka, as it does to Camus. Moreover, this radically different theater experience depends heavily upon ambiguity and ambivalence for its impact. It contrasts at once with the traditional theater of ideas, where the audience could formulate by the end of the first act the "message" of the play. Ideas are not unimportant in the new theater, but they are forced through the subjective so that they are experienced as emotions, not as ideas—so completely so that it is difficult to force them through the other way again and treat the emotions as ideas.

Consider *Waiting for Godot*, which is probably the best known of these contemporary anti-plays. Whatever else it is —and critical evaluations run from one end of the spectrum to the other—it is a center cut of genuine agnosticism, sparely served and almost totally ungarnished. The plot, what there is of it, is at bottom an analogue on the old Hebraic motif of waiting for the Redeemer. Two burlesque-type tramps, Didi and Gogo, wait beneath a tree for someone named Godot. The elusiveness of the matter is struck even in the title: Godot is a common French name and does not necessarily carry a burden of special meaning, but it may also be read, according to the will of the interpreter, as a diminutive form of the word God. By the same token, the blighted tree which is the only bit of staging paraphernalia may be simply a tree or it may be reminiscent of the Tree that has stirred the Western imagination for two thousand years now. Neither Didi nor Gogo has even seen the mysterious Mr. Godot. They are not at all sure that he will ever show up. They are not even certain that his name is really Godot. At the end of the play they decide to leave. But they do not move.

An interesting episode of the play—it is really too integral to the whole to be called a subplot—concerns the appearance of a couple of unusual characters named Pozzo and Lucky. Although Lucky is a buffoon, he has seemed to some critics to be a caricature of Christ. Kay Baxter, in fact, has declared the entire play to be one long dramatic exposition of the creedal statement, "He suffered and was buried: And the third day He rose again according to the Scriptures."[5]

The dialogue of the play is highly lyrical, though in a subdued, almost elegiac way. It is disciplined and tense and quiet. It does not leap at the audience to discover any affirmatives to it; it toys with it, like a cat playing with a mouse; it deals in undertones, and moves by hums and haws. As a statement of the agnostic temper of the times, it is much more sophisticated than the old Nietzschean statement, because it disallows unfaith as much as it disallows faith. It keeps the audience in a state of negative suspension, posing the issues and balancing them off with infinite care, so that what is left in the audience is a feeling of a void more than an explicit idea.

We can hardly wonder at the dismay of the average church-man facing such a piece of literature. There are none of the "eternal verities" in it which he has been trained by long discipline to look for. It does not sparkle with the phrases and slogans he has come to identify with the faith. Nor does it traffic in evident profanity. If it did either of these things, he would know how to handle it. But it doesn't. It defies him. Like the work of Kafka, it is too brilliant, too subtle, too vague, to attack.

Perhaps C. S. Lewis was right when he said that "a post-Christian man is not a Pagan; you might as well think that a married woman recovers her virginity by divorce."[6] Unless we are prepared wholeheartedly to agree with Mrs. Baxter about the parallelism between *Godot* and the Nicene Creed, we must admit that Beckett's plays belong in the corpus of post-Christian literature. But the sympathies they engender are not at all antitheistic ones, or, for that matter, even anti-Christian ones. They are even close enough to Christian sentiments to lend a certain amount of plausibility to interpretations such as Mrs. Baxter's.

And what is true of Beckett is true of most serious writers today. They talk a great deal about the expiration or the absence of God and thus prove somewhat unsettling to the faithful; but they are not at all ready to dismiss the idea of God. Whitehead said once that "the progress of religion is defined by the denunciation of Gods." And sometimes in our more charitable moments we are willing to admit that authors are not denouncing God, but only false gods, that they are really pushing us on beyond our favorite idolatries to what Tillich has called "the God beyond God."

Moreover, there is an unmistakable residue of the Christian point of view, or *Weltanschauung*, in such writers. The themes of modern novels and plays—lostness and redemption, loneli-ness and love, stupidity and passion, guilt and forgiveness—are highly moral in nature. They are the ones the church has always been concerned with in her better moments. Of course they do not look the same in Saturday night's play as they do in Sunday morning's homily; a certain amount of distortion is inevitable when the abstract doctrine is translated into a life situation. But the fact that the translation takes place at all, and that the connection is still recognizable in the present age, is most significant.

An example of the residue is easily discernible in Arthur Miller's *After the Fall*, which is also a play from the American scene revealing rather clearly the influence of both Kafka and Beckett. Quentin, Miller's somewhat autobiographical protagonist, has an experience akin to that of Joseph K. in Kafka's *The Trial*. He is appalled to learn one day that he is pleading his life's case before an empty bench. "I think now," he says, "that my disaster really began when I looked up one day—and the bench was empty. No judge in sight. And all that remained was the endless argument with oneself—this pointless litigation of existence before an empty bench."[7] The staging of the play is Beckettian: some gray, lavalike sculpted areas, a chair, and behind them the blasted stone tower of a Nazi concentration camp. It is supposed to represent the interior of Quentin's head, his memory, in which most of the play's action takes place.

Quentin is preparing to marry a German girl named Holga, who is haunted by the memory of what happened to the Jews in the concentration camp; she feels that no one is innocent who did not die there. Quentin is himself troubled by the question of guilt, which is brought home to him by the failure of his two earlier marriages and by the suicides of Maggie, one of the wives, and Lou, a friend whom he has been representing in the McCarthy hearings. Without the judge to acquit or condemn him, without some external spiritual authority, he finds it difficult to establish genuine relationships with other persons. He feels that he and all the other persons in his life have only touched but have not really met. So everyone wallows in his aloneness, and Quentin epitomizes the situations of Leopold Bloom and Jay Gatsby and Prufrock and Didi and Gogo and all the others who are peculiarly of the twentieth century, the century of the Great Desertion, when God has apparently left us alone to our passions.

But far from despairing of his situation, Quentin actually exults in it. "With all this darkness," he says, "the truth is that every morning when I awake, I'm full of hope! With everything I know—I open my eyes, I'm like a boy! For an instant there's some—unformed promise in the air."[8] In the end, he finds out why he hopes: it is because he *knows* the situation he is in and can accept it. "And that, that's why I wake each morning like a boy—even now, even now!"[9]

This is pretty thorough-going secularism, or at least I think it is. There is certainly no kerygmatic note, no trumpet and then the gospel. The pain is unrelieved all the way to the end. No one comes down off his cross. If anything, the invitation is simply to realize that we are all on the cross, that life is hard, that motivation is never pure, that the most we can do is make the best of it and hold each other's hands while we are doing it. And as such it is an invitation well known in contemporary letters—indeed, almost the standard invitation. Our first inclination is probably to reject the whole thing out of hand because of its lowness of vision, because the kind of hope it offers is only penultimate.

But we cannot dismiss it so easily. The emotions it touches upon are too vast for that.

Quentin's sense of guilt, by the time he reaches the final scene of the play, has swelled to include not only his personal guilt but the collective guilt of the human race. It becomes all important to find an answer. Love at first appears to be the solution, but that is too vague. Standing in the ruin of the tower Quentin looks down on the world and cries, "What is the cure? Who can be innocent again on this mountain of skulls? I tell you what I know! My brothers died here . . . but my brothers built this place; our hearts have cut these stones! And what's the cure? No, not love; I loved them all, all! And gave them willingly to failure and to death that I might live, as they gave me and gave each other, with a word, a look, a trick, a truth, a lie—and all in love!"

The answer is in the end a modest one—to know that we are guilty. "To know and even happily, that we meet unblessed; not in some garden of wax fruit and painted trees, that lie of Eden, but after, after the Fall, after many, many deaths. Is the knowing all? And the wish to kill is never killed, but with some gift of courage one may look into its face when it appears, and with a stroke of love—as to an idiot in the house—forgive it; again and again . . . forever?"

At this point Quentin appears to be interrupted by his audience. "No," he says, "it's not certainty, I don't feel that.

But it does seem feasible . . . not to be afraid. Perhaps it's all one has. I'll tell her that. . . . Yes, she will, she'll know what I mean." Whereupon he turns upstage, hesitates a moment, and then joins Holga. As they move away into the darkness, "a loud whisper comes up from all his people, who follow behind, endlessly alive."[10]

Again we protest that this is not Christian. Even if the "mountain of skulls" is an oblique reference to Calvary, it is pretty paltry, and the soteriology is not very promising. The past still snatches at Quentin, and he is not free from it all. There is no roseate glow here, such as one may be accustomed to find, say, in the post-Resurrection narratives of the New Testament. If there is faith of a sort, it is a strangely secularized faith.

Still, one cannot help wondering whether some meaningful conclusion has not been reached, a conclusion capable of releasing certain redemptive powers in the audience, and whether, after all, more has not been accomplished here than is accomplished in the average pulpit on a Sunday morning. For isn't it just possible that the God who has been pronounced missing in Quentin's speech about the vacant bench is really only one of the false gods Whitehead was talking about, and that Miller's rejection of love as the answer is merely the rejection of Eros for Agape, whose name he recognized only as "knowing and forgiving"?

What if the Christian faith *has* permeated the modern conscience? Dare we think of its having seeped beyond that corroded container, the institutional church, and penetrated into the id, the subconscious, of Western man? What if Kafka and Beckett and Miller and many others among the so-called agnostics are really, to use Amos Wilder's phrase, "uncanonical witnesses to the faith"? After all, there is precedent of a sort in the harlots and publicans who discerned the way of the kingdom in the days of the Pharisees.

The kerygmatic emphasis—"plain preaching of the gospel" —is seldom found in literature today. From the strictest point of view that is a failing, though it may represent failure on the church's part as much as on the part of contemporary authors. But if it is the purpose of poetry, of literature in general, to hold the mirror up to life, then the reflection we saw would be distorted if life were there ordered according to the promises of the gospel. Life *is* seamy—more than our self-protective unconsciousness permits most of us to realize. And literature as we conceive its nature to be in the modern age would perjure itself if it whitewashed the facts of existence.

A pastor recently complained that his daughter was disturbed by certain works being read by her high school English class—*Lord of the Flies, Catcher in the Rye,* and *Poorhouse Fair* were among the titles mentioned. On the surface at least he was concerned about the debauching of young minds by sudden exposure to rather strong doses of sensualism, profanity, and agnosticism. Deeper than that he may have been concerned about the radical susceptibility of the young to the virus of ideas—and he may have been hinting at the failure of the church to provide the young with a world view that would enable them to handle new ideas.

But the answer to his concern is not to be found in suppressing books or banning plays. This has never proved to be a satisfactory method for dealing with controversial ideas. The answer—or perhaps it is not an answer, only a reply—is for him to see that the mood of despair captured so effectively in modern literature is not a thing to be hidden, as his question suggested, but that it is the gospel's supremest opportunity. Denis de Rougemont has defined the nature of the work of art as "a calculated trap for meditation."[11] Precisely! And when literature has ensnared the consciousness and made it to look at the human condition in its rawest terms, the gospel has a chance to become the gospel, to sound in men's ears as good news!

Life itself is not a better *praeparatio evangelica* than literature. For if the novel or the poem or the play is a trap—an "oriented trap," as de Rougemont says—then it gathers up sight and sound and sense in a fashion far more powerful than that in which the unaided consciousness does it. And the sermon, the lesson, the study group that takes advantage of this groundwork has a much more direct route to success in its mission. Literature may be "sub-Christian" or "pre-Christian," even to a sacramental theology, but it ought not to be wholesalely denominated as "unchristian." When a theater audience goes out into the night after witnessing a performance of such plays as *After the Fall* or *Night of the Iguana* or *Who's Afraid of Virginia Woolf?* it is probably with a desperate sense of life's essential loneliness and the need for human compassion—and with an ear for hearing, momentarily at least, the inner truth of the gospel.

One final observation which ought to be made about the secularizing tendency in literature is that the same tendency is also at work in contemporary theology. It is not quite so radical in theology, because there are certain obvious restraints there, but it is there nevertheless. There is an air of secularism common to both areas.

There is of course a "transcendence" school of theology which has followed the lines drawn by Barth, emphasizing the otherness of the divine revelation and the radical difference between the holy and the profane. But there has been a complementary accent from those who feel that too much emphasis on transcendence denies the theology of incarnation and thus denatures Christianity. One thinks of Bonhoeffer's insistence that we cannot really understand Last Things without a proper appreciation for the Things Before the Last, of Niebuhr's willingness to accept the compromised ethical ideal, of Tillich's declaration that Picasso's *Guernica* is the most Protestant painting of our day, of the whole movement stemming from Bultmann's demythologizing of the Scriptures. And while Barth continues to be the major theologian in the eyes of most Calvinists, it is these latter figures who tend to be most talked about on college and seminary campuses and in retreats and lay institutes around the country.

A sign of the times has been the widespread interest in Bishop Robinson's controversial little book *Honest to God*, which is one churchman's attempt to resettle the Christian *Weltanschauung* in a contemporary *Weltbilt*. In a chapter entitled "Reluctant Revolution," Robinson notes our general reluctance in the church to modify the expression of our doctrines according to new understandings of the universe, of history, of language, and of the human mind itself. To question the older formulas is "to appear to let down the side, to be branded as hopelessly unspiritual, and to cause others to stumble." Pressures toward conformity from within the institutional framework are therefore almost insuperable. But Robinson extends this promise, that "as one goes on, it is the things one doesn't believe and finds one doesn't have to believe which are as liberating as the things one does."[12] Strong language, from a bishop.

It is evident that theology, like Humpty Dumpty, has had a great fall. There are some who question whether it can ever be put back together again, or whether we would want to if we could. It is suggested that the demolition of the system, of the *summa*, is one of the greatest strides toward freedom we have ever made.

Whatever the future of theology is, though, we are perhaps better able, in the face of what is now happening to it, to recognize and evaluate the secularizing tendency in literature. What are the more important authors of the time doing to reshape the general consciousness of man? How are they refocusing our thinking? What effect, if any, are they having on theology?

The long-range effect of contemporary writing on the human consciousness must, in my opinion, be described in terms of impact, and not in terms of single ideas or doctrines. The spareness of mood, the anguish, the brokenness of life, as these are witnessed to in modern letters, soon became a kind of cathartic which the mind depends upon and cannot do without. It is not a matter of this notion or of that, of any novelty of idea, but of a kind of general acidity that cuts through to the more basic modes of human existence. At first this thing is too pungent, too violent, for the consciousness. We do not like to be confronted by the ravaged "soulscape of modern man," as Nathan Scott has called it. But after a while we begin to see that anything less would be dishonest, that it would not adequately represent the turmoil and complication of the human problem in our time. Our very taste is affected. We no longer want the saccharine and flattering portraitures of an earlier year. We want things stringent and hard, in the belief that it will do us good. We favor Eliot as a "Christian" poet because he does not make the answers too easy; echoes of "jug jug jug" from *The Waste Land* still sound in his later poetry and plays, even though they are there caught up and overwhelmed in *Te Deums*. We believe that the serious author and the serious theologian alike must not treat as unreal the more grating and intractable factors of human experience, that the vision of God must come to man, if it comes at all, in unlikely places and under unfavorable conditions.

There are two kinds of reality, as Christopher Fry has reminded us—the reality which we call reality only by dint of custom, of being used to it, and the reality which is deeper, more mysterious, more colorful, and which we might recognize as such if we were only to come suddenly upon the scene of our existence instead of growing up there in the midst of things. The business of the poet or the playwright is to make us aware of the second reality. But the poet does not accomplish this without talking about the first kind of reality. He must begin with us where we are in our dull world of custom, and there make us see the magic of things. In other words, he must bring the two realities into convergence.[13]

If contemporary letters do nothing else—and I do not suggest that that is the case—they return us at a bound to the drudgeries of human life, to Sisyphus and his futile struggle with gravity, and say here, here, here you must begin. You cannot start with the second reality, even in the church. Especially not in the church! You must start where the incarnation began, in this miserable hellhole of mortal existence. Anything more is a lie and a cheat. You purchase credibility—or miss it—according to the way you talk about the facts that are common to all men, in the church or out of it.

What I am suggesting is that literature, for all its bleakness and agnosticism, has probably done more than anything else to return theological thought in our day to its ground in incarnationism, a ground from which it ought never to be separated. It has been a long time since the church was able to speak so freely of what it means to exist in the world, to triumph in the midst of the finite circumstances. Escape is no longer the church's watchword; now it is engagement. We have moved a long way of late, from Hamlet's

> The time is out of joint: O cursed spite,
> That ever I was born to set it right!

to Meadows'

Thank God our time is now when wrong
Comes up to face us everywhere,
Never to leave us till we take
The longest stride of soul men ever took.[14]

And the so-called "secular" writers have done much to help
with the moving expenses!

Of course we cannot rest forever in a mere "theology of
honesty," for such a theology is not really a theology at all.
In the end there must be some affirmatives—or at least some
reaffirmations. But the literary artist has helped us to get
down to a solid place again, where we may begin to construct
some affirmatives—this in spite of the fact that he has seldom
had any affirmatives of his own to offer. He has in one sense
been a modern mystic, treading the *via negativa* with courage
and patience while waiting for something in which to believe.
His waiting has not been simply a relaxation, any more than
Didi's and Gogo's was. Such waiting never is. It is strenuous
and demanding. It is waiting in the Hebraic sense, as if waiting were a rope stretched taut and full, with every cord bearing the strain of its antipodes, poised in action until something
gives—or the rope breaks.

Christian art, as Malcolm Ross has said, must not be merely
pious if it would be wholly relevant today, and above all "it
must not be archaic, yearning nostalgically for the ages of
faith." It must be able "to penetrate and reinfuse the historical
order—not as it was, not as it might have been if there had
been no Renaissance, no Reformation, no French Revolution,
no class struggle—but the historical order as it is, as it has
actually become."[15] It may be that literature has helped to
prepare us not only for belles-lettres that can do this, but for
a Christian faith that can do it as well!

We have seen the tidal wave come. It has washed in upon
many time-hallowed ideas and religious beliefs. It has dragged
us violently back and forth on the washboard at the sea's
edge. Institutions have toppled, dogmas have succumbed,
pretensions have been drubbed out. Here we stand on the
naked shore, tattered and weary and a bit forlorn—but perhaps also cleaner and stronger and more profoundly joyous.

An era of rebuilding is ahead. We have not clearly got to

that yet. We are still counting our dead, still crossing ourselves for fear of the sea, still watching the skies for portents, still moving slowly and wondering at the gift of being alive at all. But the time of reconstruction is coming. And the land is clear for it. And we will not forget the power of the sea for dealing with unfounded ideologies and scantly assembled dogmas. For a long time now we will build with a view to strength and meaning, to position and durability. Just as there is no blessing that is not also a curse, there is no curse that is not also a blessing. We have been washed out. But the air is clear and fresh for a new and vigorous understanding of the old and diehard faith. A new issue of life—and a corpus of genuinely Christian literature—may not be far ahead of us.

NOTES

1. *Christian Faith and the Contemporary Arts*, ed. Finley Eversole (Nashville: Abingdon Press, 1962), p. 9.

2. In *The Modern Poets*, ed. J. M. Brinnin and B. Read (New York: McGraw-Hill, 1963), pp. 198–99.

3. *Ibid.*, p. 199.

4. "The I Without a Self," *The Dyer's Hand and Other Essays* (New York: Random House, 1962), pp. 159–60.

5. "Being and Faith in the Contemporary Theater," in *The Climate of Faith in Modern Literature*, ed. Nathan A. Scott, Jr. (New York: Seabury Press, 1964), pp. 108–11.

6. *De Descriptione Temporum: An Inaugural Lecture*. Quoted by John McGill Krumm in *The Climate of Faith in Modern Literature*, p. 37.

7. *After the Fall* (New York: Bantam Books, 1965), pp. 4–5.

8. *Ibid.*, p. 5.

9. *Ibid.*, p. 162.

10. *Ibid.*, pp. 162–64.

11. "Religion and the Mission of the Artist," in *The New Orpheus: Essays Toward a Christian Poetic*, ed. Nathan A. Scott, Jr. (New York: Sheed and Ward, 1964), p. 63.

12. J. A. T. Robinson, *Honest to God* (Philadelphia: Westminster, 1963), p. 20.

13. "A Playwright Speaks: How Lost, How Amazed, How Miraculous We Are," in *The Modern Theatre*, ed. Robert W. Corrigan (New York: Macmillan Co., 1964), pp. 1042–44.

14. Christopher Fry, and "A Sleep of Prisoners," in *The Modern Theatre*, p. 1070.

15. "The Writer as Christian," in *The New Orpheus*, pp. 88–89.

The Christian Minister and the Social Problems of the Day

George W. Webber

A seasoned veteran of the inner-city ministry—in particular, that of the East Harlem Protestant Parish—George W. Webber knows firsthand the challenge that urban culture presents to the church. He also has some bold ideas as to how the church should go about meeting that challenge—which in simplest terms means finding ways to enable human life to be truly human in an environment characterized by depersonalization, rootlessness, anonymity—but also by possibilities for growth-in-community. Essential for the effective functioning of the minister in the modern metropolis, however, is a thorough-going overhaul of seminary education; as presently structured, Webber insists, it is overly academic and fails to put the minister-to-be in touch with the real world. While continuing to have a limited role on the staff of the East Harlem Protestant Parish, Dr. Webber is now the Executive Director of MUST (Metropolitan-Urban Service Training), a new venture in functional ecumenicity involving both training and action for ministers and laymen in the urban mission of the church, with headquarters at the Biblical Seminary in New York City. Dr. Webber, who is also Associate Professor of Church and Community at Union Theological Seminary in New York, has managed to find time to write two books: *God's Colony in Man's World* and *The Congregation in Mission*. His article is from Volume 1, Number 1 (Autumn, 1964) of a new periodical: *Theological Education.**

I. Introduction: The Battered Minister

IT SEEMS only fair that once in a while a speaker who stands within the parish ministry be asked by

* Published quarterly by the American Association of Theological Schools, 934 Third National Building, Dayton, Ohio 45402.

the seminaries to discuss the tensions which he faces in his work. For I am under the strong impression that for the last ten years the seminaries have been analyzing, dissecting, lambasting, and devastating the poor parish minister until he is likely to be bloody and bowed. Has any professional group ever been so threatened and criticized by its mentors as the clergy? Do law faculties spend their energy criticizing lawyers or medical faculties lamenting the demise of effective doctors? No doubt there is some of this in all fields, but examine for a moment the attacks to which the seminary professors in our time have subjected the poor parson.

First, there have been the studies of theological education, which suddenly turn out to be directed not to what is wrong with theological education but to what is wrong with the clergy. Seminary Prof. Blizzard, seeking to learn what might be done to reshape the curriculum in light of developments in the social sciences, got so fascinated with what he found was happening to the clergy of this country that no one ever did find out much about what his work meant for seminary education. But he discovered, as everyone knows, that the poor clergy spend their time doing those things they do not want to do and do not spend their time doing those things they want to do. Oh, wretched men! Then came the Niebuhr, Williams, Gustafson study of theology education with its two best read books, of course, not on changing theological education, but *The Purpose of the Church and Its Ministry*[1] and *The Ministry in Historical Perspectives*.[2] Theological education may have made some modest changes as a result of these studies, but the ministry got pinned with the label, "pastoral director" and, in spite of the intention of the study, got buried deeper in the institutionalism of the churches. Now, clearly aware that they were looked upon by the hands that trained them pretty much as a failure, it came as no surprise to the parish clergy that theological education had next undertaken, with the usual lush foundation grant, a project to develop tests that would serve to screen men out of the ministry. Obviously the seminaries were offended by the products they had been forced to train. Meanwhile, we await the results of the Lilly Studies of theological education[3] and what new insights they will bring on the perils, failures, and irrelevance of the present work of the ministry. Yes, we have tensions in the ministry—and some of them seem intensified by such studies as these.

But the formal studies are only part of the picture. Even more devastating have been the critical and unnerving articles, often in the secular press, in which seminary professors have continued the sadistic attack on the ministry. Professor Shrader demonstrated that we were breaking down. Professor Sittler discovered that we were macerated. Others from the vantage of the seminary studied our sex life and our psyches. Professor Come, taking up the implications of the recovery of the laity, seemed to imply that our ordination was a mistake. Then the renewal fad struck full blast. Books demanding new life in the church poured out of seminary studies. The clergy sought to accept these challenges from the seminaries with their implicit criticisms. They read Professor Berger and Professor Marty, they started study groups. And then Professor Winter, in a tour de force, seemed to prove that the whole thing was ridiculous, the local residential parish was dead, and ministers had best flee the sinking ship to share in Professor van Buren's "secular meaning of the gospel." By this time, battered and confused, the clergy all over the country are trying to figure out how in Heaven's name they got in the wrong fight at the wrong place in the wrong time. Yes, if we have tensions, problems, and uncertainty in the work of ministry, it is not because the seminaries have been hesitant to tell us where we were in trouble.

It is against this somewhat exaggerated background that I want to talk about the legitimate and inescapable tensions which face the authentic work of the minister in our time as he seeks to be faithful to a historic tradition in the midst of a world that has shattered every tradition and is erupting in new and utterly strange dimensions as the full impact of an urban, secular world takes shape before our eyes. There is a crisis in ministry today, as all the smoke and fire of study, criticism, and challenge make apparent. But the problem is for the minister to find out the right point of involvement, the godly tension, the significant issues that require ministry amid all the false and irrelevant patterns of his present work. What I mean to imply is that to a large degree, in finding a path of obedient ministry in the world of metropolis, the parson is largely flying blind, cut off from theological certainty and unprepared by anything in his training or experience to live as a man of God in the world outside the sacred reservation of present church life.

II. A New Orientation: The Congregation in God's Mission

I have personally been driven through a modest but rather traumatic theological reorientation since leaving seminary. East Harlem confounded and challenged the meager personal and theological resources which I brought to the task of ministry. As clergy, we had no choice but to grapple in a fundamental way with the purpose of the Church and the nature of its task in our particular situation. Only in the light of our understanding at this point were we able to deal with the particular task of the ordained clergy. Let me sketch the elements of the contemporary theological ferment that have helped us define the ministry of the East Harlem Protestant Parish.

A. THE AFFIRMATION OF AN URBAN WORLD

To our middle-class eyes, East Harlem was a terrifying and terrible slum. Here was a world of misery whose problems and despair we were called to attack with all our energy. And like most Protestants, we intensely disliked cities. The thought of living in East Harlem or bringing up our children there was utterly distasteful. This urban dislike, coupled with a rural nostalgia and a God-in-nature religion, is the pervasive Protestant ideology. It has been a terrible problem for me. When I was a little boy growing up in Des Moines I got sent to Y Camp and at night as the sun was setting we would go up on "Inspiration Point" and watch the sun go down over the river. They would say, "Here is God." God was in nature. God was in the beauty of the world, God was in the joyous happy things that take place. But we all knew what happened to a good Iowa farm girl when she moved to the big city. The devil got her! God was at work in the country, in nature, and in your garden, but Heaven help you if you had to live in cities, in apartment houses or in tenements or anyplace else. In the city, the devil, not God, is ruler. Two little six-year-olds in a profound theological discussion were heard arguing about the existence of the devil. One little boy said, "Oh, there isn't any devil." The other little boy, who was very upset by this, said, "What do you mean there isn't any devil? It talks about him all the way through the Bible." The first little boy said in a very knowing way, "Oh that's a lot of nonsense, you know. Just like Santa Claus, the devil turns out to be your daddy." Well, the devil is very real in the city, but the assumption that God is not at work in the city is a denial of a Biblical faith. God, the lord of history, seems to be putting people in cities to live.

But this is a strange and unacceptable notion to most Protestants. If everybody in the five boroughs of New York City were put in one religious category, Protestant, Catholic, or Jew, about 50 per cent would be Catholic, about 30 per cent would be Jewish, and less than 20 per cent would be Protestant, of whom over half would be Negro. Since half of the 10 per cent we've got left are not connected with any church, this means that less than 5 per cent of the 8½ million people in the five boroughs of New York City are white Protestants. We have evacuated from the cities as though they had the plague. Most of the literature of our denominations still assumes that the city is an evil place and must be attacked from outside—but Heaven help you if you have to live in it and share in its common destiny.

What I'm suggesting, then, is the need for a new stance, a new way of affirming the meaning and possibilities of life in this new metropolis which is emerging as such a clear and inescapable reality in the whole world. Can't one put it as simply as this: If God is God and if in Jesus Christ he has affirmed his direction over human life and death and destiny; if the Christian faith is true at all, then God is God of cities. The simple fact is that he is calling most men to live in these great metropolitan complexes, soon in a mass of 25 million human beings in one metropolitan unit (in our case, from Boston to Wilmington, Delaware). God is not calling men to live in these great new cities to destroy them. To be a civilized man, as the Greeks knew a long time ago, is to be a city man. In metropolis is the possibility of creativity, the excitement of varieties of human relationships and possibilities that open to all men the truly human life to which God is calling them.

In other words, *cities are for people.* Cities are a place where human life can find fulfillment and meaning and purpose—else God would not be placing life in this context. But one can take this affirmation one step further. Aristotle, who reminded us a long time before Christ that men come together in cities in order to live the good life, defined the task of politics as the art of making and keeping men truly human. We must discover for our day the art of making and keeping men truly human in an urban world which threatens men with depersonalization and anonymity. We can transpose that statement from Aristotle and put it like this: The task of the Church is to make and keep men truly human. Is that a statement that is fair to the meaning of the Gospel? Can one boldly affirm that God is at work in the cities calling his people, calling the members of his congregations to the task of making and keeping life truly human in the big cities? Now this may sound like a rather strange and jolting notion, but let it be just that for a moment. For unless we get jolted badly, unless something shatters the present introversion and complacency of the churches, irrelevant to an urban culture—we've had it!

What does it mean to suggest that the task of the Church is to engage its full energy and life in helping cities become communities in which human life can become truly human, and not warped and destroyed and corrupted by oppression or prejudice or poverty or depersonalization or any other problem? The Bible suggests that as Christians we know something about what it means to be truly human, to be a new man in Christ. In Christ we see what true humanity is. The Bible itself turns out to be a supremely political book. It is not a "religious book" that teaches people primarily how to pray or engage in private devotional exercises. It is a book about a nation, a chosen people with a particular vocation in the history of the world. It is about exile and captivity, about slavery and freedom, about the conflicts between nations, about a redeemer who comes to bring a new world and who offers the promise of a new city. Read the Bible with these eyes and see that it is a very secular book about the concrete facts of human history. We are called to read the Bible in order to understand the common events of our human destiny.

I am suggesting then that in the emerging metropolis, which so threatens the life of the Church, we are called to an understanding of the role of the Church which turns us outward, into the task of helping cities become cities of God. Christians and Christian congregations are called to join God in the task of making and keeping life human in cities.

B. GOD IS AT WORK APART FROM AND IN SPITE OF THE CHURCH

But as one discerns that precisely in metropolis is the locus of obedience for the Church, the fact becomes suddenly clear that God is at work ahead of the Church, and as often in spite of the witness of congregations. We began in East Harlem with the distinct impression that God needed us to get his work done. Christ had no other hands but ours. We went forth from the chapel at Union with the words of the great commandment urging us on, "Go ye into all the world and preach the gospel to every creature." We thought this meant we had to introduce Christ as though he were a stranger to the pagan, missionary world of East Harlem, as though we had to take him from Morningside Heights to a world from which, without us, he was absent. In the early days, with our self-righteousness, our confidence that now a radically new dimension had been added to East Harlem, we made all the social workers furious and alienated many of the devoted men and women who were engaged in the struggle for justice and brotherhood in the community. We now would humbly confess that signs of Christ's presence were there for eyes that could see, that more often than not, in beginning to enter into the life of the community, we found him coming to meet us in the needs of our neighbors and through the love that was offered freely to us.

But the truth that has been hardest for us to bear is the unmistakable fact that God has really moved outside the churches in his mission. In Acts 17, when the apostles showed up in a town it caused quite a row and the authorities were told, "Those men who have turned the world upside down, have come here also." In our world, I suggest that quite the reverse is happening. God, through his grace, is using the world to turn the Church upside down. Let me be quite specific:

1. First, the radical change in moral patterns in the city strikes any minister, particularly if he was brought up in the moralism of the YMCA, as I was, or in a typical Protestant church, as a tremendous denial of the gospel. In seminary, I had been armed with the Christian ethical position on social problems. The basic assumption, which after all these years I still must fight, is that in Christian ethics we do really have the answers so that the issue is simply one of communication or adaption. But in the sexual revolution, as we all know, the issues that are posed for the Church and for educational institutions are at points where we are simply out of this world. I am only suggesting that God here is not only judging the rigidity of our moralism, the legalism of our approach, but may also be calling the Church back from its sacred ghetto to an incarnational involvement in the real ethical dilemmas of our day which must be shared to be understood; which must be faced not only by looking into the Bible for the answer, but whose solution lies only in an honest dialogue between the Gospel and the realities of God's present world. God is calling the Church back into the world where it belongs. Our focus is not to tell people to be good but to help them become truly human.

2. The Civil Rights Crisis. Not the Church primarily, but the insistent courageous struggle of NAACP, CORE, SNCC, has opened up the reality of human suffering and degradation which a white, middle class society has permitted to exist. In the face of the segregated patterns of his churches, God has had to demonstrate elsewhere communities of genuine brotherhood that transcend all our human differences. God has clearly judged the churches, and continues to judge white Christians who even now, in large part, speak of concessions to Negroes and fail to recognize that such an orientation maintains a position of white superiority that

may be more demonic than the honest hatred of the racist. But more important, God is giving us a focus for the work of ministry. Any congregation that is not now honestly and urgently seeking in its situation to reflect cultural and racial differences in its common life, that is not restless and uneasy about its negative witness by its location in a homogeneous residential ghetto, that is not seeking to focus on a witness to the truth that in Christ there is neither bond nor free, neither Jew nor gentile, male nor female, Puerto Rican, Negro, nor white, but that in him all men are one: that congregation can hardly be called any longer a church of Jesus Christ.

3. The Gift of the City. Again, God is turning the Church upside down through the emerging urban world. We still live in our churches with patterns that were forged in a rural world a century ago when America was a Protestant nation of farmers and small townsmen. In a world of incredibly rapid change, demanding new responses in every area of life, we continue the traditional patterns in church organization, in worship and preaching, in the Sunday School literature we use, and in our emphasis upon the church building as the center of our religious life. Last summer I visited Des Moines and found a revolution had taken place in that city—nothing looked the same. It has all kinds of new industry, the buildings have changed, the downtown has been rebuilt; through TV, metropolis has intruded into every home; the whole city is different. But I went to church on Sunday—back in my home church. It was the one place in Des Moines where nothing had changed, including the soprano in the choir. It was a rather shattering experience of the irrelevance of old forms in a new world. There is a certain validity to tradition but not a tradition that is totally unrelated and strange in the emerging city.

When the East Harlem Protestant Parish was started in 1948 by a group of denominations, we simply tried to reproduce the patterns of the Church as we had known them and as we had been instructed at Union Seminary. If I may put it quite bluntly—we literally got clobbered. The kind of sermons we tried to preach, full of literary allusions, didn't ring any bells. The worst thing of all was the Sunday School literature. It isn't so much that Sunday School literature is all middle class, but because of the assumptions about the communication of the gospel. We have tried every kind of Sunday School literature—from Moody Bible Institute through Pilgrim Press, Westminster, and Seabury, from one end of the theological spectrum to the other. Sunday School curriculum materials of all denominations basically have one underlying presupposition—they all, in one way or another, say that if we want to teach Johnny about Jesus he has to live in a family where he has been loved. Then we can say Jesus is like the love you know at home. Or we explain that God is a Father by saying that God is like your daddy, a negative image for the overwhelming percentage of boys and girls in a slum community. By the grace of God, the Bible's got it the other way around from our Sunday School literature. The Bible says that I, as a human father, know what it means to be a father because of the relationship between Jesus and his heavenly Father. That is the image that men need to follow. The kind of love which is called for in a family is seen in the love between Christ and his Church.

We had a rough time in East Harlem then, because the pattern of the Church's life and the demands of the ecclesiastical structures of all denominations, some worse and some a little better, but all pretty awful, were not equipped to meet the challenge of an urban world. But when the congregation admits its failure and ceases to depend upon secular criteria of success or upon its human ingenuity to keep alive, then amid the problems of the city it finds time and again that a gracious God is offering to it the patterns for its life which it needs for God's mission. In this light we see the grim problems of East Harlem not only as problems which we must face but as God's way of leading us back to dependence upon him as the Lord of the Church. When God casts us back into the heart of modern urban America, confronts us with the predicament of the church, he is in fact offering us the gift of new life in Christ. "If you then, who are evil, know how to give good gifts to your children, how much more will the heavenly Father give the Holy Spirit to those who ask him?"

Thus we have been led to affirm that God is at work in

the world, not only judging, but redeeming and reconciling human life apart from the church. But that leads inevitably to the final theological issue that has challenged us. What is the mission of the congregation?

C. GOD'S MISSION SHAPES THE CHURCH'S MISSION

In the current study of the missionary structure of the congregation, the European working group came up with the formula: God-world-Church, thus reversing our traditional assumption that God brings his Church into being in order to minister to the world. The two great realities are God and his world, with the Church not the mediator between the two, but rather taking its shape from the shape of God's mission in the world. The Church is called to share in what God is doing in Christ, and thus its whole life must be oriented to God and the world. It must live in the world for the sake of its Lord. In every situation, the task of the Church is to discover what God is doing concretely and specifically, to join in God's work of making and keeping life truly human, and to point to what God is doing that the world see and believe that Jesus Christ is Lord. The gathered life of the Church must take its form from this missionary purpose. The work of the ordained clergy is determined by the same missionary purpose.

Always and everywhere, the shape of the Church's missionary witness and service is determined by Christ's own ministry. This is the only possible criterion, to share in the incarnation, crucifixion, and resurrection.

Incarnation: that means for the congregation that its life must be shaped by scripture and by the world. Only in this dialogue and involvement can the church discern what God is doing, where the action lies, at what point its attention must be claimed. To take the incarnation seriously means to take the world seriously, as Jesus did to affirm what is good in it, to share in it with the abandon of Kierkegaard's Knight of Faith, to express Bonhoeffer's authentic worldliness.

Crucifixion: this means that the congregation exists to share in Christ's ministry of healing, reconciliation, judgment, and forgiveness. This is to enter into the task of making and keeping men truly human. It means to live at God's pace and not our own. Now the focus is not on the moral life nor the building of an institution, but on living as "agents of reconciliation."

And the third dimension: witness to the *resurrection*. The congregation is called to be a light set on a hill, to point by its existence and its activity to the presence and power of God. When Christians gather to worship and study, they testify to the lordship of Christ over their lives. When they enter into the life of the world, it is in order to point to God's redeeming work. "Let your light so shine before men, that they may see your good works and give glory to your Father who is in heaven." The congregation that lives by confidence that God's victory has been won points through its perseverance, quiet hope, and joy to the risen Lord. The congregation that gathers around a communion table Negro, white, and Puerto Rican, rich and poor, educated and uneducated, all sorts and conditions of men, is a demonstration of the truth of the Gospel, first fruits of the kingdom, sign that Jesus Christ is Lord indeed.

III. Situation of the Clergyman

In the light of these theological affirmations, the legitimate and inevitable tensions for the clergyman begin to emerge more sharply. The ordained man is called to work within this kind of missionary congregation. He must himself live on the boundary between theology and the shape of God's present world, between the apprehension of what God has done, is doing, and promises still to do, and his personal involvement in the concrete process of history. He must bear the tension between his clerical role in the Church and his life as a man in the world. He must learn to theologize in a quite new and unfamiliar manner. That is, he has been taught to theologize about theology but never really to think theologically about the world. He encounters with utter unreality MacLeod's phrase about reading the morning newspaper to see what God is doing in the world. Bible study was an academic enterprise, not a dramatic encounter with a political textbook, the living story of how God has acted in the affairs of human history.

But above all, he finds his place amid the life of one of the present congregations of Protestantism. There, seeking to respond to God's action in history, he confronts with anguish the rigidity of present church patterns. As you know, there is a serious debate going on between those who believe that some form of renewal is possible for the local congregation and others who feel that the present residentially based congregation is hopeless. Gibson Winter, for one, is convinced that morphological fundamentalism has too firm a grip ever to be loosened. A World Council of Churches document asks whether the necessary missionary mobility can be recovered as long as we continue "the highly institutionalized and professionalized pattern of the ministry," a pattern not likely to be broken down in American Protestantism. Even a prophetic parish minister, Gordon Cosby, who has spent fifteen years in what is often taken to be the most vital missionary congregation in America, has been led to say, in a sermon to his congregation in 1963:

> The church as we know it in our time must go. This conviction has come to me gradually—I have worked with it consciously for the past 15 years and been disturbed by it for the past three. Just a few weeks ago I crossed a line in my thinking. Now I am on the side of feeling that the institutional structures that we know are not renewable. Even where there is renewal (and this goes on in many congregations) the stance of the Church is almost always the same—a stance which is contrary to the very nature of a church committed to mission.

The chorus of such voices is likely to increase in the immediate future, but their effect may well be to increase the rigidity of present patterns, rather than to call churches to mission. The discontinuity with the present sounds too great, the call to obedience too radical for many to hear and heed. The conviction underlying this presentation is that a better point of departure is to begin with the present institutional life of the church and within that context seek to find paths of missionary obedience. Out of this struggle with the old forms may come the need for new forms, bolder and more radical than we so far perceive. But this will be a process of change that accepts continuity with the past, is able to build upon the historical faith of the church even as it listens more emphatically to the need of the world. The clergyman must take his stand, for the present, or for the most part, within the contemporary patterns of congregational life—with a crucial qualification. Where there is no willingness among the people to search for missionary patterns, no concern about the mission of God, no restlessness able to be evoked about the challenges of God to the churches in our time, then the clergy will, like the first messengers sent out by Jesus, shake the dust off their feet on the assumption that a parish unwilling even to ask about its mission is not at all a parish of Jesus Christ. But in the parochial situation, part of a fellowship whose purpose is to join in the mission of God, the clergyman must find his place and face the legitimate tensions of this ministry.

IV. The Task of the Clergy and Its Inevitable Tensions

If, for the sake of our discussion, we accept this understanding of the purpose of the Church and its ministry: to share in God's work of making and keeping men truly human, then in the ministry in which I have been engaged the emerging tensions are very sharp.

A. FIRST, THERE IS THE CONFLICT BETWEEN THE ROLE OF THE PROFESSIONAL AND THE FACT OF OUR ESSENTIAL HUMANITY, THE *professional* VERSUS THE *person*.

Not only our training and our age build a professional stance, but so also the world and the church insist upon ornamenting the clergyman in such a way that he is no longer a man among men. But to serve God, the clergyman must be a representative man, facing honestly and fearlessly where he stands and who he is. In East Harlem we almost went under at this point. White, middle class, theologically trained, we were not able to transcend the image of paid

Christian, of an institutionally oriented operator, with the aura of the sacred always surrounding us. At the start, we were really cut off from the real life of the community. We were functionaries of the religious enterprise. We even went so far as to hire a rather brilliant research girl to study East Harlem, to live with the people, find out what made them tick so that we could learn to communicate to them. After six months she came back and let us have it. She said, "This is the phoniest assignment I've ever been given, because the problem is not the people of East Harlem and for you to understand their life and culture. The problem is you. You are trying to be professionals—clergy and Christian, but you're not willing to be human beings who live and share the common life of the neighborhood, who live next door and are neighbors and friends with the people in East Harlem."

In a word she pointed out to us how we had failed to take the incarnation seriously. Christ didn't set himself up as somebody special. He walked around the dusty roads of Palestine and lived and shared in its common life. We had to stop being professionals, standing on the bank of East Harlem watching the flood tide of human life sweep by, analyzing it, dissecting it, writing articles about it, analyzing it for suburban churches, but unwilling to live and share in its common life, if we were ever going to be able to communicate to anybody. What she meant was that we were phony. It was a pretty embarrassing and threatening thing to be told this: that the clergyman does not stand in the safety of his church, or protected by his education, or by his commitment to Christ, safe and secure, and throw life rings out to drowning men in the middle of an urban world. No, the ministry must always be involved in the world, as one who shares and is threatened by and is faced with the precise difficulties and problems which every other man faces. Until the staff of this parish were willing to be next-door neighbors to people, fellow parents in a parents' association in a public school, fellow citizens in the community, to share in its common life as those who were part of East Harlem, there was no possibility of sharing in God's mission. In thus seeking to express his humanity, the clergyman offends the members who look for an authority figure or an answer man. But only in this direction can the ministry recover its missionary character.

B. SECOND, THERE IS THE CONFLICT BETWEEN THE *pulpiteer* AND THE AUTHENTIC *prophet*.

The dominating place of the pulpit as the main operating base for the clergyman, as far as the inner city is concerned, is passé. As a channel of authentic communication, a well-prepared, thoughtful sermon, preached with liveliness and conviction, no longer seems to get through into the responsive centers of congregations who spend their lives in a spectator attitude and stopped reading the Bible several generations ago. The clergyman as prophet is called to use all possible resources to engage the congregation themselves in active dialogue with the word of God. He must always, in everything, seek to break open, to demonstrate and point to the present power and reality of what God is doing or requiring of men in the midst of their concrete and specific history. His task is concerned with the secular relevance of the Gospel, with the meaning of the Word in the secular commitments of the congregation. In this context, the offense of the Gospel is at once apparent. The prophet must push aside all his conditioning that demands he please people, bring about peace and harmony, at whatever cost, and live again in the freedom to speak the truth in love. He must always, with humility, speak the truth as he has been given to see it and to speak it openly and forthrightly. Only through the path of honest dialogue and of the ensuing conflict are integrity and true unity likely to emerge in a congregation.

C. IN THE THIRD PLACE, THERE IS THE TENSION BETWEEN THE CLERGYMAN AS *producer* AND AS *priest*.

So much of the liturgical renewal has depended upon a kind of showmanship. The worship service is a production in itself. I was taught about worship as though it were an end in itself, in tones that were sepulchral and mysterious . . . "we must learn to *worship*," holy, separated, special, ultimate, but unrelated to common life and daily struggles. If the congregation is directed in everything to God's mission, so in its worship its concern is for the world. ". . . your brother has something against you, leave your gift there before the altar and go; first be reconciled to your brother. . . ."[4] The gathering for worship must be honestly related to our dispersion in the world where God has placed the congregations as partners in his mission. In the parish where I worship, we symbolize this understanding of worship in several ways: the "concerns of the church" during which men and women stand and share their concerns, the issues that have involved them in mission and offer the names of those for whom we should pray. The minister then kneels and prays about these specific matters which the congregation bring before their God. Again before coming to the altar table the congregation join in the handshake of fellowship as a sign of their unity and then stand in a large circle around a table to receive the bread and wine. The loaf is an ordinary loaf of Italian bread brought by one of the members. It is passed from hand to hand, each breaking off a piece as in a family, and then all partake together. The benediction at the end is always in the form of a bidding: "Go into the world in peace; be of good courage, overcoming evil with good." In these and other ways the priestly role is to lead the congregation in intercession for the world, seek God's encouragement through Word and Sacrament for their life in the world, and then with new strength and conviction send them back into the work of mission in God's world. But as with the other tensions we have considered, the priestly role in a missionary congregation is simply not possible unless the clergyman, in fulfilling his liturgical ministry, is a worldly man. Through his knowledge of the world, his enjoyment of it and participation in it and in all the affairs of men he is equipped to perceive Christ at work there, and in the gathering of the congregation to uphold before them the meaning of the common life and offer it to God. He must live on the boundary between the community that perceives the work of Christ and the world in which Christ is at work. To live thus is always painful and difficult.

D. IN THE FOURTH PLACE, THERE IS THE CONFLICT BETWEEN THE PRESENT UNDERSTANDING OF THE *pastoral counseling role* OF THE MINISTRY AND WHAT I BELIEVE IS THE AUTHENTIC *pastoral* TASK.

To minister and laity alike in our day it is almost universally accepted as a fact that the major usefulness of the clergyman is as a counselor. And in what I suspect is an unbiblical and unhistorical manner, we have equated the traditional pastoral role with the modern phenomenon of pastoral counseling. In the process, we have simply eliminated the essential pastoral work of the clergy: that of equipping the saints for the work of their ministry. Counseling, concern with personal problems, and all the other elements that go with it are an essential part of mutual ministry in a congregation. Christians gladly bear one another's burdens. But this seems clearly the work of the whole body, not to be centered in the clergyman as his area of specialization. I have argued this point before. Here I am only making a plea to restore to the portfolio of the clergy the responsibility to give primary attention to equipping the laity to use their gifts of ministry and to focus in their gathered life on the task of witness and service they face in the world. The specialized counselor is a legitimate and essential part of a community of faith, badly needed as part of the ministry of a congregation, but this is not an essential function of ordination. The ordained man must focus on the worldly responsibilities of the laity, help in the process of consciously dispersing them into the points of service where they are called by God's mission, and in general seek not to minister to their personal needs but to enable them to minister to the needs of others.

As you may note, I have so far come down on the side of a traditional definition of the work of the clergyman, though the recovery of such a role may seem almost impossible in the face of the rigidity of present patterns. He is to be concerned with God's word: with finding ways in which it may be heard and appropriated in the context of the social situation and conditioning of those among whom he works, knowing that preaching from a pulpit may no longer be even the most important part of his task; he is concerned with the sacraments as a priest among other priests. There he is concerned to shatter the sacred-secular dichotomy that has left the church in an isolated ghetto and instead seek to witness to God's concern for the world and the responsibility of God's people to live in and share the struggles of a world to become human. And as pastor, he is concerned to discover, confirm, and train the gifts which by the power of the Holy Spirit are bestowed on the faithful. At the same time, his pastoral role involves the recognition that men gather in the church in order to be sent back renewed for God's work. We have no right to call God's people from their places of witness and service in the world—where he has placed them—into the gathered life of the church, for worship, study, and fellowship, unless this gathering prepares them for their life in the world.

E. THE FINAL TENSION IS DIRECTLY RELATED TO THIS EMPHASIS UPON THE EQUIPPING ROLE OF THE CLERGY: *Leader* vs. *Servant*.

For what is demanded is a self-effacing, servant type of role that stands in strong tension with the traditional role of the strong and able leader of the army of the Lord. *Leadership* and *servanthood* seem in some sense mutually exclusive. As Roger Hazelton has written, "the servant is one who has become expert in caring, in living for others, in obedience, and self-offering." This stands in sharp contrast to the usual notions of leadership. But precisely in the inner city, there is overwhelming need for strong and able leaders who will push aside apathy and despair and lead the victims of injustice in the struggle for human rights in a democratic society. As a staff in East Harlem, we have never been able satisfactorily to resolve the tension between our understanding of the laity as the church in the world and the necessity of ourselves taking some kind of leadership role in the struggle for justice in the community. Sometimes we argue that our ordination is only to work in the gathered life of the church. In the world, we are laity and thus attend parents' meetings, political clubs, and the like in a necktie and not a clerical collar. But we know full well that we are using, in many instances, the professional status the world accords us to achieve our goals. Or again, the tension arises when, in the face of the apathy of our congregations we can stand the routine at home no longer and go off to Hattiesburg or Albany to do something that in its own right is good and proper. But we are all the time troubled by the feeling that the clergyman, basically, belongs in the church, pushing reluctant laity in the world, not in the world, dragging reluctant laity in his wake. God is to be thanked for the charismatic leadership of men like Martin Luther King, but this is not a normative role for the clergyman in the congregation.

V. Conclusions for Theological Education

As an extended footnote, I would like to suggest something of the implications for theological education which grow out of this description of the role of the minister in a missionary congregation. I am persuaded that the seminary must itself assume a far more prophetic role than at present, determined to educate men for the congregation in mission, not for the present expectations of the churches, not the men the churches want or think they need, but the men they ought to have. Overshadowing all else, of course, is the need for the seminaries to produce what, in rather grandiose terms, might be described as "worldly men in Christ." For the congregations of our day need men whose lives are informed by Christ but who live as men in God's world, as free to embrace the world as did their Lord. This means that fully as important as academic study is concern for what the Catholic seminary calls "the formation of the priest."

Many theological seminaries are discovering that they can no longer take for granted the religious maturity and commitment of their students. Unsure of their vocation, confused about the meaning of their faith, critical of the institution of the church, and hesitant before the radical claims of Christian obedience, this student generation is simply not prepared for the ministry through a program of academic study and theoretical reflection. At best, they may suppress their doubts sufficiently to enter the work of the ministry but without any prophetic insight or convicting faith. Training demands that we focus upon helping students and clergy become "worldly men in Christ." This is the task of formation.

Several years ago in a careful study of Christian seminaries in Africa, Asia, and Latin America, Yorke Allen was intrigued to discover that Roman Catholic and Protestant seminaries were, in their curriculum and program, parallel at every point save one. In a Catholic seminary, almost as much attention was given to the formation of the student as a man in Christ as to his academic studies. But in Protestant seminaries, there seemed to be no parallel concern, even on a rather vestigial basis. The Roman Catholic Church can teach us something at this point; not, perhaps about method, but simply about the necessity of conscious attention in the seminary and training facility to helping the student to grow in his commitment to Christ and to discover the channels of grace through which God may deign to direct his life. We cannot leave this matter of formation to chance or assume that somehow it will happen in the ethos of the institution. Each man is different, but all need help, encouragement, and direction in preparing themselves as men for the work of ministry. They may even need to learn something of the cost of obedience. Four elements in formation seem important:

A. THE EMPHASIS UPON FORMATION MUST TAKE SERIOUSLY THE NEED TO BE WORLDLY.

A number of sobering studies of theological students and clergy indicate what basically sheltered lives most of them have led. The kind of men who enter the ministry have these tendencies: they made their decision in high school; they relate more easily to adults than to their own peers during the teen years; and they begin their ministries with relatively little acquaintance with the realities of modern life. The honest and open worldliness to which Bonhoeffer calls the Christian is hardly possible. Theoretical exposure to the world through academic study in seminary does not face the issue of helping the student, as a man in Christ, to gain some personal understanding of what it means to take seriously the incarnation, to dare to live as a Christian in the world, without the protection at all times of the institution. This suggests clearly that for men brought up in the cocoon of the church—youth fellowship, denominational college, and academic understanding of the world—some new involvement in the world is required. Church field work or an intern year, still in a church somewhere, is no answer. Perhaps a genuine secular involvement for a summer, or better, an intern year that involves secular work and commitments, coupled with a program of disciplined study, is one possible direction.

B. IN THE TRAINING PROCESS, THE CONCERN FOR THE FORMATION OF THE STUDENT AS A WORLDLY MAN IN CHRIST INVOLVES THE HABITS OR STYLE OF THE CHRISTIAN LIFE.

This means that the institution itself must with some self-consciousness focus upon the student as the subject matter of the curriculum. Without trying to deal here with the obvious dangers of overlooking the claims of subject matter, academic disciplines, etc., and without any brief for training as group or individual therapy, I suggest that we must discover, if we do not know it now, how to help those in our care grow or develop in terms of their obedience to Christ. The key to this process, I suspect, is discipline. This rather unpleasant word to most of the younger genera-tion can be replaced, if you wish, by the term "habits of the Christian life." In Christ a man is given a new freedom, but this must be expressed in a whole new orientation of his life. The habits of thinking, feeling, and responding, appropriate to the Christian life, must replace the old habits with which men begin their life in Christ. In the *Screwtape Letters*,[5] C. S. Lewis describes the efforts of the old tempter to console his nephew who has just lost a victim to the enemy (the Church). He reminds the young tempter that the intended victim is not yet lost, for all his old habits are still in their possession. Unless they are changed, the man will soon fall away from Christ and they can claim him again.

We fool ourselves badly when we think that all patterns of life will be displaced by the fervor of a new commitment to Christ or the decision to enter the ministry. Only by the long-term work of building new habits in the place of the old can we hope to be sustained in a pattern of life which will express the freedom is made possible only by discipline. Only when men have learned to make the many small decisions of life that reflect their obedience or disobedience to Christ out of habit are they able to exercise genuine freedom in the larger issues for which no habit is adequate.

C. FORMATION MUST ALSO FOCUS UPON A NEW APPROPRIATION OF THE BIBLE.

In the Word of God is the link between Christ and the world. The clergyman must learn again to see the world with eyes of faith, as the arena in which the God of history, who is revealed in the Bible, continues to act and in which his promises will be fulfilled. But in the seminaries with which I am familiar, Biblical studies do not find their focus at this point. Is it unfair to say that by and large they are either academic and scholarly or entered into for the sake of preaching? The seminary student has firmly before him the twin images he encounters: the dynamic preacher, breaking open the word—like Buttrick or Steimle; and, stimulated and thrilled by lectures in Old Testament from Muilenburg, he can hardly wait to gather his flock during Lent for a series of lectures in which he can play the role of teacher. Of course, I am not suggesting that preaching and scholarship are to be downgraded, but rather to affirm that in our day men and women, including seminary students, do not stand under the Word of God, or become drenched in scripture, or begin to see the world through eyes of faith until and unless they are engaged in regular, long-term, corporate Bible study, focused on themselves listening to God's word to them, in light of their work in the world. At one leading seminary last April, thirty-eight seniors had still failed to pass a required examination on the content of the Bible. But they had all taken the required courses and more in Old and New Testament, been in preaching courses, and were otherwise ready to fulfill the traditional role of preacher and teacher. But they did not see the world through eyes of faith. Last fall at Union a group of twelve students were offered a course on Bible study. They were expected to prepare carefully, but the seminar hour consisted of corporate study, with no introduction or critical background. The students, who did their homework carefully, as for an exegesis class or for a sermon, were really amazed at how their preparation, instead of making the hour and a half boring, made it immensely interesting, stimulating, and often quite literally a source of revelation and new understanding of what God was saying through the scriptures. Precisely this pattern of Bible study is the only way that the laity in the parishes we serve will ever be brought back to any degree of Biblical literacy and themselves live under the Word of God. In a congregation thus engaged, preaching and teaching may again become primary channels of grace; but without this preparation, the words fall on rocky soil indeed. Thus I suggest that a normative part of a man's seminary preparation must be his personal involvement in the kind of corporate Bible study that offers him as an essential part of the armor for his ministry the strong, clean sword of the Word.

D. FINALLY, I WOULD SUGGEST THAT IN THIS CON-
   CERN FOR THE FORMATION OF THE CLERGYMAN,
   THE MOST VALUABLE INSTRUMENT OF TEACHING
   IS THE LIFE OF THE SEMINARY COMMUNITY
   ITSELF.

Here is a teaching vehicle that either serves as a parable for the young minister as he approaches the life of his parish, or points in quite the wrong direction.

As a hypothesis, I suggest that theological seminaries are called to grapple in their academic and community life with the problems which at a given period of history are those same issues that most deeply trouble, perplex, and confuse the churches. Is not theological education at its best and most relevant point when it is seeking through Biblical, historical, and theological reflection to understand the shape of the Church, the task of ministry, and the work of God in the concrete context of its own historical situation? Thus at the turn of the century a crucial issue was in the field of Biblical interpretation. Fundamentalism was as much a problem for the parish minister and the local church as it was in the seminary. Again, the social gospel movement was an expression in Protestantism of the confrontation of the churches by emerging industrial life in America. In the seminaries and in the churches the same issues were important. I have already pointed to the need for a new appropriation of the Bible. Worship is another central emphasis.

Congregations are struggling to find patterns of worship that take seriously their life in the world and enable those present to enter as participants into a corporate act. The liturgical renewal in many places is no fad or gimmick, but an impressive recovery of an authentic part of our life in Christ. But in some seminaries, the chapel pattern has undergone no change in generations, the worship life of the institution is meager, and the faculty is not particularly interested in discussing the matter. Above all, the ultimate problem for the present parishes may turn out to be "morphological fundamentalism," that is, the rigidity of our present structures so that change is almost impossible and renewal unlikely. The processes of change and a theological perspective on institutions are both urgent concerns in the committees of the World Council and in the life of local congregations. In seminaries, they are matters for minor attention in the "practical field."

The seminary is called to express through its style of life its central focus as called to be an instrument of the present work of Jesus Christ. The community of scholars, practitioners, and students is in need of a style of life that reflects in its situation the appropriate marks of obedience to Christ. Just as much of American Protestantism, for a variety of reasons, has virtually eliminated any concern for church discipline and search for an appropriate style of life, so the seminaries, of whatever type, seem really unable to face the necessity for a creative style of life. The denominational schools are often still seeking to maintain a pietistic community life, unrelated to the life of the congregation in our time, while the larger seminaries, like the churches as a whole, have simply decided to forget the whole matter, often under the guise of freedom. I argue here not for some particular pattern, but only that a seminary dare not leave aside the matter of its appropriate style of life.

Not only does this seem necessary for the integrity of seminary life in Christ, but in facing the task of discovering a style of life as a seminary community all those so engaged are being prepared directly for dealing with the problems of every Christian in the world today. And such preparation is not primarily going to take place in the classroom but in the whole context of seminary life: chapel, the discovery of personal discipline, small groups that are studying the Bible, the debate over house rules, and all the rest.

As theological educators seek clarity about their task in the midst of the fantastic changes in our day and in light of the emerging purpose of the church in God's missionary work, it may be that they will discover that our present seminaries are not required to fulfill the entire task of the education of the clergy. Secular involvement, continuing education in the light of a man's particular focus of ministry, and increased possibilities for specialized training may all suggest a delimited understanding of the proper role of the seminary. In that case, the diffusion of "practical" courses might be checked and the seminaries, insofar as they are professional schools, might concentrate on their particular, but only partial, task in the total preparation of the clergy.

NOTES

1. H. Richard Niebuhr, *The Purpose of the Church and its Ministry*, (New York: Harper, 1956).

2. H. Richard Niebuhr and Daniel D. Williams (eds.), *The Ministry in Historical Perspectives*, (New York: Harper, 1956).

3. Study of Pre-Seminary Education, Study of Education for Practice of the Parish Ministry.

4. Matt. 5:23, 24 (RSV).

5. C. S. Lewis, *The Screwtape Letters*, (New York: Macmillan, 1943).

6. Yorke Allen, *A Seminary Survey*, (New York: Harper, 1960).

Fidelity to the Living: Reflections

Daniel Berrigan, S.J.

Jesuit poet Daniel Berrigan offers a moving, mind-stretching essay delineating the dimensions of a viable Christian witness in our age. Among his motifs are the radical distinction between religious magic and Christian mystery, the nature of servanthood, the paradox whereby "one must consent to live at the edge if he is ever to reach a true center." Father Berrigan, like his brother Father Philip Berrigan, has long been involved in the civil rights movement, and both have been dissenting voices in regard to United States involvement in Vietnam. At present Associate Editor of *Jesuit Missions*, Father Berrigan is the author of a number of books of essays and poetry. His two most recent books are *They Call Us Dead Men* (essays) and *No One Walks Waters* (poetry). His article is from the Spring 1965 issue of *Continuum.**

TRADING IN one talent can be a noisy thing, as the single coin rattles about in an empty metallic life. In contrast, the gentle effortless flow, not of currency, but of the spiritual energies of life, on the part of those whose existence is the tipping of a great available vessel; "And the house was filled with the odor of the ointment."

Some make of the faith a kind of lofty Olympian tundra where they tread and breathe an air too cold and pure for ordinary mortals. Such heights allow one to dismiss with contemptuous ease the common man's expectation that Christians too will take into account "justice, and the law."

The pure in heart are in the nature of things defenseless. Before the world. And also before the Church.

One lives in a room after a while, with an eye to his grave. The furnishings are unimportant. So after all, is the view.

* Saint Xavier College, Chicago 55, Ill.

"When time has made all equal. . . ." Which of course time will never do; it only offers occasions for a more complex structure of injustices. The key: the end of time.

The attitude of faith is no more easily described than a glass of water: colorless, tasteless, odorless; but still, mysteriously refreshing. And when held to the light of day, a prism that captures all the delight and mystery of the world.

Several figures of the Church seem to verify themselves in turn throughout history: the church as House, the church as Exodus. One, the "dwelling" figure (Pauline, perhaps by way of the Greek view of the universe as *amplissima domus*); men build when the times are kind, when a certain overflow in nature and life offers a pause, a measure of freedom from mere subsistence, a universe that is "benign and ample." Secondly, the Exodus figure; wars, famines, destitution, personal sinfulness, exile in Babylon, the necessity of leaving the "low-vaulted past," the transcendence and uniqueness of the summons (from what direction coming, in what direction leading?). These are perhaps features of the Exodus image.

A third image seems also to perdure; it is large enough, and mysterious enough, to express the opposition contained in the other two. "You are the Body of Christ." The body—open, permeable, needy, in service, at rest and on the road, beset with suffering, growing and becoming, contemplative and creative, unique and generated. The metaphor implies man's personal body, jealously protected, cherished, fed, and clothed; and it implies man as a world body, acknowledging his debt to mother earth with every breath, and always foreshadowing in his poverty and dependence, the day of return, the dust yielding to dust.

As early as Feuerbach: "Individual man does not contain man's being in himself, either as moral being or as thinking being. Man's being is contained only in community, in the unity of man with men, a unity which rests however, only on the reality of the difference between I and Thou."

"The characteristic of greatness is the carrying out of a will which goes beyond the individual. The great individual knows what the nation's will should really be and carries it out, because the force and capacity of infinitely many is concentrated in him. There appears here a secret coincidence of the egoism

of the individual with the greatness of the whole." (Burck-
hardt, *Reflections on History*) True; as far as it goes. And
moreover, a profound critique on Nietzsche's unlimited "will to
power" as an ingredient of greatness. One reflects—(1) given
the corporate nature of mankind, and its growing consciousness of being corporate in all phases of life, a decision, however enlightened and far-seeing, is of little value as long as it
is arbitrary and unrelated to those in the grouping; (2) Burck-
hardt's idea seems related to the principle, medieval and
ecclesial, "What is of import to all, should be discussed and
approved by all"; (3) the greatness of decisions and ideas is
to be measured by their availability, rather than by any striking originality or thrust of power, by their ability to express
the unformulated, obscure hopes of many; to seize upon and
vitalize human life, a new soul for an old. The aim of great
ideas or great art or great policy, is incarnation, embodiment;
a new man, a new form, a new community.

That styles of religious life are changing is news to no one.
It is no longer really important to defend change, or to accept
change. What is crucial, and will be for several years, is the
effort to understand the nature of change, and to act in such a
way (both as subject and initiator of change) that what is
sacred, real, valuable, comes through as new world and new
Church. The task is of course very difficult. One is simultaneously subject to change and yet must bring change about.
There are no pure spectators, and yet there must be enlightened observers; in a way, we must be Protestants at a
catholic process.

Certain things will always endure, if change is not to become chaos. There is no need to become dogmatic here, or to
compose a new chain of "things to be believed." The real
point is living faith, charity, a Christ who is present. And
from the human point of view, the retention of good humor,
courage, suppleness of heart, openness to conversion, inward-
ness. Literally everything else is worth sacrificing for these.
And these cannot be sacrificed for anything else.

What must be prepared for, and actively experimented with,
is the creation of new forms of life. And there is no reason
why such experiments, such active tribute to the unknown,
cannot be paid within the framework of the old. For the

old is a nest of the new; and unsuspected life is always longing to be heard, and to be heard from, within the old.

One will always respect the truth of tradition, at risk of becoming a mere destroyer. On the other hand, the gospel nowhere urges us to remain within a decaying nest.

It is remarkable how new forms of life continue to come to us, like unsuspected hidden springs, from within the most unpromising and suppressed areas of the world; one thinks of Christians under Marxism today, and of what they have had to say to the whole Church. And one is led to think of the ambiguous play-acting that goes on among Christians in the West, the poisoning of the air to which we contribute, the arrogant assumption that "the others" cannot produce art or disinterested research—or indeed a Church. Meantime, the Spirit breathes where he will.

Bonhoeffer speaks of a "sense of quality." The development of this sense has a price tag attached. It means developing a sense of the genuine over the merely phenomenal, of reserve over assertive speech, of listening over persuading, of reading and reflection over sense stimulation, of the individual over the big gain, of suffering and submission along with action, of prayer along with initiative, of anonymity over headlines, of personal change over bureaucracy.

A sense of mystery as contrasted with a devotion toward magic. Mystery is effected, according to Catholic belief, when a symbolic activity, quite modest and concrete, brings about a meeting of two freedoms: the divine and the human, and the opportunity of creative change in human life, a climate of choice. Magic, on the other hand, announces an automatic possession of the divine by humans, and its manipulation toward human ends: the genie in the bottle.

The renewal of the life of faith can be seen from this point of view—it must be purified of its subtle magical appeal. The test of whether mystery or magic is at work will always be the changes being wrought in the community itself—its tightening into a closed fist of selfish exclusivism, or its gradual opening out on the will of God and the hope of man—at whatever cost. Magic costs nothing, except in the tender of a given society; one pays his entrance fee, becomes an initiate, and in every formal activity reinforces his sense of belonging, of earning salvation through bribes, and of excluding the "impure." But mystery creates the individual and his community anew; it breaks up the old molds, forces open hearts and hands, introduces the mind to the real world, awakens responsibility toward it.

Properly speaking, magical rites have no symbolic content, no depth. Their pretention to the miraculous really leaves no distance between the god and the initiates; there is no task, no journey between the divine and the human. So magic ends by destroying those who place their trust in it, because it falsifies human life into a closed circuit for those (literally) lucky enough to be in touch. Magic allows for no growth, no pain, no human response or cost. There is no incarnation in magic, for incarnation implies the ultimate tribute to man: an entrance of God into what is unfinished and therefore perfectible by human hands. Magic leaves us only the indistinguishable dream world of the *Odyssey*: gods and the humans couple and wage war and connive, a classic cosmic impurity rules everything.

Holding on to mystery, on the other hand, means precisely letting go. "Cast off into the deep." It is only a very mature community that is worthy of being trusted with the mysteries. The early Church understood this. An adult community had come to the faith by way of a profound world experience. It was to be thought that within Christianity, the world experience would continue; under a different aspect, of course, but inevitably.

How different our situation today! The conscience of Christianity has permeated the world, the world has even gotten beyond Christians. Many unbelievers surpass Christians in their purity of outlook, their sense of reality, their sense of the neighbor. The protest of *The Deputy*, the Negro revolution, the social gains made by Marxist societies, are extremely unsettling to a society of believers that thought it contained and expressed the conscience of man, once and for all. Being a Christian needs redefining in every age; and every age hesitates between two great choices: that of insecurity in the world, and that of a security which merely draws on what has gone before, and remains on safe ground. The real effort, never really done with, is to discern what Christ is saying to us from within the real world. . . . All else is a mortician's job, or a child's game.

Change is always painful; at least part of the pain is the effort toward agreement on what needs changing. Almost everyone has his own version of what should be swept aside, and of what is worth saving. It takes little insight, however, to see that every form of triumph, even of sacramental or liturgical triumph, is only another bind. Nor to see that the proliferation of Christian projects, structures, groups, is in large part an obsession of security, a thicker wall about the in-group.

We are possibly moving to a point where the effort to verbalize mystery is becoming more and more self-defeating. The world is too much with us; too complex to box, too omnipresent not to threaten even the most tentative statements, especially when these are put in the way of religious claims. To live the faith is the point.

What leads we have from Christian lives that are making no claims are a sort of radiant symbolic activity. That, first of all; no proofs, many signs. World issues are quietly assumed to be religious issues or, let us say, Christian issues. And one puts his life in that breach. This is also a clue as to why the most viable theology of the last twenty years has come from (1) those among the priest workers who left a few letters and notes, and died before they were heard from; (2) the prisons of Hitler; (3) the theologians of central Europe. Much of the rest smells of some obsession: to speak in abstractions, to attempt a presumptuous synthesis, unaffected by suffering and exposure.

The world says it needs only itself, needs contact only with its own deepest instincts, in order to run its own version of providence. Empirically it cannot of course be proven or disproven that the world has resources to heal its own wounds and to arrange its own future. And Christianity at its best has not been overly interested in proving anything about itself, or the character of its mission in the world. It has announced a mystery: the divine gift, forgiveness, hope, eternal life.

Every use and teaching about the sacraments which merely announces a divine activity as such, is a perversion of the will of Christ. Every use and teaching about the sacraments, on the other hand, which attempts to embody human hope, to lead the facts and struggles of life beyond themselves, is a service, i.e., a liturgy. The first tactic announces an a-historical God, an idolatry, the Christian obsession to be "out of it," to create a god who is himself "out of it." The second announces the incarnation principle as a continuing fact, the God who is "in it." Thus baptism must embody conscience and responsibility, and the eucharist must summon men and women to sacrifice.

The critique of Bonhoeffer and his commentators concludes that with the forward movement of history, God has been proven more and more "unnecessary." Man has passed through one stage of growth; God as overseer and guardian is dead. So we are in a better position to see what he was from the beginning. The statement, taken in the sense that his relationship to us has altered, is not offensive to believers.

And what is the basis of a new, mature sonship, that is looking to no false hopes or props? that is looking to be only son and brother, in him? For it seems that faith in God is at its purest precisely when man is closest to asserting his freedom, his wholeness, his domination over creation. At such a time he has the chance of a real choice of God, one at greatest distance from "thunderbolt religion"—a controlled, mature, fully conscious faith.

One can protest that we have as yet no solid reason for asserting that man, in his personal and social aspects, is about to fulfill all the postulates of maturity. The new societies and the "new man" of the Marxists have had no sufficient historical testing as yet to prove they have made it, or that their new societies have made it. And the dominion of man over nature, claimed by science, would surely have to include freedom from suffering, freedom from psychic disorder, from social selfishness, the acknowledgement of a minimal human chance for all men. It is by no means clear that the blueprint is about to be realized. Man has not as yet created himself in any real way, as "new" man. As the first generation of Marxist ideals fades, and as East and West tend to homogenize, we are seeing that the "new" man was largely a historic exception, created by the enthusiasm of a new start. But it is at least doubtful that he can reproduce himself.

In a time when so much is in question, and when the best

men seem to question most deeply of all, it is good to recall what was seen as essential by the first Christians; not by way of cowardly regression, but of an effort to touch the springs of our being, "our fathers in the faith." When all has been said, the Christian is a man; he knows that Christianity has never scouted or despised the simple requirements by which men live—justice, altruism, conscience. But he knows that these gifts do not make the Christian. He waits on God. No effort of his own can effect the "difference"; no boasting of his can assure it.

For this reason a Christian is unassertive and modest; he knows that he stands under judgment, and that the love that summoned once, gently and irresistibly, may one day be drowned out. "Today if you hear his voice, do not harden your hearts."

The opposite of love is not hatred; it is indifference. When we have learned indifference, when we are really skilled and determined at the business of ignoring others, of putting our own well-being, our own options, first, of thrusting our own ego into life, as the ideal form of life itself, we may be quite certain that at that point, life has become hell. We need be no more thoroughly damned.

Christians without personality. It is as though not the world, but their faith, had choked off everything living in them. Which is of course impossible. What has happened, more nearly, is that they have fastened on some form of cultural or sensual substitute, which has gradually sucked dry whatever living capabilities their faith would have brought to flower. What is left is a shell of dreams and fantasy. No heart, no mind, no horizon. No sense of the direction or intensity of life around them, or of the response expected of a man of faith, who knew that faith is destined to incarnate itself or to die.

What form of life will summon men as powerfully as war does? will attract them, unify their energies, make of even the most nondescript among them, for some few hours, a very lion? Religious passion, except for some few, has been no substitute. Neither have ideals of public or intellectual service. All of which is not necessarily a judgment on these latter; under proper stimulus even a nonentity can put on a lion's skin and play his part ferociously. And the instinct for violence lives so nearly under the skin as to leap into action with the slightest provocation.

When all this has been admitted, it remains true that religion issues no more than the most vague and tardy summons to heroism. What it offers in its sermons and the embarrassing evidence of Christian lives, is a way of evasion, a quiet moral minimum, a blameless passive life by the fireside. Not wonderful if few have the clairvoyance to get beyond all this to the fiery summons of Christ.

Apart from the state and the blood line, there are very few loyalties to which men feel bound to cling today. In normal times, one's bonds to the state are inert and meaningless, a response to minor annoyance—keep traffic laws, pay taxes. Blood loyalties are another matter. Who has not seen even the least passionate or concerned parent transformed into a fury when family values (money, security, the tribal good) were challenged by a son or daughter who had come to see something beyond?

When loyalties of spirit grow weak, loyalties of blood become consuming. To invoke gods other than those of the tribe is assumed to be a sacrilege against nature. And of course a sacrilege against idolatrous nature is exactly the form Christian virtue must take in such a case. "I have come to set husband against wife and brother against brother."

Even the best of our theologians have not shed much light on the nature of revolution in the Church. And least of all when revolution implies the duty of blessing unpopular causes and urging their value on Catholics. We are assured rather that the Church will not grow hotheaded or yield her tradition into the hands of the impatient. All of which is a way, more civilized perhaps but hardly less damaging, of tipping the weight of tradition in favor of prudence and reaction. Which hardly allows for a profound analysis of the workings of spirit.

Against a call to single-minded obedience, there is no end of obstacles, even of those which call themselves sacred. They amount to an unscalable, massive roadblock; is it not wonderful that all but the most courageous lose heart? But in the final analysis, the same Christ who calls, must create the response; obedience is a gift, not a human capacity.

The Christian failure: not to confront men with choices. But it still may be a providential irony that many of the real choices today, on behalf of God and man, are made outside the Church.

Christianity has always implied responsibility toward structure. From the beginning, the apostles took others in charge: their human welfare, their worship, their conscience. So there were choices at hand, and adjustments to human weakness, even the presence at times of a pernicious spirit, of mistakes that cost dearly. But our situation is not comforted when we consider the early Church, in spite of superficial likenesses. The average conversion when believers gather today reveals the anomalies. We indulge in the good common small change of an in-group, concentrating on money, good order, and gossip. We are obsessed with the well-being of the inheritance, without seriously considering whether in fact it ought to be spent abroad; most terrifying of all we consider the sacraments and Mass in exactly the same way as a lawyer or medico looks to his accounts, his regular returns, his expanding accounts.

A church with place for sinners?

A church which serves the poor?

A church which is itself poor, as contrasted with the group which gives some hours a week or month to "going down to the poor."

It is said sometimes that we must match our apostolate to the poor by one to the urban and suburban rich. Give equally good priests to the affluent, and equal results can be predicted. . . . But the theory neglects the facts of life. Who or what in Christianity can help the rich become poor in spirit? A priest who serves the poor with any seriousness cannot fail to become poor in spirit. But who will teach poverty to the priest who serves the rich?

In question here is not poverty and riches at all—but the quality of faith that governs a life. And who is to say in any case that priests generally have more faith to communicate than the faithful do?

Interpreting the call of Jesus, in all its pressing historic complexity: The anguish of choosing among the mysterious good things the gospel offers us, the fear of choosing, the fear of not choosing, the fear of inevitably choosing badly—all these are relieved when we choose according to the *sensus ecclesiae,* the Spirit of Jesus, speaking in his body.

But where is one to come on that consensus? So vast a rhythm governs the consciousness of the Church that the wave of knowledge and holiness gathers to a crest only with extreme rarity, once or twice in a century perhaps. And what if the gathering wave does not meet my insistent need? The Spirit who speaks in the whole church, in the hierarchic Church, in the sacramental Church, speaks in every Christian. In me.

A false literalism demands that we become what we are not: contemporaries of the historical Christ. An illusion. A true literalism demands that we submit to sonship: as contemporaries of living men in the one Body. Reality. Right use of the world implies the willingness and capacity to be used by the world, as God's man.

Does God live on in the believer? does God live on in the world? The "signs" seem to be correlative; it is not possible to accept one hypothesis without accepting the other.

"To be free of this or that . . ."—always of course as a way to freedom. Which is possibly the heart of illusion. Since freedom in the nature of things is bound up with a certain undissolved slavery.

If one were free to be in every respect the man whom his sins prevent from coming into existence! This is the nub, the reality of guilt one must stay with. Man can only touch or taste his sins, remotely, from afar—which is a curse of the state of sin itself. And he touches his sinfulness in the moments when he knows beyond any doubt his refusals and selfishness. This knowledge is, on occasion, quite concrete. Man's sinfulness, at its worst and best, confronts the radiant love of Christ as a disease is touched by health; or more intellectually, as one absolute opposition touches another. What happens then is part of a continuing unresolved process; I believe in his healing. . . .

The act of faith is colored and made concrete by Christ—both as Act and as Thou. He draws one to faith; faith is in him. He stands as healer, he acts as healer. Healer of what?

The sensual games one plays; self-love, a corollary of the esthetic, insofar as this has not yet confronted Christ.

Despair, hallucination, unpurified ambition.

Fear of the future, fear of the demands made on health by a virile dedication to others.

A demand for freedom, and insisting on its presence, without being willing to pay, or even to discern clearly, its demands.

A moral life based on quality invincibly joins one to Christ and to community. Such a life also implies inevitably a sense of mystery Whose presence to one's inner life is signaled by signs, hints; one can never, strictly speaking, "rule in" or "rule out" either God or man.

We find it more natural to give ourselves to a performance than to a principle. This is why the God of history reveals himself in Act; *Verbum Caro factum . . . crucifixus pro nobis.* . . . Theologizing comes later, and is natural and needful. But in the gospels, God reveals himself by action. Almost in the dramatic sense; on a stage which widens its arms to include.

"Creating and recreating our spiritual destiny piecemeal, as we go along" (Henry Aiken, *Reason and Conduct*). Not as though nothing were given. But as though nothing were given until it is taken. The horrendous possibility remains; that is, of leading such an outside, formalized life that even persons and sacraments are no more than enticements on a tree of life. And on the other hand, nothing really possessed until it is given. An instance of the final, adorable mutuality: "I am in the Father, the Father is in Me."

One knows others, one loves and experiences others. One can live in a room, content in the thought of his friends. But one must also break free into the world, a bodily presence, affecting and affected by. The world "groaned in travail" for the Incarnation; as the garden was a perpetual autumn, until man.

To share in the tragedy of man: sin, malice, despair, the plenary horror. To share in the works of God: life made bearable, the partial resolution of the tragedy, the cry rising from our hearts to him, the "unutterable groaning of the Spirit in us."

Clairvoyance: "This will come to pass."

Abnegation: "This will come to pass, but not through me, nor in my hour."

Faith: "This will come to pass, through God and in his hour."

Resolution in hope: ". . . which I submit to, as my hour also."

Man's sense of sin is often adolescent, abstract, unproductive of change, of holy fear or renewal—an inverse of his sense of God. Man is creator and victim of the plateau he lives on; its killing monotony, its mirages, its emptiness. And when he has added nothing; assumed to the landscape, one with it, a zero within a zero.

A sense of being, altogether compenetrated with a sense of being inadequate. To be at all is, in the gospel sense, to be blind, leper, beggar, to live in a ditch, to throw up one's miserable dwelling and have the storms bring it down again. But who or what can help a Christian come to a sense of this unless God himself? A sense of the precarious misery of life, the fate of the majority of men, joined to the spiritual capacity to realize the meaning of such life, as ground for salvation.

Sin: the shaping of a heart without capacity for God; in a sense incapable of God.

The breathing area of freedom, and the discipline of obedience; both of them radically necessary in an age like ours. The best men are proudly and passionately conscious of their dignity, and speak a great deal of their need of freedom; but in so speaking, they express without saying it their longing for obedience, for someone to give themselves to, for a communion and friendship, for a counterpoise of thought which will contain, interpret, and direct their experience.

Authority is an organ of the authority of Christ when it too, and more deeply, and perhaps at greater cost than to the one who obeys, is obedient to Spirit.

Tradition is brought to bear on the present when the imagination of Christ lives on, both in men of authority and in obedient men. What does it mean to live in the real world? The question is one which the gospel both answers and refuses to answer. Answers: in the world experience of Christ, in his obedience and release into time. Refuses: in its open ending, "Live on in me, as I in you. . . ."

Authority which takes on a special style of life, or demands immunity from the fate of the majority, can never hope to ask the right questions, let alone to answer them.

A formula for fanatics:

1. Conceive a principle.
2. Baptize it "Absolute Claim."
3. Ignore its performance.
4. Canonize it.

A temptation of great men in face of the inevitability of death; to place some act to which their memory will be indestructibly attached. The absence of this temptation; an absence of greatness? Not necessarily; perhaps death, which is another name for the hand of Life laid on us, has already begun his purifying work.

The history of the world; the transformation of matter in spirit, the increasing availability of spirit. So true is this that forms of performance are either equivocal and destructive (where existing apart from spirit or in conflict with it) or merely useful (as dwellings and structures for spirit).

Why a Christian depends on the intercession of others—not precisely because he knows his own unworthiness (the question has little interest, either before the believer, or before God; an inert fact) but because only the "cloud of witnesses" can express in worthy measure the value of the "strong cry and tears" of our Lord.

The living space in the iron cage—"I am with you all days."

Placing ourselves in the Church, placing ourselves in the world.

Is this not a formula of faith; to realize the depths and heights and breadth of this compenetration?

To place one's self in the world, not as passive integer, but as witness; source of new life, of vision, of the service of God in time.

Placing one's self there by submitting to be placed there; a man of providence, neither rebel nor idle servant nor vagrant innovator.

Constantly exploring and enlarging the known frontiers of the kingdom, the visible geography of spirit, so that the kingdom is not a limbo of the restless disembodied, but a community of incarnate consciences.

As prophet, from above; as servant, from within. Teacher and taught; man of communion, man as listener.

Agent of faith in the Transcendent, a faith that includes the world.

In how many ways one must consent to live at the edge if he is ever to reach a true center! In order, that is, to become recognizably Christian, accepting the new life as a gift, not as a bride of a muscular achievement. And in order also to help the Church become recognizably Christian—not as an exercise in rebellion or public rhetoric, but as an epiphany of one's being, a postulate of love. This "edge" is where Christ is found. It is also the only true center, the "still point." The only locus of the new creation. "Come to Me."

One comes to him, not by moral integrity nor a lighter yoke of law, but by a submission that ties, destroys, and fires anew one's being.

What may count as apologia is that in the twentieth century a certain number of Christians did not give up, in spite of all provocation to do so. On the contrary, artists became artists, writers writers, scientists scientists. And in their troublesome, exacting, and dedicated tasks, they were supported by the Church, which did not condemn nor put heavy or untimely burdens on their consciences, but trusted them as sons. And in this enterprise, the honor of Christ and the needs of men were served.

But reading the story of Teilhard, how much of this ideal was violated! And how much honor and service undone, because many good men who lacked his fiber and faith simply disappeared as far as unusual gifts were concerned.

How necessary the healing work of the Spirit is, in those who are called to obey, and much more, in those who command intemperately.

Who else can unite the terrifying divisions of human life, except only Christ? or the terrifying divisions within the person? One who has not sensed these divisions to the quick, and sensed their parallel character, can have little idea of the horizons of Christianity. We are going so far as to say that work done on behalf of unity, even by those who are unconscious of Christ or against him, is still done in his Spirit. He draws together the world's limitless volcanic energies, its power of creation and self-destruction, its marvelous intellectual gifts, its biology and spirit, its suffering, violated, and hopeful flesh. And his action, it goes without saying, has nothing to do with the procedures so loved by this world—by the officious, the bureaucrats, the specialists of overcontrol, the trainers of rebellious beasts. But in a mystery, within and without simultaneously, as spirit always acts on spirit: within, a gentle unkillable immanence that is patient, unfearful, viable, that approves life in all its unpredictability and beauty; without, the invitation into the end of things: Come. A victory to assure our victory. A transcendence to vindicate his immanence. A person to modify and breathe on human systems. One impassioned of community, as a man is of his body, as a bridegroom is of the bride.

The appeals to "what Christ would do if he returned" strike one as rather crude and beside the point. The village Rabbi could not of course return any more than time can be rolled back on itself. And the Risen One has never departed; only his life is now and until the end a mutation in existence. So our appeal to him as sign is always modified by his presence as reality: sacrament, community, the substance of history itself attests to him. . . .

All of which does not make the task of fidelity any the easier; it only places it under a mystery. Does he communicate with the believer? Yes: "I am with you all days." He has become a life-giving spirit. "Wherever two or three are gathered together in my name, I am amid them." Fidelity to the mystery means fidelity to the One who is present neither as memory nor image nor law, but as Event in all events, Man in all men, victory beyond all defeat, a continuing defeat and a delayed victory.

Willingly to pay the cost of living in the real world. A world that is comprehended, even exhausted, in Christ. But to grow into him, as the price of knowing him at all, rather than identifying with this or that cultural or religious counterfeit.

"I am ready for today, if you are ready for the day after tomorrow." (Abbé Godin, to the French Bishops)

"I'm Not So Sure T... As Hateful As You Want Everybody To Think You Are,"

Honey whispered. "That's why I parked in front of your house—so we'd have a chance to get acquainted and start off on the right foot."

"Why, you little schemer. You said you didn't fool around—"

"Because I wasn't fooling around. My job was to meet you." She smiled impishly, defiantly. "I'm going to stop you, Mr. Cameron. Your old tricks aren't going to work. I think you're just as scared of all the things that scare everybody else."

"You don't know a damn thing about me."

"I know a lot more than you think." Honey seemed to catch herself. "Everybody's scared, Mr. Cameron. Even..." she paused, trembling slightly, perhaps because his powerful body was edging closer "...bullies like you."

"Is that what you think I am?" he demanded quietly.

"That's what you just said you were." Her tongue slid out to trace the dry outline of her soft pink mouth. She drew away from him. "We should be natural enemies."

His breath caught. His eyes were fixed on her mouth. "Baby, if you're smart, you'll run."

"I can be foolish sometimes...."

Dear Reader:

Welcome to Silhouette Desire – provocative, compelling, contemporary love stories written by and for today's woman. These are stories to treasure.

Each and every Silhouette Desire is a wonderful romance in which the emotional and the sensual go hand in hand. When you open a Desire, you enter a whole new world – a world that has, naturally, a perfect hero just waiting to whisk you away! A Silhouette Desire can be light-hearted or serious, but it will always be satisfying.

We hope you enjoy this Desire today – and will go on to enjoy many more.

Please write to us:

Jane Nicholls
Silhouette Books
PO Box 236
Thornton Road
Croydon
Surrey
CR9 3RU

ANN
MAJOR
WILD HONEY

Silhouette Desire

Originally Published by Silhouette Books
a division of
Harlequin Enterprises Ltd.

All the characters in this book have no existence outside the imagination of
the Author, and have no relation whatsoever to anyone bearing the same
name or names. They are not even distantly inspired by any individual
known or unknown to the Author, and all the incidents are pure invention.

First published in Great Britain in 1994
by Silhouette Books, Eton House, 18-24 Paradise Road,
Richmond, Surrey TW9 1SR

Silhouette, Silhouette Desire and Colophon are
Trade Marks of Harlequin Enterprises B.V.

ISBN 0 373 59112 8

22-9402

Made and printed in Great Britain

ANN MAJOR

is not only a successful author, she also manages a business and runs a busy household with three children. She lists traveling and playing the piano among her many interests—her favorite composer, quite naturally, is the romantic Chopin.

Other Silhouette Books by Ann Major

Silhouette Desire

Dream Come True
Meant To Be
Love Me Again
The Wrong Man
Golden Man
Beyond Love
In Every Stranger's Face
What This Passion Means
*Passion's Child
*Destiny's Child
*Night Child
*Wilderness Child
*Scandal's Child
*The Goodbye Child
A Knight in Tarnished
   Armor
Married to the Enemy

Silhouette Special Edition

Brand of Diamonds
Dazzle
The Fairy Tale Girl

Silhouette Sensation

Seize the Moment

*Silhouette Christmas
   Stories 1992*
"Santa's Special Miracle"

*Silhouette Summer
   Sizzlers 1993*
"The Barefooted
            Enchantress"

*Children of Destiny series

Prologue

———

Why is it so hard to say you're sorry? To admit you've been wrong? Hypocrite!

Her desire to return to the fold had nothing to do with unselfish motives.

Honey shivered with dread as she tiptoed gingerly up the pink marble steps. It was a magic spring evening in Pacific Heights, San Francisco's lovely old neighborhood with its magnificent houses hugging their steep hillsides. Far beneath her, past the dark forests of the Presidio, a lavender fog rolled beneath the Golden Gate Bridge.

As always the air was characteristically soft and fragrant with the scent of jasmine. Bright stars were popping out in a darkening indigo sky. The beauty of the night and the neighborhood achieved movie-set perfection, exactly the sort of perfection her father sought to achieve in every aspect of his well-ordered life.

Honey hesitated, feeling uncertain of her welcome and vaguely intimidated as she stood in front of the massive door of her father's mansion.

It was chilly for the first of May, and Honey wished she'd worn more than her flowered light cotton blouse and green shorts. For one thing her father would disapprove. Nor would he like her vinyl boots, nor the wide-brimmed green felt hat that concealed her hair even though the vivid color brought out the green of her eyes. He'd always complained that she was too much like her artistic, bohemian mother and not enough like him, so, to please him today, she hadn't worn the bangles at her ears and wrists she'd wanted to wear. Instead she'd selected gold studs and a single gold bracelet.

She touched the doorbell with trembling fingers, then jumped back when it buzzed loudly.

It was not too late to run.

She glanced down the steps at the tired-looking, battered green car she called the Bomb. The old instincts were still strong. But she had run before, thirteen years ago, to escape her father's deplorable tyranny. Or so she had said. She had married a free-spirited man and lived the nonmaterialistic kind of life that her mother would have applauded.

When her father had disowned her, she had laughed with defiant glee—on the surface.

Well, Mike was dead, and Honey was beginning to realize her life with him had been more rebellion against her father than the life she should have chosen. Coming back to make peace with her father was just one step among many in the painful process of self-discovery.

She rang the bell again.

The door was answered by a small Japanese woman in impeccable white who did not recognize her.

Honey should have known the housekeeper would be someone new.

"I'm Cecilia Rodri—Cecilia Wyatt. Mr. Wyatt's daughter."

The housekeeper's face was politely blank, giving no indication that she was surprised Hunter Wyatt's daughter wasn't slimmer and more beautiful and more elegant. That she wasn't perfect—like him.

"I—I teach school here.... Well, not exactly here." *No, not here in this exclusive enclave for the rich and powerful, but in a small privately funded school for the disadvantaged in one of the city's toughest neighborhoods.*

The door widened. "Welcome."

Honey smiled at the irony of that word being used on the threshold of this house where she'd always felt left out.

Honey was ushered past the bold surrealistic mural her mother had painted in the last days of her unhappy marriage into an ornate white room with white couches and white walls and golden-edged mirrors. She remembered that her father did not inspire loyalty in the people nearest him. Help came and went. He had had three wives, her own mother having been the second. Both his children had run away.

The cold, formal drawing room oozed with the unabashed splendor of elegant carved moldings, parquetry and marble, tapestries, antiques and rich brocades. Hanging from the high ceiling in the center of the room was a huge golden cage with a white cockatoo in it.

The room was like a stage set for a grand opera, not a place for real life and real people. For a fleeting instant Honey saw it filled with vibrant warmth and slapdash color as it had been in her early childhood.

Because of the many tall windows and wonderful sunlight, Honey's mother had appalled her father by turning the room with the grandest potential into her studio. Honey remembered the smell of paint and turpentine, the brilliant splash of sensual colors on chaotically stacked canvases. She and her older brother, Raven, had loved watching their mother paint, especially since her studio had been a sanctuary from their overbearing father.

Honey went to the cage and spoke softly to the bird. She lifted her finger and the bird moved closer to nibble at it. The cockatoo was making animated, growling sounds of pleasure when Honey's young stepmother glided down the white marble stairs.

Astella was as beautiful as ever and as golden as the room she had designed. One of San Francisco's most famous socialites, Astella was written about constantly in all the society columns, columns Honey would never have admitted to anyone that she had the slightest interest in reading, columns she secretly devoured.

Astella wore a white gown of drifting silk and a thick gold necklace at her throat. She had that rare kind of charisma that would stand out even in a room filled with the city's most glamorous people.

"Cecilia, darling. This is ... a surprise." Astella's husky voice was cool, unwelcoming. "Do sit down. Make yourself at home."

Impossible—in this house, with you here and Mother dead. Honey looked at the stiff white couches and lingered near the cage so that Astella was forced to come to her.

The slim, long, scarlet-tipped fingers that touched Honey to guide her to one of the narrow couches were tense and cool.

"The room, the house—you've done wonders," Honey said, feeling like a wayward gypsy surrounded by such frosty elegance.

"That's all I do," came that cool, faintly exasperated tone.

"It wasn't always."

"No, but I stay busy." Astella used a scarlet lacquered nail to flick an invisible speck of dust off the golden tassel of a white pillow. "As you know your father expects perfection in all things." Her gaze slid from the battered green brim of Honey's hat down the wrinkled blouse and shorts to the scuffed vinyl boots.

"Yes," Honey agreed dismally. "That's why he married you."

"Thank you." Astella said, continuing to look her over. "You shouldn't hide your hair. Or wear such big flowers."

"I—I know I've put on ten extra pounds ... since Mike died. Every day I tell myself I'm starting a diet."

"You should exercise."

"Yes, well, right now it's the end of the school year. It's hard to find the time."

"You don't *have* to teach."

Honey shifted nervously, defiantly. "Yes, I do."

"Oh, yes. Your precious independence—so you can support Mario and prove to us all that you don't need the Wyatt name or the money. You could send Mario to live with his grandmother."

Honey's mouth tightened rebelliously at the mention of her teen-aged stepson. "She doesn't understand him."

"You're only his stepmother—"

"Astella—"

"We could go shopping together. I could help you choose a more flattering wardrobe."

"That I couldn't possibly afford."

"I could help with that, too."

"No." Honey's gaze traveled to the brilliant greens and reds in the foyer. "I'm glad you left Mother's mural."

"Your mother was a wonderful artist. The mural is famous."

Famous—that was why it had stayed.

Once, Honey's father had said that her mother had preferred her art to him. He hadn't cared for it until she'd made a name for herself.

Astella plucked a white rose from a vase and began to twirl it in one hand.

"Don't you ever get tired of just keeping him happy, running his homes, arranging his parties?" Honey asked.

"Perhaps if I were a talented artist or a devoted teacher..." Astella had begun to shred the rose. "A woman in my position has no need for a career."

"Women with money have all sorts of needs."

"As your mother's daughter, I'm sure you would know." Astella's fingertips froze as a dozen petals fluttered to the white carpet. Then she rang for the housekeeper.

The same old tensions had crept into the room.

After the petals had been gathered and thrown away and Astella and she were alone once more, their conversation resumed.

"I know you don't want me here, Astella."

"Only because of conversations...like this. Only because you always upset your father by being prickly and defensive, by pretending to be such a socially conscious little do-gooder."

Honey shot out of her couch. "Prickly! Defensive! Me?"

"I shouldn't judge you. I'm sorry."

Honey sat back down.

"Look, Hunter's not himself. He's not up to one of your battles." Astella looked genuinely worried.

"What's wrong?"

"His heart's been acting up again. He's been under a lot of pressure lately."

"So have I, but I can no longer stand it that we live in the same town and we don't even speak to one another on the phone. The only thing I know about my father is what I read in the paper."

"You should have thought of that before."

"I was running for my life. Astella, are you going to let me see him or not?"

"There was never a question of that. He was expecting a call, and I heard the phone ring." She frowned as if something about the call bothered her. "But he should be through by now. I'll go look for him."

As soon as Astella had gone Honey got up and began to pace restlessly, not daring to look at her reflection in the long gilt mirrors because she knew they would magnify the many faults of her bohemian costume as well as those of her figure.

Prickly? Not her! Hadn't she spent her life being kind to others, fighting for the rights of the underprivileged? Defensive? Of course not. She'd outgrown all that—years and years ago!

But deep in her heart she knew that the minute she stepped into this house she became the unhappy, guilt-ridden, rebellious child who'd grown up here; the child who'd never fit in to this glamorous life, the child who'd secretly longed to belong, the child who'd had to prove she could live without it.

Honey moved near the partially opened windows and heard the faint rumble of her father's angry voice coming from the pool area.

She opened a tall glass door and stepped out onto the balcony, hesitant as always about going too near any ledge, even though this one was only a one-story drop.

Her father looked up at her. His handsome, weather-beaten face was as grim and unsmiling as on that long-ago day when they'd quarreled and she'd run away. She lifted her hand and waved down to him.

His frown deepened when he saw her. Her fingers froze in midair as all the light seemed to go out of his eyes. His face contorted. Honey's fragile smile died and she swayed nearer the ledge. The flagstones blurred sickeningly.

In spite of the air rushing into her throat, she couldn't breathe.

She should have realized how hopeless it was—expecting his forgiveness.

Slowly he set the phone on the table and took a single agonized step toward her. Then his hands went to his chest, and he doubled over lifelessly. He staggered, slumping headfirst into the pool. His body, a rigid deadweight, sank instantly.

Dear God! He'd had another heart attack. The very sight of her had killed him.

Honey forgot her terror of heights and bolted down the stairs.

Hunter was lying face down on the bottom of the pool when she reached him. Astella screamed from an upstairs window.

Honey yelled, "Dial 911!" Then she dove into the pool and grabbed her father. She struggled to tow him to the shallow end.

Honey would never remember what happened next. Somehow the housekeeper and Astella were there to help her lift him from the pool. He was so heavy, it took all three of them to turn him over.

When she felt for his pulse there was none. She tilted his chin back and lifted his jaw, opening his mouth, placing her ear there to feel for his breath.

"He's not breathing!"

Honey pinched Hunter's nose shut, opened her mouth, took a deep breath and blew two full breaths deep into his chest. She did this again and again. Then she began to compress his chest, repeating the cycle and praying silently for what seemed an eternity until she heard the siren far below, screaming faintly at first and then louder and louder as it climbed the hills.

After the ambulance arrived, she sank onto the grass, numb and shivering, chilled to the bone, utterly exhausted as she watched the frantic flurry of white-uniformed men fighting to save her father.

Her father's face was ashen. Never once did he move or speak.

Astella brought Honey towels and one of Hunter's white gym suits. "You can change in the bathhouse." When Honey only looked up at her stepmother with dazed, bewildered eyes, Astella pressed her arm. "For God's sake, hurry!"

Like a robot, Honey obeyed.

When she came back, dressed in her father's huge sweat suit with her wet hair wound in a towel, her father was on a stretcher being rushed to the ambulance. She was about to race after him when the cordless phone her father had set down so carefully before his collapse rang.

Honey picked it up as she ran after her father's stretcher.

"Hello." A man's rough, violent voice assaulted her. "I want Wyatt. He hung up on me a few minutes ago. When I called back the first time, the line was busy."

Honey was too drained to feel anger at the caller's rudeness. "I'm sorry. He can't talk now."

"The hell you say! You tell that bastard—"

"That...that *bastard*..." now she did choke on a sob "...that bastard...has had a heart attack or something. Who is this?"

"You tell him it'll take more than a fake heart attack to stop J. K. Cameron."

"No way, Mr. Cameron!"

She was passing the mailbox when she stared wildly around the front of the house for a place to get rid of the phone. She lifted the mailbox lid and defiantly knocked the phone against the metal sides before dropping it inside. Then she rushed after her father's stretcher and climbed into the ambulance.

Dear God! How could anyone, even a stranger, be so callous? Her father's lips were blue now, his face grayer. As she touched his icy cheek, she wondered if he was still alive.

"You'd better sit down and put your belt on, ma'am."

Honey sank against Astella.

As the ambulance sped down the hill, all Honey could think of was that her father was either dead or dying, and she could do nothing to help him. Would he die without ever knowing that despite everything, his imperfect, rebellious daughter had always craved to be the perfect daughter he had wanted?

J. K. Cameron had been utterly forgotten.

All Honey knew was that if her father died she would blame herself forever. She had killed him by favoring her mother even after her mother had died, by never pleasing him, by rebelling against his life-style and his marriage to Astella, by stubbornly marrying the wrong kind of man just to spite him, just to pretend she was morally superior, by never admitting that despite his faults she secretly admired him.

Years after she had married Mike, Honey had learned that her father had suffered his first heart attack the night she had run away.

Yet he had never called her.

Nor had she called him. Not even after the devastation of the earthquake and the almost total destruction of his hotel.

Yes, if he died, it would be her fault.

One

―――

Hatred filled Joshua K. Cameron as he shoved past people in the white hospital corridors without bothering to smile or apologize. Not that he was much different today than any other day.

Hatred for one man, Hunter Wyatt, and the need for revenge were the fierce emotions that had fueled Joshua's monumental ambition ever since he'd been a boy of eleven. These sentiments had propelled him out of a tough, impoverished neighborhood, and had governed nearly every aspect of his life—even his meteoric successes.

Only today the hatred was so strong, he almost felt overpowered by it. Suddenly the white walls on either side of him seemed to sag toward him crushingly. He reeled as if he were in an earthquake. Then he realized that the floor was steady. The hospital walls weren't falling. It was the defensive walls in his mind that were crumbling, deluging him with unwanted memories.

He saw a boy screaming as he ran through similar endless white tunnels. He saw that same thin-faced, frightened child clinging helplessly to his mother's skirts, looking up with frozen, bewildered eyes as he watched the big nurse with the contemptuous smile hand his mother his father's pitiful things in plastic bags.

Damn it. Not once had Joshua set foot inside a hospital since those bitter days. He had thought the memories were safely buried, that time and the hardships of his life had dulled the pain. But the memories were like the stabs of an ice pick gouging out his heart and the old agony was as intense as ever.

Beads of perspiration broke out on Joshua's brow and his tanned hand jerked his tie loose. He caught himself. Even though he felt as if he were suffocating, he resisted the impulse to give into his weakness. Instead he took a deep breath and then straightened his designer tie, drawing the knot even tighter before he rushed toward his destination with an even stronger resolve.

He stopped suddenly in front of the intensive-care waiting room. For a long moment he stood in the harsh light, taken aback by the outward perfection of his own reflection in the gleaming steel doors.

Ebony hair, ice blue eyes, hard mouth and jaw—women thought Joshua Cameron movie-star handsome until they found he had no heart, no tenderness. His black suit had been hand tailored in London, the soft, lightweight wool excessively costly. His silk shirt and tie had been bought on Rodeo Drive. The man Joshua saw wore his clothes with such ease there was no way anyone could have guessed that once he'd worn rags, that he'd grown up in the garbage-strewn, gang-infested streets of one of the roughest parts of this city.

Joshua took no pride in what he saw. He hated the man he was now just as much as he hated the boy he'd been, and he didn't pause long to reflect on either of them. He flung the doors open and raced inside like a shark dashing through bloody waters toward wounded prey that would prove a certain kill.

Wyatt was a fool if he thought he could escape Joshua Cameron by fleeing into a hospital bed. Another foe might have let up, but long ago Wyatt had squashed out every drop of compassion in Joshua's soul.

Use or be used. Take or be taken. Destroy or be destroyed. Those were the credos Joshua lived by.

At first glance the waiting room appeared to be empty. Then a shadowy figure at the far end of the room sniffled. A magazine tumbled from a sloppy stack on a low table and a woman bent over and picked it up. Joshua's eyes flicked toward her and then quickly away, his intuitive male radar having informed him the disheveled, slightly plump female was not worthy of even his most casual attention.

Joshua grabbed a paper from the receptionist's vacant desk, scanning it until he found Wyatt's name. Then, ignoring the No Visitors sign, Joshua headed toward the doors that led to the unit and pushed one open.

"Wait! I mean stop! You can't go in there!" came the woman's choked whisper from behind him.

Joshua whirled, incredulous. Who was this nondescript creature who dared tell him no?

"I'm sorry," the creature persisted weakly, her feeble courage seeming to vanish as she shrank more deeply into the shadows.

"Who the hell are you?" He growled, surly now at having been crossed by such a shabby little nobody.

He stalked toward her, his rolling, easy gait the predatory swagger of a street fighter's.

Uneasy, she coughed and sniffed again.

She had a hell of a cold.

"I'm Ho...Cecilia...." she began.

He cut her off. "Do you think I give a damn who you are? I meant do you work here?"

"No. I'm a visitor—like you."

He despised inefficiency and messiness. From the look of her rumpled, ill-fitting, stained white sweat suit, she'd spent the night on that hard vinyl couch, something he would never do. He saw chocolate candy wrappers and grimaced at the thought of her gorging herself on junk food. He couldn't see her hair because it was hidden by a white towel that was messily wrapped around her head like a turban, but he was sure the color of her hair would be as nondescript as the rest of her.

In no way was this plain, no—worse than plain—this slovenly, very forgettable female remotely like himself. He felt like a fool for having allowed her to waste even a second of his valuable time.

She tilted up her sunglasses as if to inspect him as closely as he had so arrogantly inspected her. The defiance in that gesture caught his attention. So, even this dimmest of female bulbs could burn with more wattage than he would have given her credit for.

He leaned down, and she let her sunglasses fall instantly. Because of the shadows and her glasses he couldn't make out the color of her eyes. All he could see was that they were long lashed, that beneath them there were dark smudges, the telltale traces of tears. Her mascara had run down her cheeks as well. He saw the box of tissues on the table beside her and the wadded tissues in the ashtray, the lopsided stack of dog-eared magazines she'd tried to read in the long hours to distract herself.

He decided to leave her to whatever misery afflicted her. He was about to go when suddenly she smiled up at him in a way that was somehow quiet and bravely defiant and surprisingly engaging.

She was a fighter.

Like him.

He felt an odd, tingling warmth. Not pleasure! No way! Why would he feel pleasure that this plain woman was being friendly when he had the phone numbers of dozens of the most beautiful women in California? When he had Simone. He never took the slightest interest in any woman who wasn't rich, famous or beautiful.

But the warm smile continued to draw him, and his own response continued to puzzle him. He raked a hand through his thick black hair.

"You must really be worried about someone," she said softly—somehow extending herself beyond her own problems and sensing his.

He felt in tune with her—which was idiotic. He didn't tune in to people; he used them. Nonplussed, he decided it was way past time to cut her dead and be done with this ridiculous encounter.

"Look." He edged nearer, screwing his black brows together in his most ferocious scowl.

She merely sat up taller, uncowed. "Yes?"

Slice her to ribbons. Now!

Her trusting smile was both brave and defiant.

He faltered. "I mean—"

She kept smiling at him in a way that was somehow so special, that somehow made him sense she was putting up an extraordinary fight to appear brave. She was like a kitten battling a lion.

This was absurd. He balled his hands into fists. She was plain, dumpy even. She was a stranger he hadn't the slightest use for, someone he should rid himself of instantly.

Yet the emotion she aroused in him was mushrooming. It wasn't hate and it wasn't sexual. Nor was it predatory. What he felt was an incredible and bewildering empathy. He sensed a terrible sadness in her, and it expanded inside his chest as if it were his own.

He understood her odd stillness, her uncertainty, her trapped look—too well.

Again he had a vision of that dark-haired little boy of eleven, caged in by white walls, white uniforms. The boy was pulling a man's gold watch out of a plastic bag.

Damn! Joshua closed his eyes to shut out the memory of those small, trembling fingers closing around the cold gold watch. The anger that had propelled Joshua across San Francisco at breakneck speed was gone. Something about her, about this hospital scene had made him touch base with the gentle boy he had once been.

"What's your name?" she asked quietly.

He growled, "Joshua."

What the hell? He never used his first name. Not since he was eleven. He went by J.K. or just Cameron.

He looked at her pale, smudged face. Why was he Joshua to her?

"Where's the receptionist?" he demanded more gruffly, determined to dispel his own incomprehensible mood of sentimentality.

"I'm afraid I sent her in to check on my father," the dumpy young woman said. "She'll be back in a moment." She paused. "You're obviously a busy man. I'm sorry if you have to wait because of me."

"Look, it's okay," he snapped, irritated because he didn't feel irritated enough.

"I've been here a while. I sort of know the ropes. Maybe I can help. Who did you come to see?" she persisted gently.

"Hunter Wyatt." How had he gotten the name out without a trace of the loathing he felt for the man?

Her head jerked toward his, startled. "My father?" Her voice was choked again. And surprised. "You're the first friend to come up. I didn't know he still had any." She cast her eyes down as if ashamed to have admitted that.

Joshua was shocked into speechlessness. She was Hunter Wyatt's daughter!

"Not many, I'm sure," Joshua said coldly.

"You remind me of him."

"I remind you of him?" Joshua's fury rushed back like a tidal wave. He edged menacingly closer, but before he could reach her, his knee hit the low table beside her. He yelped as dozens of magazines and candy wrappers and a book, *Losing Those Last Ten Pounds—Forever* tumbled to the floor.

When he knelt to pick them up, he knocked the box of tissues and a plastic ashtray down, too.

"Hell!"

"Hey, take it easy," she said softly.

He picked up a bunch of magazines and threw them back onto the table.

"He's going to be okay. We have to hang on to that," she said reassuringly.

Joshua avoided looking at her, and she misinterpreted that, too. He felt desperate to escape her, but before he could say or do anything, she took his hand.

Then it was too late, because he felt something extraordinary and totally inexplicable. Her touch didn't arouse the sensual variety of electricity he might have felt for a beautiful woman, but her gentle fingertips were like her smile. They brought a kindly warmth that was infinitely pleasant, that drew him like the heat of a fire when he came in wet from a cold sail on the bay. She had touched him to comfort him—as a friend, and just for a second her quiet warmth dissolved all his cold hate and fierce need to destroy. *It was a nice feeling.*

Her hand was soft and small, treacherously gentle. It seemed to belong in his. He hadn't experienced such a powerful connection to another human being in years. Not since before his father had died.

With a supreme effort of will he blocked those memories. A strange lethargy prevented him from jerking his hand free of hers. The same weakness made him sit down beside her.

She said haltingly, "I'm glad you're here. You seem to understand, and that helps. You remind me of him, you know. I mean the way he was at his best—hard and strong. I used to hate all that. Now I'd give anything if he'd wake up and bite my head off. I've been alone here for hours."

Joshua's hand tightened on hers, his brown fingers threading themselves through hers. *Somehow she was a perfect fit.* "I'm sure it's been difficult," he muttered in an odd, strangled tone.

Though she was tearless, he sensed her profound desolation. Even as Joshua wondered silently what he was doing, he drew her into his arms and comforted her, an action that was as totally out of character for him as his every other response to her had been.

"Yes. It's difficult," she whispered brokenly against his collar, her lips so close, he felt the warmth of her every breath flow through his silk shirt to his skin. "You see, if he dies—I killed him."

"What?"

Her fingers curled into his shoulders more tightly. "It's my fault—the attack. We've been estranged for years. I went home today for the first time in a long while. He was on the phone. He looked up and saw me. It was such a shock, he collapsed. I...tried to save him. I had to drag him out of the pool."

Joshua winced guiltily as he remembered her tortured voice on the phone, his unthinking cruelty to her.

"So that's why you've got a cold and are shivering." He caught the scent of chlorine clinging to the damp towel wound around her hair.

She was blaming herself—for what he had done. His raspy voice was filled with terrible remorse. "Cecilia, it wasn't your fault."

"You don't know! I was a terrible disappointment to him, you see. But he was to me too." She sounded even sadder, as if her childhood memories upset her as deeply as his did. "I'm afraid he never had much time for me when I was a child. There were reasons why I resented him—especially after he divorced my mother. My father remarried. My brother ran away, and I tried to rebel against everything my father believed in."

"All that's in the past."

Cecilia didn't seem to hear him. "My stepmother told me not to come. But do I ever listen? I'm always so sure I'm right. Always trying to pretend I'm the little miracle worker." Her voice cracked. "Who am I kidding? I'm no different than they are."

Joshua smoothed her cheek. He almost touched her lips before he realized what he was doing and pulled his hand away.

"They're talking about putting some little balloons in his arteries or open-heart surgery. Like I said, he's always been so strong and tough. At home we called him the iron man."

"Yeah." His one word was grim.

"Now he could die at any minute. One moment he was yelling on the phone. The next he saw me and passed out. I guess that shows you—underneath the hardest masks, we're all human."

"Not all of us, honey."

She began to tremble, and Joshua clenched his hand over hers more tightly.

"I killed him," she whispered tearfully.

"No, you didn't." Hesitantly Joshua brought his other arm around her shuddering body, discovering she wasn't as overweight as he'd thought. She was just well endowed, and the jogging suit was too big and added bulk.

Her body felt tight and firm and surprisingly small at the waist. She felt good, better than he could have ever imagined her feeling.

He hadn't comforted anyone in years—the women he dated didn't need comfort. Not even his daughter, Heather, and her fierce teenage pain could touch him.

Why did he have the strangest sensation that this woman belonged in his arms? She seemed to think so, too, because she continued to cling as if she would trust her life to him.

Holding her brought a vague softening in his chest that was almost painful. Long ago when he'd waited in the hospital, he'd wanted his mother's arms about him, but she'd been too lost in her own grief to comfort him.

The woman cried soundlessly against his shoulder for a while—until a doctor was paged on the overhead speaker. Then she tensed, listening to it, drawing back, looking up at him wonderingly before she blushed.

"I—I don't know why I said all those things to you," she whispered, feeling awkward suddenly.

"I guess you needed to."

"I'm sorry." Her color deepened. "I know you're his friend, but please don't tell him . . ." She slid further away.

He got up abruptly.

While she straightened her rumpled suit, he watched the way the thick white cotton outlined the curves of her breasts.

When she looked up at him a little breathlessly, her hand pausing beneath her breast, he yanked hard at the knot of his tie. He tore his eyes away on a hot flush. Damn! He was behaving like a raw adolescent.

What the hell was wrong with him? She was Wyatt's daughter. Joshua should hate her for that alone.

But he didn't. Maybe because she didn't seem a thing like her father. Not with her soft heart and sad, plain face and unglamorous costume. She wasn't beautiful or stylish, but she was class—the real thing. Her father was a fake and so was Joshua Cameron.

The unit doors swung open and the receptionist barged into the waiting room. "Miss Wyatt, your mother went out the back way. You can go in and see your father now. He's sound asleep and he won't know you're there."

Strange words.

Honey smiled faintly, profoundly grateful to the nurse. "Thank you."

"Be quick. If the doctor catches you, I could lose my job."

Honey turned back to Joshua. "Thank you, too—for your kindness."

Again Joshua was surprised that her sweetness brought him so much pleasure. He couldn't remember when anyone had thanked him for a simple kindness. Maybe that was because he couldn't remember bestowing many simple kindnesses.

Cecilia Wyatt wouldn't thank him—when she knew the truth.

Joshua took her hand and pressed it. She pressed his back. Even though her fingers were small and soft, they warmed him through.

She broke their handclasp, not he. Then she knelt to pick up her things.

"Sir, can I help you?" The sharp-eyed receptionist was looking him over. "Sir?"

"No." He exhaled a deep breath and straightened his shoulders. "I'll come back later."

"I'll tell Daddy you came by, Joshua."

"Right." Joshua couldn't think of anything to say. He clumsily backed out of the room away from both of them.

Joshua dashed through the corridors as if a dozen demons chased him. He took the stairs because he was too impatient to wait for the elevator, plunging down them two at a time, coming to a sudden stop when a final vision, more horrible than all the others, loomed before him. Joshua fell against the wall and buried his dark head in his hands, struggling to block the memory.

But it didn't matter whether his eyes were open or closed. Either way, he saw a dark, impassioned boy quivering like a coward before Hunter Wyatt's giant-size desk. He remembered Hunter's relaxed, awesome power. He remembered how quickly the boy's hate had degenerated into an awful terror and sickening impotence when he'd yelled desperately up at the man, "If I had a gun I'd shoot you." Joshua heard again the roar of Hunter's laughter, the purr of that hateful voice that had lacerated him with its hard-edged contempt as he ran away.

"You wouldn't have the guts, kid. Because you're as weak and spineless as your failure of a father."

Joshua had made a vow that he would never be weak again, and he had kept it—until today. Until her.

Joshua sat in the bar, hating the golden whiskey because he wanted it so much. Cecilia Wyatt had driven him to this. Funny, how the more he tried to remember her, the more her plain, smudged features became a blur. He could barely remember what she'd looked like. Was she tall or short? What were her eyes like? He didn't know. Her hair?

All he could recall was her grief. All he could feel was his own guilt because he was the cause of her pain.

As once her father had been the cause of his.

Joshua looked up gloomily. What the hell was the matter with him? For years he'd allowed himself to feel nothing except an overwhelming obsession for money and power so that he could use them to get revenge against the enemy he hated. For years he'd moved through life like an unleashed natural force building an empire of his own because he'd always known someday he would use it to destroy Hunter's.

Now suddenly when he could finish Hunter as easily as he could smash the glass before him by throwing it against the wall, Joshua felt only a bleak emptiness and a curious listlessness at the prospect of doing so.

Without hate, who was J. K. Cameron? Without the hate was there even a man?

Hunter deserved to be destroyed.

Why couldn't Joshua do it?

Because Cecilia would believe she had killed her father. Because her anguish took Joshua back to the most dreadful hour in his own life. Because her pain seemed like his own when he'd been a young boy in a hospital waiting room—terrified he'd lose his father.

Because he knew the agony and the hopelessness of the long years of dark, guilty emotion after a death when you blamed yourself for it.

Joshua picked up the glass and brought it to his lips, and only barely resisted the temptation. Furiously he slammed it back down onto the bar, spilling the whiskey. Then he got up and left the bar. The Golden Gate Bridge was backlighted by the red fire of a sinking sun as he hurried blindly down the hill toward the bay where he'd left his car.

Joshua could almost hear the roar of Hunter's gloating laughter. "You wouldn't have the guts, kid. Because you're as weak and spineless as your failure of a father."

Destroy or be destroyed.

A parking ticket was fluttering from beneath his windshield wiper when Joshua reached his sports car.

He grabbed the ticket, shredded it into tiny bits and threw them into the gutter. Savagely he yanked open his door.

He had to finish Hunter off. He had to forget the girl and her absurd power that made him as soft as that ineffectual boy who'd run out of Hunter Wyatt's office to hide.

Joshua had learned long ago that there was nowhere he could hide. Not from himself. Not from the hatred that ate at his soul. Not from this new weakness that had crept inside him.

Hunter was his enemy.

So was she.

Joshua stomped down hard on the accelerator and pulled out into the traffic. Horns blared. Brakes squealed. He heard the crunch of chrome fenders behind him. Shouted curses. A man on the curb was jotting down his license number.

To hell with them all.

Joshua sped into the stream of cars, his mind on Hunter Wyatt and his daughter.

When he destroyed Hunter, he would destroy her, as well.

Two

Was she completely crazy?

Not only had she been disloyal to Mike's memory, but Honey actually felt worried about the hard, bitter man who had stumbled out of the waiting room.

Joshua. She'd upset him as much as he'd upset her. But because he'd helped her through a difficult moment, she hoped he'd be all right.

When he'd stalked so menacingly toward her, his ice blue eyes glaring at her, she'd thought him cold, remorseless even. Then something extraordinary had happened. When she'd looked at him again, she'd seen her own pain mirrored in his beautiful, compassionate eyes. When he'd taken her in his arms, she'd felt an instant bonding with him—the bonding of two souls.

For an infinitesimal moment she'd no longer been the rebellious daughter or the guilty widow determined to grieve forever. He'd no longer been bent on whatever dark goal seemed to consume him.

Now it seemed crazy to think such a thing. Incredible. All Joshua had done was look at her, hold her. He was a friend of her father's. Any man might have offered her such simple kindnesses.

But Joshua was not any man. Somehow she intuitively knew that his actions had been out of character for him.

Honey remembered Mike's sweetly loving nature and felt ashamed that she had been drawn, even for an instant to someone as pitiless as Joshua. Joshua was everything she'd run from when she'd rebelled against her father and his cold, self-serving life-style. Her heart belonged in the grave with Mike.

But there was no denying that Joshua's touch and the warmth in his eyes had woven a magic spell. Just as there was no denying that deep down she wasn't really as noble and altruistic as she'd always pretended she was.

She shook herself. She would have to forget him as Joshua had probably already forgotten her. She didn't want to be drawn to selfish, hard-driven men. He was too glamorous looking. No doubt he had an equally glamorous showpiece wife or girlfriend.

Still, as Honey followed the nurse across the waiting room, she secretly wondered what his last name was. The heart that should have been buried in Mike's grave beat too quickly as a little voice kept asking, "Joshua? Joshua what?"

Hunter Wyatt lay like a sunken doll beneath a labyrinth of twisting tubes, the machines on all sides of him seeming more alive than he. Monitors bleeped. His breathing machine made rhythmical, gurgling, sucking sounds.

Honey pulled back a curtain. High-tech medicine. Why did it have to be so dehumanizing?

Her father's skin was white to gray—the waxen color and parchment texture of death. His tall, athletic frame seemed to have shriveled. The sight of her once vital father looking so terribly ill made Honey feel paralyzed by her guilt and sorrow.

She had lost so many years by being at war with her father—almost her entire lifetime. Now everything that had divided them seemed so foolish. She took another step toward him and made a silent promise that if he lived, she would make it up to him. It wouldn't matter that he'd never said he'd loved her.

Her hand curled over his lifeless fingers and she shut her eyes and prayed that he would get well, that he would open his eyes and tell her he hated the way she was dressed, that he hated the way she never made friends with the right people.

Suddenly she felt his fingers twitch against hers—ever so slightly. Excitedly she squeezed his hand back.

He stirred restlessly.

With a start she realized that he was conscious, that his dark lashes were fluttering weakly against his colorless cheeks. He was looking at her—calmly.

She leaned nearer, still holding his hand. "One of your friends came by, Daddy. Joshua..."

Hunter's gray eyes focused fixedly on her face. Then they widened. She thought he hadn't heard her, so she repeated the name.

His fingers moved wildly. The old unmistakable dislike flared in his eyes before they rolled back and he began to sweat and twitch, jerking his hand agitatedly from hers.

Loud beeps erupted from his machines. Chaotic rhythms danced across his cardiac monitor. His face turned purple. His body seemed to shrink.

An army of nurses rushed in, followed by Astella. The technicians pushed Honey aside and began to work frantically.

Her father's eyes closed slowly, perhaps forever.

Astella's cool voice was faintly accusing, "We'd better go. I don't want to risk his waking up again and finding you still here."

"No..." A sad smile drifted across Honey's face. She wondered if her legs had turned to stone as she let her stepmother turn her and push her leaden body out of the room.

Nothing had really changed. Hunter Wyatt had never wanted his daughter.

He still didn't. Not even on his deathbed.

Astella was tracing the chipped edge of the yellow plastic table in the hospital cafeteria with the sharp tip of a glossy red fingernail. Her large diamonds sparkled. Honey sat across from her sipping a diet cola. An unopened chocolate bar lay in front of her beside her book, *Losing Those Last Ten Pounds—Forever.* As always even when they were silent, the atmosphere between them was coldly charged.

Astella's golden hair had an artificial windswept look. Bold silver earrings flashed at her ears. She was too elegant and sleek for the cafeteria, too glamorous for ordinary life, and yet she looked wonderful. Every time she got up, people watched her. The male cashier fawned excessively. She was a trophy, one of the many Honey's father had collected during his long successful life. Honey knew that her own madcap mother, the famous artist, had been a trophy, too.

Honey could barely remember Astella when she'd been a young, immensely ambitious executive in the management of a rival hotel chain. First her father had bought her away from his rival. Then he'd grown jealous of her abilities. On their wedding day, Hunter had fired her.

"Do you want something to eat?" Astella fingered her white leather wallet. The words were kind; her voice was cold.

Honey pushed the diet cola away and twisted her plain gold wedding band round and round and then remembered she should hide it under the table. "No."

"You haven't eaten anything except candy bars since Hunter—"

Defiantly Honey placed her left hand back on the table on top of her book. "I never thanked you for coming to Mike's funeral."

"I came because your father was too busy—as always—to come."

"Yes, as always." Honey pressed her lips tightly together as she remembered the turmoil of that day. "I didn't expect him to. I know how he felt about Mike and our life together. About Mario. We weren't something he could brag about to his friends—"

"Cecilia—"

"You're right. I'm being...prickly...defensive.... Astella, I'm sorry I came yesterday. I should have waited."

"If you hadn't been there Hunter would have died."

"He saw me. That's why he collapsed."

Astella looked at her with sudden understanding. "No, Cecilia. No matter how I feel about you at times, I—I can't let you believe that. Hunter had taken a call from J. K. Cameron. It was Cameron who upset him, not you. You saved his life. I could never have done what you did. Your father's alive because you came."

Was that true? Honey stared at her in silence, wondering as she remembered the rude man on the phone for the first time. Nervous, Honey began tearing at her paper napkin. "I want to know about Daddy and this Mr. Cameron."

"Hunter's been under a lot of stress. For quite a while. There's a business rival of his, a Joshua K. Cameron, who's determined to ruin him."

"Joshua?" Honey's voice barely came out in a whisper. She felt an alarming spasm of fear in her throat.

"Apparently he was buying your father out—at such a low price that when Hunter pays his creditors, he will have worked his whole life and lose everything. It's almost as if Cameron hates your father personally."

"Who is this...this Joshua Cameron?"

Astella opened her big purse and dug, finally pulling out a magazine and throwing it onto the table. "There. Read all about him. No doubt he paid someone to get him on the cover. He owns a chain of rival hotels, as well as several casino hotels. He owns an airline, land, and I don't know what else."

"Joshua..." Honey's hands froze. *Why had he been kind to her?*

Honey almost moaned as she picked up the magazine.

His incredible eyes were darker on that glossy cover than she remembered, and his beautiful mouth seemed harder and more insolent. He was standing on the top of a skyscraper he was building, looking arrogant and self-assured as if he thought he owned the world. Honey's gaze flickered—she felt the beginning of a tear—as she devoured each handsome feature.

She had known he was glamorous, too glamorous, for her. He was someone you read about, someone you might secretly dream about.

Her palms began to perspire. Her throat felt tight and dry.

"Cecilia, what's wrong? Do you know him?"

"No. Well, I mean ... not exactly." Honey's voice was faint, dying away. "He ... he came to the hospital today."

"He was up to no good."

"He was kind to me."

Astella's beautiful face grew as quiet and still as stone. "You must have misunderstood him. He hates your father—therefore he hates you, because you're Hunter's daughter."

"But why?"

"All I know is that when he was just a boy, he broke into your father's office and told him he wanted to kill him."

"If he hates Daddy so much, why didn't he?"

"What makes a cobra decide to strike or not to strike? I don't know. Your father says he was a coward."

"Why didn't Daddy ever tell me?"

"Your long suit has never been communication with your father."

Honey felt a wave of fresh guilt. Not only had she betrayed Mike by finding this ruthless Cameron monster attractive, she had betrayed her father—again.

Honey flipped through the magazine until she came to the article on Cameron. Astella sat in silence as Honey read, pausing over several paragraphs about the beautiful women in his life. There were several photographs of a beauty named Simone. She was pencil thin, so hatefully skinny that she looked dazzling in her skintight sequin dress.

She looked good in Joshua's arms, too.

"Pretty girlfriend," Astella commented. "His wife was rich. All his women are at least beautiful."

Honey forced herself to read more. Joshua had grown up in the same poor neighborhood where she taught. He'd fought his way out. It seemed he was still fighting.

There was a section on Cameron's magnificent five-story mansion on Telegraph Hill. Photographs were included of his modern art collection. In his spare time he was waging war on his neighbor, Nell Strohm, a longtime Telegraph Hill resident, because she was the owner of the apartment building directly downhill from his house.

Nell was an old friend of Honey's—they'd been sent to the same boarding school. Honey bit her lip and wondered if Nell could be useful. Apparently Cameron wanted to tear down Nell's building because it blocked his view of the bay. He planned to extend his garden. Nell and her tenants were up in arms.

There were several blistering quotes from Nell as well as insolent, sexist-sounding rebuttals from Cameron.

Honey snapped the magazine shut without finishing the article. How could she have found comfort in such a brute's arms? Even in her ignorant state she should have sensed his shallow, debased nature; she should have felt a natural enmity toward him.

Maybe it was that secret side of her, that side that was both attracted and repelled by surface glitz that found him appealing.

He had known who she was. And pretended to comfort her.

Joshua Cameron was a ruthless, selfish bastard, a swaggering ghetto punk who'd acquired money and power so he could bully and ruin others. He would destroy everything he touched—unless someone stopped him.

Dear God. This was beginning to feel like one of her vendettas to right some social wrong. Honey groaned deep in her throat like a frightened animal.

Why me?

Aloud she said, "Astella, we've got to stop him."

"But how? Your father is sick, maybe dying.... Cameron's no fool."

"First, you're going back to work."

"Me? I wouldn't know where to begin. I haven't worked in years."

"You were good."

"Hunter has forbidden me to work."

"Like you said, he's...sick." Honey couldn't say the word dying. "I'd do it myself, but you know the hotel business." Honey sucked in a tight, frightened breath. "I'll work on Mr. Cameron in my own way."

"Hunter will never forgive me."

"Or me."

"You're used to that. You'd probably like to drive a wedge between us."

"Astella, if we don't do something quickly to stop this monster, Daddy will be dead and you'll be out on the street."

"Since when did you ever care about me?"

"I don't want to lose my father."

"You walked out on him thirteen years ago."

"Astella, we're going to have to work together—not against each other—if we're to have even the slimmest chance of success."

"Why do I feel we're doomed?"

Honey couldn't look at her stepmother, for fear she'd give up, too. Instead she let her gaze fall to the glossy photograph of Joshua Cameron. His blue eyes seemed frozen over with some darkly chilling emotion, his handsome, chiseled features unrelentingly cruel.

Honey swallowed. "We've got to stop him, Astella."

* * *

A dozen of Joshua Cameron's top executives and his lawyer, Johnny Midnight, were in his hushed elegant office for a meeting. Cameron was leaning tensely over the model of the grandiose hotel one of his South American corporations was planning to build in Brazil. He felt frustrated as hell about all the delays on the project. Most of his executives were bunched together near the mauve drapes at the windows, staring out at the magnificent views of the city and bay forty stories beneath them, waiting for his next move.

The executives wore dark suits. In his black leather jacket, wild tie and jeans, Johnny Midnight stood out. He didn't look much like a Stanford Law grad, but he was—Phi Beta Kappa and all. His intense black eyes were on his boss.

"Midnight, we've got to get this thing built. We're losing millions per year in interest alone."

"I'm with you, J.K. But what about the Wyatt chain? Their stock took a real dive last night. Do you want me to buy more—"

"Damn it, Midnight, I told you to wait on that. I'm talking about Rio."

"Right." The deep, velvet-edged drawl sounded cool, uninterested.

Yet Joshua knew differently. Midnight's sudden tension was quick and hot like a fever. Even though Joshua was looking at the model, he could feel Midnight's burning black eyes on him.

Midnight could see in the dark. Joshua knew he could damn sure see through him. Joshua's own fists tightened. Midnight already sensed something, but then Midnight knew him like nobody else could ever know him.

"So what do you want, J.K.? Say the word." Midnight shrugged his shoulders and drawled in that casual, gravelly voice that wasn't casual at all.

Joshua looked up at the one man he trusted, his only friend, his right-hand man. Back-street alley or executive boardroom, Midnight could handle himself in a tight spot

anywhere. Joshua and he had fought together on both bat-
tlegrounds.

Joshua was tall, well over six feet, but Midnight was taller,
leaner, swifter—deadlier. In high school he'd been a star
athlete. Joshua's own daughter adored Midnight. Hell, except for his driving, Midnight excelled at everything—business, kids, women.

Then Joshua remembered Lacy. With women Midnight
had had one notable failure.

Midnight's hair was blue black except for a narrow, distinctive streak of white above his right temple. His strong,
handsome face was deeply tanned and extraordinarily alive.

"Say the word, J.K.," Midnight repeated, his voice
deadly and still.

Before Joshua could answer, the phone rang. Ticia's voice
flowed from the speaker phone. "Mr. Cameron, It's Ms.
Cecilia Wyatt again."

Midnight's brows arched. His beautiful mouth seemed
ready to smile, to laugh. Instead he exerted cynical control.

"I know you said not to interrupt you, Mr. Cameron, but
this is the fifteenth time Ms. Wyatt's called. Every time I
hang up, she calls back."

Defiance. The kitten dangled the one string the lion was
tempted to chase.

Joshua felt a wave of powerful, unwanted interest. He
turned away from Midnight so his friend couldn't detect it.
"For all her softness at the hospital yesterday, she's every bit
as bullheaded as her father," he muttered.

Joshua didn't realize he'd spoken aloud until Midnight
chuckled.

"I knew there was a woman. Is Cecilia Wyatt the reason
you don't want me to buy—"

"No, damn it!" Joshua brushed past Midnight and
grabbed the phone. "Ticia, put Ms. Wyatt through." He
covered the mouthpiece. "Midnight, postpone the meeting
till I finish with her."

Midnight nodded swiftly and then ushered the other executives out of the room, returning alone. He picked up a sheaf of legal documents that dealt with the Brazil project.

"Mr. Cameron? Is that you?" Ms. Wyatt asked just a bit too sweetly.

Even with her thick cold, her voice was gentle and soft. Too soft. Joshua didn't like the way it affected him even over the phone. Suddenly he wished he'd told Midnight to leave, too.

"J. K. Cameron," Joshua said coldly, giving her no other greeting. Grim initials and his last name should set the correct tone. He picked up a rubber band and began stretching it with his free hand.

"Thank you for talking to me, Joshua."

Joshua. The sound of his own name raced through him like electricity.

"Get to the point," he growled.

Across the room Midnight sank down into a leather chair, his long legs sprawling. He seemed to be flipping papers with more gusto than was necessary.

"We met yesterday in the hospital waiting room," she said. "You may not remember me—"

What he remembered was the way his skin had crawled with heat when she'd touched him so gently. Joshua didn't like the memory—especially since his neck was getting hot just thinking about it. Especially since he knew Midnight was hanging on every word, on every inflection.

It was maddening the way she always drew out every exchange. Joshua began stretching the rubber band.

"Plump. Rumpled white sweat suit. No makeup. How could I forget?" Joshua demanded cynically. The rubber band he had been stretching popped loose and flew toward Midnight.

"Ouch!" cried Midnight, springing up instantly, rubbing his tanned cheek.

"Sorry." Joshua waved Midnight back down.

"Forgiven," she replied.

"I wasn't apologizing to you," Joshua snapped.

Midnight chuckled as he picked up the legal papers.

"Oh," she said, the one word both defensive and defiant. "I didn't really expect an apology from a man like you."

Defiant. Again. Why the hell did he have to be so drawn to that?

"I didn't realize who you were yesterday," she said.

"I figured that out for myself," he said grimly.

"You must have thought I was a fool—leaning on your shoulder for sympathy."

"No." For some inexplicable reason, in spite of Midnight rustling his papers so maddeningly, Joshua was uncharacteristically gentle with her.

"I'm not sure I want to know why you were there. What I do want to know is why you're trying to destroy my father—"

"Ask him."

"He's in no condition to answer me."

"Ms. Wyatt, I'm a busy man."

"Then I'll make this short and sweet."

"Short will do."

"I want you to back off."

"No."

"Please."

"Please doesn't work with me."

"What will, then?"

"Are you offering to sell your soul to the devil?"

"Something like that." She lowered her voice. "I would do anything to save my father."

"Sorry, not interested." *Liar.* He paused, shaken by his secret admission. "Look, Ms. Wyatt, women . . . beautiful women . . . or at least their bodies are a dime a dozen for a man like me."

"Simone?"

How the hell did she know about Simone? "Damn it! I'm not in the market for souls—if indeed that was what you were offering for sale. As for your body . . ."

He let the last word hang in the air.

A crisp paper flipped noisily on the opposite side of the room.

"You misunderstood me," she said in a low, shocked tone.

"Ms. Wyatt, I've been propositioned before, by women who are far more desirable than you."

Another page of that maddening legal document Midnight was pretending to read crackled.

"I'm sure you have," she said, her voice fainter now.

"Is that an insult . . . or a compliment?" he countered.

"It was just a fact. It wouldn't kill you to wait, would it?"

"I like doing things fast."

"Why can't you quit buying our stock for ninety days?"

"Why should I? It's at rock bottom right now."

"Because of the rumors you've paid that slick Stanford lawyer of yours, Mr. Midnight, to spread among the right people."

"You're wrong there, Ms. Wyatt."

"My father's sick."

"That's his problem. As soon as I've got enough stock, I'll leak word that I'm buying. Your stock will go through the ceiling. Whatever I do then, I'll make a profit."

"My father will die if you don't ease up."

Joshua felt himself hesitate—inwardly. Why could she bring on this weakness? He forced a coldness into his voice. "Then I'll get control of your hotels even quicker."

"Is that all you care about—business? Doing a deal fast?"

"With your father it's personal."

"You hate him that much?"

Joshua said nothing.

"Yesterday . . . you seemed like a nice man."

"First impressions . . ." But Joshua could feel the sweat breaking out on his brow. He didn't like remembering yesterday or the way he'd behaved with her. His fingers itched to claw his tie. But Midnight would see and understand.

"Mr. Cameron, please . . ."

"Ms. Wyatt, cut the...the niceness. Feminine charm won't work with me. Especially not from a Wyatt."

When her soft voice began to beg, he couldn't bear it. He held the phone away from his ear. Then he slammed it down.

Almost instantly it rang again. Defiance, again. Joshua picked it up before he thought.

"Then I won't be nice," the gentle voice said firmly. "If my father dies, you'll never get his hotels. Because I'll see that you don't."

"Do you really think you can stop me?"

"Oh, yes. I'll do anything to get even with you."

He laughed harshly. "Revenge? I was playing that game when you were still in diapers."

"Are you always so hateful?"

"If I told you, you wouldn't have the fun of figuring me out for yourself."

"You're an arrogant, self-centered, conceited bastard."

"Whatever works."

This time *she* hung up.

Joshua set the phone down slowly, thoughtfully. She was fragile, inexperienced, afraid. A woman like her didn't know the first thing about fighting a man like him. He could crush her easily.

But she was brave and defiant. And nice. Damn it. But she was a kitten toying with a lion. He would smash her anyway.

Midnight got up and strode toward him, his dark face alive, his black gaze more intense than usual.

"What are you looking at?" Joshua's growl was thick, embarrassed.

"Maybe nothing, J.K. Or maybe something that might prove damned interesting."

Once Midnight got an idea in his head, he hung onto it like a dog with a bone. Joshua ignored him and punched a button on his telephone. "Ticia, refuse all calls from Ms. Wyatt."

"Too hot for you to handle, huh?" Midnight taunted softly.

Take or be taken. Destroy or be destroyed.

Joshua glanced angrily away from Midnight. His stubbornness made him a damned good lawyer. At the same time it could make him a damned annoying friend.

"Buy all the Wyatt stock we can afford," Joshua ordered. "And get the hell out of my office."

Midnight just stood where he was and laughed.

Three

_____

Hunter's raspy command erupted from the bed. "Mario's not our kind. You're to send him to his real family, quit that dangerously insane job in that poverty-stricken sewer, and move home. And another thing—stay away from J. K. Cameron, or I'll disown you."

Same lyrics. Same tune. Honey's fingers knotted rebelliously against the curtains of the window as she looked down at the pool where her father had collapsed three weeks earlier. "You already did that—thirteen years ago, Daddy. It didn't work then—"

He pressed his chest as if he were in pain. "So you're going to keep on pretending you're not one of us and refuse to obey me—as always?"

Honey's mouth tightened. "Why change a winning father-daughter relationship at this point?"

The immense bedroom grew tense and silent. Honey left the window and began to pace.

Distaste filled Hunter's eyes as he watched her. "Why don't you ever wear anything that flatters you? Where the hell did you get that awful green hat?"

"A flea market," she said with false cheerfulness. "I thought it was eye-catching."

"Why do you always cover your hair like your mother did?"

"That's why."

"She did it to keep from getting paint in her hair," he said.

"Okay, maybe I'll stop—but, that's not a promise."

"You're stubborn and mean and defiant."

"Who do you think I take after, *Daddy?*"

That was a chilling thought for both of them.

Fortunately before their inane quarrel could escalate, Astella glided into the room. Honey suspected her of eavesdropping.

Glamorous as usual, Astella's golden hair was secured in a tight, gleaming coil at her nape. She was dressed in a white silk business suit.

"You're looking flushed, Cecilia," Astella said coolly as she went to her husband and kissed his brow. "Why don't you open the window and let in some fresh air?" To divert his anger, Astella began to lecture Hunter on medicines and his diet, repeating all the latest complaints of his nurse.

"Mrs. Compton's a battle-ax," Hunter muttered angrily.

"She says even worse things about you, darling."

"I'd fire her except I'll be back at the office too soon to bother."

"Oh, no—"

The conversation had changed abruptly to business.

"You're to stay the hell away from my office, Stell, before you destroy everything I've spent my whole life building."

Astella glanced nervously toward Honey.

Honey exchanged an anxious look with her stepmother before rushing to her. Their alliance was still an uneasy one.

"Astella can't do that because I—I can't fight Mr. Cameron without her."

"Damn it! I told you to leave that bastard alone."

"Believe me, I hate him even more than you do, Daddy."

That was an understatement. These days the mere thought of J. K. Cameron was enough to make Honey's blood heat with fury. "I didn't tell you this, but last Tuesday when I tried to see him he had his guards throw me out of his offices like a common criminal."

"We saw it on TV," Astella admitted quietly. "The mayor was here when they handcuffed you."

"On TV! The mayor!" Honey groaned.

"I think all the mayor could see was the back of your head."

"Then you saw that there were at least a dozen police cars—two dozen cops. You would have thought I'd robbed a bank the way they threw me up against the wall. Why...if that slick Stanford lawyer of his, Mr. Midnight, hadn't come down and said that the handcuffs wouldn't be necessary if I'd promise to quit harassing his boss, the police would have carried me off to jail. Cameron's a monster. A—a—" Honey reddened as she relived the humiliation.

"He's all those things and worse," Astella agreed. "But at least after that initial rather vengeful shopping spree, he's slowed down on buying our stock even though he's manipulated the price so it's at rock bottom."

Astella's cool mind was on business, not passion. She turned back to Hunter. "I'm afraid I've drastically cut our hotel staff."

"Damn it! Neither one of you featherbrains knows what you're doing! Cameron's a spineless wimp like his father. That's why he quit buying. He hasn't got the guts to take on the Wyatt chain."

Honey shivered at the memory of Joshua's ice blue eyes, his hard determined mouth. "I think you're wrong, Daddy."

"*You* think. *I* know. *He's a coward!*"

"Darlings," Astella began briskly, taking a new tack. "We're vulnerable right now. We're overstaffed in management. We need to remodel. We haven't been aggressive enough at promotion. We've lost market share. Our stock's almost worthless. You're sick. . . ."

"I'll be dead if you two keep this up," Hunter roared. "I don't need your help. I don't need either one of you. I never have."

Astella knelt gently, her slim fingers smoothing satin coverlets until Hunter pushed her hands away. He eyed his daughter with equal fury.

"We'll go now, darling," Astella said, "so you can rest." She grabbed Honey by the hand and dragged her toward the door.

"Don't give me that phony darling stuff," he shouted after them.

Close to tears, Astella shut the door. When they reached Honey's car, Astella attacked. "Do you see what you've done? He hates me now."

"Would you prefer that he die? Do you want to risk everything because you're afraid to stand up to him? He's not competent to run his affairs right now. You are."

Astella bit her lip.

Honey adjusted her ugly straw hat, so that its tilt was even more precariously defiant than before. "Look. I'm sorry I always upset him. I made things worse, as usual but, Astella, we can't give up."

"I—I guess you're right."

"You've been wonderful at the hotel. I feel terrible that I haven't done anything," Honey said. "But as soon as school's out, I'll do more."

"Like what?"

"Since he won't talk to me at his office, I'm moving down the hill from Cameron so I can sneak up on him from his blind side."

"Are you crazy? Cameron saw you in the hospital. He knows you. You hate him! You'll attack him the way you do your father and make things worse."

Honey opened the door of her battered green car. Then she turned back to her stepmother. "I've been trying to figure a way around that. I've got to be different than I was that day."

"He's a very dangerous man—a man you dislike."

"Believe me, I know that better than you do. I've got the handcuff bruises to remind me."

Astella was looking at Honey's enormous green hat. "Your father was right about that hat. It doesn't do a thing for you."

"You *were* eavesdropping!"

"If you're going to take on Mr. Cameron, you're going to need a whole new look. You really should let me help you pick out a new wardrobe."

Honey hesitated. She felt like she'd be selling out to make herself look attractive for *him*.

"We're supposed to be working together," Astella said. "You can't catch the shark if you don't bait your hook with something appetizing."

"Shark bait..." Honey shivered as she remembered Joshua's ice-cold predatory eyes, but she managed a brave smile. "I—I'm warning you, Astella. You're not going to like where I shop. And you're not going to like how I have to try on twenty outfits before I find one that makes me look slimmer."

At least half a dozen men looked up from their menus as a fashionably dressed Honey followed a waiter to her table in the posh restaurant. The waiter pulled out the chair by the window. Honey felt uneasy, not herself, like a child playing grown-up in her mother's clothes.

Honey started to sit in the chair, and then she looked down. Fourteen stories down. The sidewalk and rushing pedestrians blurred sickeningly.

Shuddering, she glanced quickly at her waiter. "Could I please sit over there?" she asked pointing to the chair on the opposite side of the table.

"Of course, Madame. Most people prefer the view—"

"I—I'm sure it's lovely."

As Honey turned her head away from the window, the sunlight streamed through the glass and turned her hair to flame. She had cut the remarkable silken stuff into a sleek, shoulder-length pageboy.

A smartly dressed, beautiful young brunette passed her by.

Honey stood up, her green eyes sparkling. "Nell—"

Nell turned. Her brown eyes widened. "Why, Honey. I—I didn't recognize you. Stand up."

For once Honey obeyed, even though she felt more ill at ease than ever.

"You look thinner."

"I'm not," she said defiantly, guiltily. "It's the dark solid color."

"More glamorous, then."

"Astella helped me pick out my clothes. I—I wish they weren't necessary."

"And your hair—! You have the most wonderful hair in the world."

"Astella's hairdresser cut it while she told him how. But . . . this isn't me."

"Makeup, a new hairdo, a gorgeous green suit that flatters you instead of those awful jeans and bangles." Nell sat down. "Does this metamorphosis mean you've learned the error of your socially conscious ways? That you're finally going to relax and enjoy being the spoiled little rich girl?"

Honey smiled at her friend even more defiantly. "I bought this suit on sale—and I manage on my own."

"Ah— Well, a girl who's too proud to ask Daddy has to be clever. And you always were clever except when it came to men and money—two very important exceptions, love. Speaking of which, what's the occasion? A new man? Could this be love—again? Mike's been dead . . . what is it . . . three years?"

"Two." Honey blushed guiltily. "In 'hate' would be more accurate."

"Mmm." Nell smiled. "*He* sounds interesting."

"*He* is. But not in the way you think. He's dangerous."

"He's not like Mike, then?"

Honey flushed. "Hardly. This guy is bad news."

"Great! Mike may have been nice, but I never thought he was right for you. He took himself too seriously."

"His life meant something."

"Maybe, but if he was so great why did you go to pot while you were married to him? If a man is good for you, you improve."

"I—I did improve, but in ways you can't see."

"You're right there," Nell admitted matter-of-factly. "But, I can definitely see an improvement since you met Mr. Wrong."

Honey stared back, her eyes huge and betrayed, completely nonplussed. "Nell, please—"

"Sorry."

There was an awkward silence. Then Nell started talking again.

"Honey, I was thrilled when you called."

"I had a reason. I read that you moved out of your apartment on Telegraph Hill because a certain neighbor keeps running off your managers. Sounds like you need someone to live there and manage your apartment building. I'm volunteering."

"For combat duty?" Nell laughed.

"Exactly."

Nell signaled the waiter. When he came she ordered a very fine wine.

"But, Honey, you teach on the opposite side of town."

"And I've no experience managing apartments. But I've got the summer off. And I'd work very hard. I've checked several books out from the library on apartment management. Tenants can't be any worse to deal with than the kids I teach."

"My tenants are the most demanding eccentrics in all of San Francisco."

"I'm used to difficult people."

"Then you'll probably love them."

"Is that a yes?"

Nell sipped daintily from her wineglass. "It's maybe. And only until I can find someone with experience. And only because I'm desperate."

The waiter reappeared and Nell ordered their meal—lobster with black bean sauce and pine nuts, two stir-fried noodle dishes and a stew of diced chicken in a light cream sauce.

"How's your father?" Nell asked when the waiter had gone.

"A bear. Which means there's room for hope. He's got to cut back on stress. He can't even go near the office for another six weeks."

"At least you're together again."

"Not exactly... and maybe not for long."

"What do you mean?"

"My father has an enemy who's deliberately trying to destroy him. An enemy who won't stop." Honey hesitated. "Nell, unless I do something—fast—I'll be burying my father, and my stepmother will be penniless."

"Good Lord! Who is this man?"

Honey pulled the magazine with the article about Joshua out of her purse. "Your famous neighbor."

"J. K. Cameron? The same disgusting jerk who's determined to buy my building and tear it down? Honey, no..."

"Nell, I despise the man, but I *have* to get acquainted with him... on a personal basis."

"Are we talking seduction?"

"Are you out of your mind?"

"Then what? Why the hair? The new you?"

"He saw me in the hospital a month ago. I—I couldn't take a chance that he might remember me. Fortunately I looked terrible that day. No makeup, or rather what makeup I did have was running all over my face. I had sunglasses on. My hair was wet and wrapped in a towel. I was wearing one of Daddy's old jogging suits."

"Honey, forget it. J.K.'s sharper than you think."

"Nell, we grew up together and you walked right past me."

"Well..." Nell studied her friend and silently conceded that point. "Even if he doesn't figure out who you are, even if he was the kind of guy you could befriend, you'd be crazy to pick my building. He absolutely loathes it and everyone who lives in it. He made me the most abysmal offer for it. Not that I want to sell to him at any price. Some of my tenants are dear, old things who've lived there for years. If he buys, he'll kick them all out."

"What's he like?"

"If you know enough to despise him—?"

"I mean...details."

"Oh, he's just great if you like utterly ruthless, ice-hearted, egotistical, womanizing barracudas."

"I was raised by one."

"Honey, he'd sleep with you in a second, and still finish your father off without a qualm. Quite a change from your sensitive, socially conscious Mike."

"Yes." Honey clenched her napkin. "I've tried calling Mr. Cameron, but he won't talk to me any more. I don't have an entrée to the crowd he socializes with, so I can't get to know him that way. Nell, you're my only chance."

"He'll eat you for lunch, darling and then nibble on some other beauty for dinner. He's got a daughter, but he shipped her off to boarding school when his wife left him."

Honey shivered. "Nell, please give me the job."

"You're going to be miserable there. The apartment is post-earthquake—1906, that is. People kill for a parking place up there. You'll have to pay someone to haul your garbage up the Filbert Steps. My tenants are a real hassle. Mario and his friends and his drums won't fit in there."

"If I promise no drums, will you hire me?"

Nell nodded slowly, dubiously.

"Thank you. You won't regret this."

"I'm not so sure. But as I told you, I'm desperate."

With renewed fear, Honey remembered Joshua's black-lashed icy blue eyes, his cruelly sensual mouth, his chillingly harsh voice over the phone. But the most terrifying memory of all was that of her own vulnerability when he'd gently held her in his arms at the hospital.

Honey sat frozen across the table. ''Oh, Nell, I'm desperate, too.''

Four

———

Honey had awakened that morning with a sick stomach and a fluttery heart. Now she had the beginnings of what felt like a migraine. Today was the day she was moving into Nell's apartment.

The Bomb seemed to be as reluctant as she to make the final climb up Telegraph Hill. When Honey pressed hard on the gas, the engine wheezed. Something under the hood popped.

Honey stomped harder. Her car made a final gasp and rolled backward.

The taxi driver behind her honked frantically, and she braked just as the Bomb's bumper nudged his.

Union Street was so steep, it would have been hard for the Bomb to climb it any day, but this afternoon the struggle was even worse than usual because she had loaded it to the brim with schoolbooks, boxes of papers to grade, Mario's broken guitar and her kitchen appliances. Not to mention her cat, Mr. Right.

She turned her key in the ignition. The Bomb started, only to die and roll backward when she put it in gear and touched the gas pedal. The taxi driver kept honking furiously. She twisted her key again and stepped on the gas, flooding the engine. Again she tried, only for her car to sputter to life and die the second she took it out of neutral.

She threw up her hands, gesturing helplessly at the cabbie, but instead of getting out to help her, he swerved past her, screaming in Italian, shaking an angry fist over his roof. Mr. Right began to meow anxiously from his cat carrier on the floorboard.

Dear God. Starting the car once more, she revved the motor, determined to warm it up before she tried to climb the hill again. She nibbled on a chocolate candy bar—forbidden stuff now and, therefore, all the more delicious—while she raced her engine and wished she'd waited till next weekend to move in, when school was finally over and she felt braver. After three full minutes in neutral, she threw her empty candy wrapper onto the floorboard, put the transmission in first and inched up the hill, fluttering her toe against the gas pedal the whole way.

She turned onto Montgomery Street. At the bottom of the slight hill beneath the trees that hid Coit Tower, she saw Joshua's five-story ultramodern pink mansion hugging the right side of the hill beneath her. Beyond them both the blue bay glittered.

Of all the damnable good luck! Usually the narrow, tree-lined street was jammed with cars. Why couldn't it be today? What was that roomy parking space doing directly in front of the Filbert Steps right where she was going?

She drove past it and parked in the illegal space in front of Joshua's house, deliberately blocking the entrance to his garage. Tilting her sunglasses up, she twisted her rearview mirror and defiantly fluffed her bright bangs. That quick glance told her that there was no way Joshua would ever associate the pretty, albeit chaotic-looking creature in the mirror with the grief-stricken wreck he'd met in the hospital waiting room a month earlier.

Hurriedly she got out of her car, first making sure Joshua's windows were dark and that he wasn't watching before she opened her hood. Her guilty gaze flicked to the distributor cap and then away, her frightened heart thumping. She couldn't resist a second wary glance up at Joshua's closed miniblinds. Then, fast as a rattler striking, her hand darted inside and yanked the emission-coil wire loose. She closed the hood, scanned the darkened windows again and began whistling softly, innocently as she pretended to watch two puffy clouds sail over her head.

The battle lines were clearly drawn now. She couldn't be the little coward she wanted to be.

She dusted off her hands and then dug for a scrap of paper in her purse. Licking the tip of the pen for inspiration, she leaned over her hood and wrote furiously, her breezy note telling Joshua where she would be in case he needed in or out of his house. When she was done, she tucked the paper under a windshield blade.

Mr. Right meowed, perhaps appreciatively, as she lifted his cat cage out of the Bomb along with a box of bedding. Telegraph Hill was so steep that Filbert Street, which crossed Montgomery, became nothing more than a charming easement which was used for a garden by the residents. Narrow wooden steps provided pedestrians access to their homes on the hill and to the streets below. Because Nell's building fronted on the steps and the garden, Mr. Right would be able to be both an indoor and an outdoor cat for the first time in his life with no danger of being run over by a car.

As Honey descended the famous Filbert Steps, she walked nervously past Joshua's front door. Picking her way carefully in her high-heeled green sandals as she walked to her new apartment, she saw another cat prowling through the ivy investigating bees and plump roses. Mr. Right meowed again, and Honey smiled. Even if their new apartment was too near Joshua's house for her own comfort, at least her cat would have a perfect environment.

Before entering Nell's building, Honey looked up again at Joshua's house. He was right. Nell's building did block part of his view of the bay.

Once inside her living room, she forgot Joshua and opened Mr. Right's cage, smiling when he slunk out to investigate. The three rooms of the one-bedroom apartment were large and airy. As she followed Mr. Right through them, she imagined the walls white and the trim apple green—to match her curtains and furniture.

She took out a dust rag, but when she ran the cloth over a windowsill, loose paint flicked to the worn carpet. She left off dusting and decided to make her bed.

The apartment was half the size of the one she and Mario had been living in. Mario was going to have to sleep on the living-room couch. As she draped a fresh sheet over her bed, she wondered how they would get along in such a tiny space. Where would he practice his guitar? Where would he entertain his buddies? Where would he park his motorcycle? Could he survive three whole months without his drums?

Honey went to the window. The sun had vanished below the roofline of Joshua's mansion, and his house cast its long shadow over hers.

Her hands shook as she remembered his words. *Are you offering to sell your soul to the devil?* He had spoken then, not of women's souls, but of their bodies being cheap commodities to a man like him.

She remembered how safe she'd felt in his strong arms, how she'd felt an instant treacherous bonding between them. He'd reversed himself and been coldly insolent over the phone and brutal when he'd ordered her arrested outside his offices.

Who was Joshua Cameron, this man who could be both kind and cruel to the daughter of a man he hated? She was afraid as she'd never been before, but it was too late to turn back.

Challenging Joshua Cameron on his own turf would be like diving into the deepest, coldest waters of San Francisco Bay and deliberately seeking out a man-eating shark.

Dear God. She dreaded tangling with him again. She had enough problems already, and all of them would be made worse by living here. Just trying to park would be a nightmare. Enduring Mario's lip-curling complaints when he found out he would have no privacy, listening to him practice—not to mention moving everything they both owned—would make her life far from comfortable.

But worst of all there would be Joshua.

The long, slanting shadow of Joshua's house blocked out all light.

Suddenly it all seemed like too much.

But she had no choice. Her father's life was at stake.

Joshua's right temple throbbed painfully as it always did when he talked to Heather and she complained about the posh, overpriced school she was damn lucky to attend. Only this was worse.

Joshua leaned against the stark white wall on the third floor of his home and wished he'd let his machine answer the phone.

"You're not listening. Daddy, I've been expelled!"

"Young lady, I want to talk to Mrs. Stanton."

"It won't do any good. Even if you bribe her again with some huge donation, I'm not staying at this snotty place one more day. The kids all hate me, and I hate them. They're spoiled rotten—"

Joshua's vision clouded with red as he remembered the bleak, graffiti-spattered walls of the dangerous schools he'd been forced to attend as a child. "Spoiled! Look who's talking."

"Just come get me," she commanded as imperiously as he might issue orders to his underlings.

"Heather, I've got an important appointment at six."

"Am I ever important, Daddy?"

Through gritted teeth he replied. "Of course you are...sweetheart."

The line went dead, cutting his clumsy endearment in half.

She had hung up on him.

Teenagers! If only they could be bottled with a tight cork and locked in a vat like fine wine until they matured.

Joshua slammed the phone down. Then he raced past the dozens of fabulous paintings that decorated his stairwell, down the graceful, five-story spiraling staircase that had cost him more than most men spent on their entire homes.

He set his burglar alarm. Then he opened the door that led to his garage, groped through the darkness and got into his low-slung sports car. He took a deep breath, but the rich smell of leather in no way soothed his taut nerves. He wished he was good with kids—the way Midnight was. Joshua was almost afraid to pick up Heather in his present mood. He'd be too harsh.

With one hand he punched the automatic garage-door opener. With the other he dialed Midnight on his cellular phone.

"Midnight, Heather's been expelled from the Stanton Academy for Girls. You've got to pick her up from her school."

"What about the Brazil meeting?"

"I'll have to handle it without you. You're better with Heather than I am."

"You're her father, J.K."

Joshua exhaled bitterly. "And not too talented at the job."

"Heather's the one thing I envy you, J.K."

"Good. Then you won't mind picking her up for me."

"I'll look forward to it."

"I know I should do it myself—"

"Maybe after we wrap this Brazil deal you could take her somewhere special, just the two of you. Let her pick the place."

"Thanks, Midnight. I'll owe you."

"That's mutual."

"And Midnight—keep to the speed limit as long as you have Heather in the car."

Joshua pressed a button and broke the connection. They never bothered with goodbyes.

The garage doors rose slowly. Brilliant sunlight streamed inside.

He was about to start his car when he saw *it* parked in *his* driveway.

Whatever *it* was, *it* was immense and painted an awful shade of the most piercing psychedelic green.

His black head jerked around. What the hell—

His blue eyes froze on dented green steel. Some sort of horrible jalopy, some weirdo's junkyard creation, was jammed at a crazy cockeyed angle across his drive. It had a Chevy body and a Buick grill. A green note fluttered saucily from a windshield wiper.

He felt like ramming the heap. Hell, the thing was probably built like a Sherman tank.

Joshua got out of his own car and tore the note from beneath the blade, his hard gaze swiftly skimming the jaunty handwriting. Just as swiftly, he crumpled it up.

He unwadded the paper slowly. His gaze narrowed on the swirl of black ink as he reread the name and apartment number.

Honey Rodriguez. Who the hell was she?

From the address he figured out that she was Nell's new manager.

Which meant she was J. K. Cameron's new adversary.

He peered inside the filthy windows and saw that her garish wreck was piled to the roof with old boxes. She was obviously moving in.

Into *his* neighborhood.

Joshua smiled grimly at the prospect of meeting her. Maybe if he was very ugly to her today, he could run her off before she got settled. He felt like being ugly. Maybe it would help him get his mind off his impossible relationship with Heather.

As he strode forcefully toward the Filbert Steps, he heard a soft, unhurried voice singing a currently popular love song.

Some people had nothing to do.

He stopped at the top step. Beneath him, a voluptuous young woman in tight green shorts and spiked green heels was singing to herself as she climbed up the wooden steps, as if she had nothing else to do but to enjoy her life.

He looked at her closely. The instant he did some feeling that was rich and hot let go inside him and seemed to flood his veins. He felt he knew her, that he'd shared some important intimacy with her.

He'd never seen this indolent, harum-scarum creature before.

Not in this life.

And he didn't believe in any other.

Five

———

Joshua stared at the whimsical, gypsylike creature in green.

Then it struck him. She had a thing for green.

Green car. Green note. Green shorts. Green heels.

She was Honey Rodriguez. He knew it in his gut. Suddenly he forgot the packaging and viewed the contents with a mixture of surprise and pleasure.

Golden-toned ankles and lushly curved calves. Voluptuous thighs.

She wasn't skinny—the way he liked *his* women.

But she wasn't bad.

Joshua tightened with hot excitement. Which was ridiculous. His mission was to destroy her before she even moved in. Besides he liked sleek glamour, women who made other men envy him.

She stopped singing and knelt for a moment to touch a lush green fern and then to smell a fat yellow rose, her every movement charmingly sensual and lethargic. A hummingbird buzzed by her nose and she laughed.

How could this chaotic creature block his driveway and then waste time in the garden?

Her red hair caught the sunlight and seemed to gleam with a fire all its own. He had never seen hair quite that remarkable dazzling color. It was a dozen different shades of red, and all of them were ablaze.

She kept her glorious head down, even when she resumed climbing and singing, so he couldn't see her face. He wondered if she was deliberately keeping it hidden from him.

She was wearing green walking shorts and a long-sleeved, green, cotton shirt. Huge bangle earrings danced at her ears. She was big at the top and a shade hippy, but her waist was small. And somehow on her, her hips and legs were gorgeous.

"Excuse me," he growled with calculated fierceness. "Are you Honey? Nell's new manager?"

She jumped back, choking in the middle of a word. She looked up at him slowly, warily. Then her infectious smile lit her face and brightened something inside him, too. Again he felt the oddest sense of familiarity.

He had to tell himself that the face that was tilted up to his wasn't beautiful. It was merely animated and eager to please. And yet she seemed beautiful, in some special way all her own.

The softness of her mouth and skin registered, too. She licked her lips nervously, and he felt a sudden stirring in his loins.

She climbed nearer, and he realized anew how voluptuous she was.

Too voluptuous. He didn't like lushly feminine women.

"I asked you a question!" he repeated.

"Honey—that's me," she said softly in a slightly trembly voice, as if she were afraid and yet determined not to appear so.

But he liked soft.

She drew a nervous breath and fluffed her glorious hair. He watched the ripples of fire playing through the satiny softness as it cascaded in waves against her creamy cheeks and throat.

It was now an effort to force anger into his low tone. "Then this is your...er...car, I presume?"

"You mean the Bomb?" Again the faint tremble in her voice.

At least the vehicle was appropriately named.

"Did you know you're illegally parked?"

"Oh, my— Yes." She didn't look at him. "Didn't you get my note?"

Now she tilted her sunglasses up and looked at him quizzically, and for that brief brave moment there seemed something oddly familiar about that pert gesture. *Damn it. He was sure he'd seen her somewhere.* She put her glasses back down quickly. But not before he had seen her eyes.

He would have remembered her eyes if he'd ever seen them before. They were as startlingly lovely as her remarkable hair. They were vividly green, long lashed and wonderfully slanted. But their bright spark had quivered as if with fear when she'd looked at him.

Why did he imagine her in his bed, afraid of him no longer, her legs wrapped around him, her fiery hair brushing his chest, those green eyes darkening with desire, her arms and lips passionately clinging?

Hesitantly she joined him on the top step. She stood close, too close for either of them to feel comfortable. It was becoming an effort to remind himself that he liked sophistication and experience as well as glamour in his women, an effort to remember that he couldn't possibly be attracted to some naive, offbeat creature who seemed to be stepping out of a sixties' time warp.

Ms. Rodriguez wasn't his type. Not at all.

Why then did he see himself reflected in her sunglasses as if he were a man spellbound?

"I'm sorry if I'm blocking you," she said in a defiant voice that made him wonder if she really was.

He was aware of the elusively provocative scent of jasmine. Again he told himself that he had always preferred slim, glamorous, sophisticated beauties.

Glamorous and sophisticated *she* wasn't.

Alluring in her own special way *she* was.

She scared the hell out of him.

"It'll just take me a sec to start my car. Then I'll be gone." Her smile quivered as she tilted her sunglasses up once more, dazzling him again with the innocent heat of those frightened green eyes.

For some reason her smile unnerved him and put him off balance. Again it seemed vaguely familiar. Which was ridiculous. He couldn't have forgotten those eyes. That hair. Those legs. Her smell.

He couldn't have forgotten her.

"It's nice to meet you, Mr. . . . ?"

"Cameron." Even though he gritted his teeth, his growl was lower, less angry.

"I always like to know my neighbors."

"I usually try to avoid knowing mine."

"Usually?" She laughed then, as if she were forcing herself to relax, and held out her hand which was soft and small.

The closer her hand came to his, the more it trembled.

Rudely he ignored her hand even though he felt drawn to take it. Because of her fear he found it impossible to be as ugly to her as he had originally intended to be.

He would size her up. He could save the ugliness for later when he knew more about her vulnerabilities.

"Nell warned me about you," she said.

Why the hell was that such an unpleasant surprise? "Start your car," he said grumpily, determined to end this encounter as soon as possible.

"Aye. Aye." She saluted him mischievously and tripped jauntily toward her car.

Never had big hips seemed so deliciously feminine as they swayed in those tight, boyish shorts. He couldn't help a slow grin of aesthetic appreciation.

No way could he have ever forgotten that walk. And yet
that vague sense of familiarity lingered in the back of his
mind. *He had definitely seen her somewhere before.*

She turned, her long hair flaring flirtatiously like a cop-
pery fan before it fell back against her neck and shoulders.
She smiled. "Coming?"

She seemed to be growing more self-confident by the
moment. She didn't wait for his answer, but hopped into her
car. When she tried to start it, the engine turned over but
didn't catch.

That figured. He raced after her. She was still trying to
start it when he yanked her door open. "You're going to run
the battery down doing that," he muttered.

"Would you like to try?" she asked, scooting over. Not
that she could scoot far, since her front seat was jammed
with boxes.

When he got in, his hand accidentally brushed hers. Light
fingertips, satiny and warm, skimmed against his. Joshua
felt an uneasy prickle of male interest and was gratified
when she quickly jumped away from him.

She would be an easy conquest for a man of his experience and sophisticated expertise. *Not that he was interested.*

"You have to put your foot on the gas. Gently. Like this,"
he whispered authoritatively.

"Oh." Her big green eyes watched him. "My!"

He pressed the gas pedal while he turned the key. The engine cranked endlessly just as it had for her.

Which infuriated the hell out of him. "Something's
wrong," he growled.

"I know."

He pressed the hood release and got out, grabbing the
loose emission-coil wire the instant he saw it. "Have you
been fooling around under here?"

Her eyes were wide, almost fearful again. "Who me?"

Ridiculous question. A woman like her wouldn't know
the first thing about cars. As he leaned over and reattached

the wire, she got out and began removing boxes from the other side of her car.

"It should start now," he said a short while later, slamming her hood closed.

"You already fixed it?"

He liked the way she sounded impressed as she set her box on the sidewalk. "A wire was loose."

"Thanks a lot." She picked up another larger box and turned toward the wooden stairs that led down to her apartment.

"Hey!" he yelled, freshly irritated. "What the hell do you think you're doing now? I started this thing, so you could move it out of my way. Put that damned box down. I've got a meeting."

When she stepped backward, her green heel caught on the curb. The heavy box she was holding caused her to lose her balance and she tumbled back, dropping the box. Its contents spilled, rolling downhill toward him.

Before he could jump aside, a runaway paint can with a bit of green lace tangled around the wire handle slammed into his shin.

"Ouch!" He danced on his good leg.

She got up slowly. He doubled over to wrench his pant leg loose from the can. Expensive wool fabric tore.

"Oh, I'm sorry." Unhurt from her fall, she rushed toward him.

He didn't look up from the hole in his slacks or the paint can. "Are you always this clumsy?"

She bent down beside him. "Always—when someone screams at me."

Her gentle, frightened voice brought an unpleasant emotion that he was not accustomed to—guilt. But before he could react to it, she touched him. Her fingers pushed his trouser leg up and her fingers slid against his bare leg to inspect his injury.

Her nearness and that light caress of fingertips made it impossible for him to control his breath and chaotic pulse.

He grabbed her hand. "Hey, I'm okay," he said roughly.

"I'm glad you're okay. I—I'll buy you a new suit...."

"There's no way you could afford to."

"I—"

"Forget it!" he snapped.

He picked up her paint can and untwisted the bit of green lace. He was embarrassed when he saw that it was composed of two cups held together by green satin straps—her bra. As he stood up with the flimsy strips of lace dangling from his brown fingers, funny little darts of feeling flooded his stomach.

First she took the paint can from him. Then with eyes and cheeks as bright as his, her bra. But not before he had imagined full, soft breasts, their pouting dark nipples cupped pertly by green lace. Not before his heart had begun to pound with fresh violence.

"I'm afraid I can't resist green," she said, her eyes full of humor and mischief now instead of fear.

Apparently neither could he. Because even though he was late for his meeting, he helped her gather her things. When she began to reload her box in a haphazard, lazy fashion, he couldn't resist lending a little of his male expertise.

Sinking back on those voluptuous haunches, she watched him pack the box with amazed pleasure and gratitude. When she handed him a last bundle of towels, their hands brushed again. This time she didn't pull her hand away quite as quickly.

Tell her to move her car so you can go. Run her off.

"I'll carry this down for you," Joshua heard himself say in a low, gravelly tone he scarcely recognized as his own. "It's the least I can do after causing you to fall and spill everything."

Fool! What the hell are you doing—helping Nell's new manager to move in?

When they reached the door of Honey's apartment, she slid through the opening with him.

"Where does this go?" he asked her, suddenly more aware of her than ever in the small, closed apartment.

"Just set it down in my bedroom," she said, her voice light and breathy. "Here—I'll lead the way."

It was impossible for him to ignore her sexy walk. He was openly grinning when they reached her bedroom. He glanced around. "Where now?"

"On my bed."

He tensed. "Right."

The green bedspread was the same color as her bra. A huge gray cat with a green rhinestone collar lay in the center of the bed.

"Green collar, I see."

"I told you my weakness . . . for green."

Her eyes were wide and inquiring and no longer fearful. Did she sense she had somehow acquired the upper hand? Her mouth was moist—delicious looking.

"One of many—" The words rasped over his suddenly dry vocal cords.

"Yes, I'm afraid so. I'm very messy, very disorganized. I have a weakness for chocolate and for bubble baths on lazy Sunday afternoons—"

"I like chocolate, too." His eyes were on her face. "You're very lovely."

She recoiled warily and glanced away.

Slow down, J.K.

When the mattress dipped under the weight of the box Joshua set down, the cat meowed, stretching a lazy paw indignantly.

Joshua hated cats. "We've disturbed someone's nap," he said, pretending an interest in her pet.

"Meet Mr. Right," she said more easily, now that their subject was safer.

Mr. Right and Joshua stared at one another. Mr. Right flattened his ears.

"He looks like a stray."

"I collect strays." She paused. "They make the best pets." Her eyes touched Joshua's. "Thank you for carrying that down. I didn't expect you to." She paused.

"You're...not at all what I thought you'd be like. I mean—" She edged away.

Suddenly he was thinking of the green bra and the green bed, as well as the fact that he was very much alone with her in her bedroom. He imagined her lying on that bed, stretching her hands up to him invitingly.

She must have read his mind because she moved even further from him, out of the bedroom and through the front door. She stepped onto the porch, folding her arms across her chest, heaving a nervous sigh. He followed her outside, glad to be out of the apartment.

He said in a matter-of-fact voice, "Nell's old manager lived here, too."

"I'll just be the summer manager," she said a little defiantly.

As always, defiance compelled him. "Don't get too comfortable. You won't make it through the summer here."

Her green gaze dared him. "Says who?"

"I'm going to buy this firetrap and tear it down."

"What about the people who live here?"

"They're not my concern," he said. But he had turned away to avoid her quick look.

"No. They're mine," she challenged softly from behind him.

He whirled, edging closer, cornering her when she tried to run past him off the porch. The scowl on his dark face was not nice. "Don't even think about taking me on. I crush people who try to stop me."

Fear flared just for a second in her eyes, and then that damnable, charming defiance was back. She forced a smile. "How do people defend themselves against people like you?"

"They don't."

Although she said nothing, her eyes sparked.

He eyed her just as grimly. "I'm glad that's settled."

"Did it ever occur to you that I might motivate you to change your mind?"

Joshua towered nearer. "What do you mean?"

"I mean," she whispered, "that I'm not so sure that you're really as hateful as you want everybody to think you are. Oh, I know that you've harassed all Nell's managers into quitting."

"What?"

"That's why I parked in front of your house—so we'd have a chance to get acquainted and start off on the right foot. I'm afraid I even pulled those wires under my hood loose."

"You what?"

She smiled impishly, defiantly.

"Why, you little schemer. You said you didn't fool around—"

"Because I wasn't fooling around. My job was to meet you."

"To harass me."

"I'm going to stop you, Mr. Cameron. Your old tricks aren't going to work. I think you're just as scared of all the things that scare everybody else."

"You don't know a damn thing about me."

"I know a lot more than you think." Honey seemed to catch herself. "Everybody's scared, Mr. Cameron. Even..." She paused, trembling slightly, perhaps because his powerful body was edging closer. Her gaze slid up his dark rugged face. "Even bullies like you."

"Is that what you think I am?" he demanded quietly.

"That's what you just said you were. Nell said so, too, but... I—I think, or at least I *hope,* that you could be very nice if you wanted to be."

His gaze touched her eyes and then her mouth. "And your special mission in life is to manipulate me to be nice?"

"Manipulate is your word."

"Changing me is an impossible mission."

The light of the sun was in her mussed hair. Her determined lips parted into that infectious smile.

He drew a deep breath. "Honey, you're in way over your head."

Her defiant smile caused his pulse to quicken. He started to say something cutting and found he couldn't.

Hell, he was swimming in deep, uncharted water himself.

Her smile vanished. Fear had replaced defiance in her eyes, and he wished it hadn't.

He liked her.

Not that he understood this sudden, incredible affinity he felt for her—a stranger. Nell's manager. His adversary.

Besides that, she was poor and he was rich. He knew all about being poor, all about what men and women would do to better their cash flow. He had been chased by lots of women who were after him just for his money, women who wanted to use him. Usually he used such women—as long as they pleased him.

Her tongue slid out to trace the dry outline of her soft pink mouth. She drew away from him, shaking her head. "We should be natural enemies." A red tangle fell softly against her cheek.

His breath caught. His eyes were fixed on her mouth. "Baby, if you're smart, you'll run."

"I can be foolish sometimes. Besides, I have a job here."

His immense frame eased closer.

She swallowed. Then she looked over her shoulder uncertainly at the Filbert Steps. "But who says it's a crime to follow sound advice?"

She took a single faltering step away from him. Then she made a wild, defiant dash across the porch.

But he was faster.

He caught her by the wrist and eased her against the wooden wall of her house, his body pressing into hers, his hands and arms securing her against him as she cried out softly, trying to free herself.

"I thought you told me to go."

Women were easy for him. It had been a long time since he'd had to chase one. Something wild and dangerous was smoldering to life inside him, something that had been dead for years. "Maybe you're too tempting to resist."

She balled her hands into fists and pushed at his chest. Her eyes blazed with defiance.

He lifted her chin and stared into her eyes' hot, burning light, which so turned him on. He crushed her effortlessly to him, her breasts pressing against his wide chest, her hips pushing into his thighs. A fierce white heat consumed him. Every movement of her body as she struggled against him brought fiery surges of pleasure.

But his voice was gentle. "Honey...Honey, I'm not going to hurt you."

Very slowly she stilled.

A vast silence seemed to envelop them as he held her. Her face seemed lost, devoid of all hope. He, too, felt overwhelmed by the same bottomless despair. Instinct told them that each had the power to annihilate the other. And yet neither of them wanted to run.

She stared up at him without breath as he flexed his big brown hand and brought it slowly toward her to smooth the wayward red tangle away from her soft cheek. Then his rough-textured fingers traced lower, along her satiny, high sculpted cheekbone, down the slender curve of her warm golden throat, lingering against her quivering heartbeat before he turned her face gently up to his.

"I've never known a woman like you."

Her frightened, luminous eyes held his. Again she seemed to stop breathing as he continued to explore every inch of her face.

Like one mesmerized, Honey watched the slow descent of his mouth. The instant his lips touched hers, he felt her quicken. As he deepened his kiss, he felt her arms slowly come around his neck, her fingertips tightening reluctantly against the corded muscles of his back as she arched herself nearer.

She accepted his tongue when he flicked it inside her lips. Her velvet mouth was hot and moistly delicious.

She was everything he had imagined and more—hotly alive and tenderly naive, all at the same time. One kiss, and wildfire raced through his veins.

More than anything, he wanted to carry her into the house and have her naked and writhing on that green bed beneath him. He imagined her nipples, budding tight and hard against his mouth. He knew she would be good—better than those piles of fancy skeletons he'd been sleeping with for years. He was a man who usually took what he wanted without a qualm.

Instead, even when every cell in his body throbbed to have her, he relaxed his grip and let her go.

What the hell was wrong with him?

All he knew was that he felt different with her.

Alive. Almost human.

He drew in a deep, ragged breath and then let it out in a long, frustrated sigh. "What is going on here?"

Too weak to stand, she sank against the wall and laughed shakily, a little hysterically. "It's called animal attraction. Instant chemistry. I never believed in it before."

It was more than that.

"Dangerous stuff," he muttered fiercely, running a light finger across her lips that caused them both to shiver.

"The kind of chemistry I teach to seventh graders is pretty tame," she said.

"Then it's nothing like this."

"No... I—I wish it hadn't happened."

"Some things can't be undone."

"Mr. Cameron, please... You're the last man I would choose to feel like this about."

"Thanks."

"I—I know what you must think of me. What any man—but, especially a man like you—would think."

"A man like me..." He felt a smoldering cynical fury. Toward her. Toward Nell, who had obviously thoroughly brainwashed her. For the first time in a long time he regretted his nasty reputation. "I doubt that you do."

"Nothing like this has ever happened to me before."

"Likewise," he said very coldly.

Her golden skin reflected the pink light of the sinking sun. He looked at her passion-swollen lips and despite his anger, he felt as if he were starving for them.

He wanted to taste her again, and not just her mouth. He wanted her hands on his body, too. But she wasn't the kind of woman who could endure the easy kind of passion he had in mind. There was an intensity about her, a true innocence in her soul that even he, jaded though he was from a hard life and too many easy women, didn't want to despoil. Not just for her sake but for his own. Because he would hate for her to despise him when she learned what kind of man he really was.

"I don't want this to happen again," she said.

"Neither do I." He ran his hands through his unruly black hair that had tumbled over his brow. "Baby, if you're smart, you'll stay away from me."

"Because your intentions are not honorable?"

He set his hot, insolent eyes on her until her lips quivered with fright. "Nothing about me is honorable, Honey Rodriguez."

"Do you always warn women away?" she asked, her voice husky with fear

"Not usually. Take another summer job. Anywhere but here."

"I—I can't do that."

"It will be dangerous for you—living near me. I usually take what I want. And I want you, Honey Rodriguez. But you're not my type, and I probably wouldn't be interested very long."

A twinge of genuine hurt and then fright crossed her white face. "You were in a hurry. I'm sorry I kept you so long."

"My pleasure— Honey." He smiled wolfishly.

Silently, she walked to the Filbert Steps. He followed right behind her.

As they ascended the wooden steps together, he did a curious thing. He picked the fat yellow rose she had admired and gave it to her.

"You shouldn't pick the flowers. They'll wither and die sooner than they should," she said quickly. "You should leave them for other people who come after you to enjoy."

"I've picked a lot of flowers I shouldn't have picked—for my own personal pleasure. I've never given a damn for those who came after me."

As she took the rose, she caught the dark note in his voice and knew intuitively he wasn't talking about flowers.

"Do you believe a man can change, Miss Rodriguez?"

"If he really wants to."

"Then you are not as cynical as I."

"I wouldn't want to be."

He did a second curious thing. He never confided any of his personal problems to anyone. But he found himself doing so—with her.

"I was upset when I found your note."

"I meant to annoy you."

"No... My teenage daughter was expelled from her private school this afternoon for some very unladylike conduct, conduct that I'm deeply ashamed of because of my own background... or rather my lack of proper background."

"That's probably why she did it. Kids always go for the jugular."

"Well, I was proud when my daughter was accepted to such a classy school. Then when she told me about this crazy thing she did, I felt like wringing her neck."

Honey smiled at him, her fear gone. "That's a normal impulse. But don't do it. Be kind. Try to find out what's troubling her. She probably just wanted to get your attention."

They had reached her car. Joshua opened her door and she got in.

"I'm afraid I'm not very good at kindness. I didn't experience much of it growing up. And I haven't spent much time with her. You're probably good with kids."

"Not always."

"I grew up on the street. I've tried to give her everything I never had, but she throws it all back in my face and rebels."

"Then she's a normal teenager. Don't give up on her, Mr. Cameron. That's the main thing."

"I never give up—when I set out to do something."

She started her car. "Neither do I."

Twilight had fallen, and he noticed that she had begun to shiver.

She held out her hand in farewell.

"Then you'll heed my warning and stay away from me?" He took her hand, knowing deep in his heart that the last thing he should do was touch her.

Her green eyes were unreadable. "Goodbye, Mr. Cameron."

"Joshua," he murmured.

"Joshua," she repeated, but very softly and a little defiantly.

There were no words to describe how good he felt when she said it. There was no way he could resist leaning into the car and kissing her goodbye, either. When she tried to pull away, he wouldn't let her.

His kiss was soft and gentle and possessive, and after it was over they were both more afraid than ever.

Six

"**M**idnight, get me a list of the casualties!" Joshua strode grimly beyond the steel deck of the new high-rise tower he was erecting as an expansion of his hotel.

With the grace of a cat, he sprang across the naked girder and stared down through the unfinished walls and floors at the ruin of concrete walls and the overturned crane many floors beneath him.

Midnight was a few feet behind him. "No casualties, J.K. You were lucky as hell. When the crane collapsed, the crew had shut down for the day."

Joshua turned and saw his own profound relief mirrored in Midnight's jet gaze. They'd both seen too much violent dying to ever forget the pain that went with it.

Back in his office an hour later, secure in the knowledge that no one had been hurt, Joshua fought to concentrate on what Midnight and his architect were saying. What frustrated the hell out of him was that he'd been distracted at work all week.

Joshua was glad when Midnight and the architect finally left. Maybe he could pull himself together before either of them came back and bombarded him with more legal or architectural problems.

Joshua got up slowly from his desk and went to a window. The city beneath was silent like a dead dream city. He watched the cars glide through the downtown with quick, quiet purpose. He watched the Golden Gate Bridge disappear as fog rolled in from the Pacific. He saw sailboats on the bay and felt the need to get out on the water himself. He wanted the icy wind on his face; he wanted to breathe in the tangy smell of the sea. Impossible—he never took off in the middle of the week.

He felt trapped in his glassed-in cage, lost, not himself. He ran his hands through his black hair. He hadn't been worth a damn ever since he'd met Honey Rodriguez one week ago.

Not that he'd seen her again. She'd avoided him as though he had a fatal disease; she'd done exactly what he'd said he'd wanted.

Damn it. Why couldn't he forget her? Why did he keep remembering the way she'd smelled? The way she'd tasted? Why did her sweet, defiant smile continue to haunt him? Why couldn't he work with his usual ferocious energy? Why did he search every narrow side street on Telegraph Hill for that green monstrosity of a car every night when he drove home? Was he crazy? And why did he feel like he'd met her before?

A man with his problems didn't have time to moon over a woman like some lovesick teenager, especially a woman so totally unsuitable. He had had constant hotel-renovation and construction hassles. Then there had been all the frustrating dead ends with the Brazilian project. The Wyatt takeover wasn't going well, either. Only today he'd found out that Hunter's wife had blocked him from buying more Wyatt stock.

How the hell an amateur like Mrs. Wyatt had scraped up enough cash, lured in a partner and financed the purchase of that run-down casino hotel in Vegas, he would never know. But since Joshua already owned the maximum number of casino hotels he could own by law, he couldn't take over her chain, without selling one of his own highly profitable casinos. He'd been stopped—cold. By a woman. He remembered Wyatt's daughter and realized she'd made good on her threats.

His own daughter, Heather, compounded his business problems by making his time off a living hell. She was even moodier and more argumentative than she'd been after Monica had first left them. When she wasn't hysterical about some tiny problem, she fought with him constantly.

Two nights ago he'd blown up at her for watching a trashy television show at two in the morning. She'd yelled back, refusing to listen when he told her that if she stopped staying up till dawn and sleeping through lunch she'd feel better.

Not that she ever did anything worthwhile when she was awake. She did her long blond hair, which stayed lank and stringy no matter how many hours she combed it, or she listened to awful music and talked incessantly on the phone. When he'd offered her a part-time job, she'd refused to work in his office.

In desperation he'd decided that she had to go to summer school. He'd insisted until she'd sulkily agreed—if she could pick the school. Then she'd made the worst possible choice by selecting one nobody had ever heard of, just because it was near the house and she could walk and make friends with the neighbors.

She constantly criticized him.

Joshua didn't like thinking about Heather, so he went back to his desk and tried to work. When he hadn't finished by seven, he crammed a briefcase with hotel blueprints and went home anyway.

In his kitchen sink he found the remnants of Heather's soggy peanut-butter sandwich. He ate alone and went up to his office, spread out his blueprints and resumed work. He'd just begun to really get somewhere when Heather's choked voice came from the door, interrupting him.

"I know you don't want me here, Daddy."

He looked up. She was dressed sloppily—in a big black T-shirt and black shorts. *He hated black on kids.* He hated the way she didn't know how to dress yet. Her forlorn blue eyes were glassy bright and huge; her complexion was mottled with livid red spots. Her blond hair was untidily plaited into a crooked French braid. She was at that coltish stage—too skinny and long legged. She was ill at ease with her newly budding feminine body. She didn't know what to make of herself, and neither did he.

She needed a mother—to help her dress, to do her hair. To help with the other important stuff.

"I know you don't want me to bother you, Daddy."

He damn sure didn't. His hand clenched around his pencil.

"I was trying to work, Heather," he said, deliberately keeping his voice calm.

Her bottom lip quivered. "I know I'm just in your way."

How the hell was he supposed to answer that? He couldn't say she was right, so he'd said nothing.

"When Mother went away I felt I was less than nothing, that I had no one."

A frown crept into his eyes. That's the way he'd felt, too. Not that he could admit it. He set his pencil down carefully and raked his hands through his hair.

"Why did Mother leave me and then have a new baby when she won't even let me come see her?"

Hell, she left me for another man.

Heather's tear-filled questions filled Joshua with rage against Monica. His fingers tightened against his scalp.

"Daddy—"

"For God's sake, don't ask me about your mother."

"You won't ever talk about her."

His mouth thinned. His bleak eyes stared at Heather, almost hating her when she came to him like this, pleading and in tears, because she reminded him too much of Monica and all the hopeless years he'd wasted with her.

"Did you ever love her, Daddy?"

He shoved his chair back from the desk and got up. Striding across the room, he threw open the glass doors and plunged out into the cold, damp air that brought the salty smell of the sea.

His hands gripped the balcony railing as unwanted memories of his ex-wife deluged him. The brutal truth was that he'd married Monica for her money and family connections. Not that he hadn't tried to make their marriage work. Monica had been a spoiled socialite who'd considered herself better than the poor bad boy from the bad neighborhood she'd found herself curiously attracted to, though she'd married him anyway. He'd thought she was class. She was pregnant before either of them realized he hadn't held her values. Not that they both hadn't been climbers. It was just that they were clawing their way up different ladders.

He hadn't understood her fierce competitive desire to establish them in society by spending their entire lives at endless parties he'd considered silly. She hadn't understood why he worked so hard in his own business when she had all the money in the world. He hadn't known how to play up to the kind of people she considered socially important, people who made him feel empty, bored, unsure—inadequate. Not wanting the same things, they had torn each other apart. In the end Monica had left him for someone with old money.

"I'm leaving you because I've found a man with real class," Monica had thrown at him as she'd slammed the trunk down on her suitcases and punched the garage-door opener. "You're still just a cheap hood who hasn't learned that money isn't class."

"Oh, I learned, Monica," he had said softly, edging menacingly closer to her in that shadowy garage, causing her to panic in that last moment and quickly jump into her car and snap her door locks. "Maybe you shouldn't be too hard on a cheap hood just because he was attracted by your shallow glitter."

When Heather made some soft sound as she stepped out onto the balcony, too, Joshua was jerked back to reality. He forced himself to relax his hands on the railing. Monica was gone. For good. She had a new family now. He turned toward Heather wearily. All he wanted now was to forget Monica and live in peace.

But Heather wasn't about to let him. "Why did Mother leave us, Daddy?"

"Damn it! Don't push me."

Her young, unhappy face crumpled. "Why?" Her one word was a desperate plea.

"Because of me. Because she thinks I still stink of the gutter I was raised in."

"She's not like that."

"If you don't like my answers, don't ask me questions."

"Why can't you ever be a real father? Why can't you ever...just once...make me feel better—the way Midnight does?" A strangled moan escaped her lips.

Because he didn't know how. Because he wasn't talented the way Midnight was with kids. Joshua swore in a brutal, frustrated undertone.

"You always hurt me," she whispered. "Always."

"Damn it, Heather. What the hell do you think you do to me?"

"But I don't want to hurt you, Daddy. I want to be with you."

Her pleading eyes held on to his for a painfully drawn out minute. A tear slid down her cheek. She waited as if she actually expected him to touch her, to comfort her as Midnight would have done. But a dark bitterness stole over Joshua. When he just stood there she backed slowly away from him, sobbing as if he were a monster.

"Heather—"

He followed her as far as the darkened circular stairwell and listened to her footsteps flying down the stairs. He flicked on the light so that she wouldn't stumble on a stair.

Her door slammed and he turned the light off again, glad to be alone once more. It was no use going after her. She was right. He'd been hurting people so long, he didn't know how to do anything else.

Inadvertently a perverse thought struck him. Honey Rodriguez would know what to say, how to be kind and patient and understanding.

Damn Honey Rodriguez. She'd avoided him.

He went back to his desk and stared down at the blueprints. All he could think of was that he longed to see Honey—again.

He cursed viciously. He felt out of control, furious. With a single frenzied swipe, his brown hand raked across the desk, sending blueprints, notepads, pencils and pens flying. Then he stomped over the jumbled sheets, not caring that he ripped one of them on his way out to the terrace.

He barely saw the glittering blur of the Oakland Bridge, of faraway lights across the bay. The garden four stories beneath him was dark. He drew in a deep ragged breath. He had to get himself back in hand.

Muted laughter drifted up from the garden, and he looked down, seeking anything that might distract him. A pair of lovers embraced tenderly on the Filbert Steps in the shadows beneath the palm tree. The sight of them made him feel even crazier and more alone as he stood on his empty terrace and looked down on a city of hundreds of thousands. When he wrenched his gaze away from the entwined pair, a golden light snapped on—high up in Honey's apartment building.

Her light. It seemed to glow brighter than all the other lights in the world. Joshua's pulse accelerated.

He held his breath when, a few minutes later, Honey came to the window and stared up at his house for a long moment. His breathing became labored and harsh as he imagined her eyes seeking him in the darkness. Slowly, almost reluctantly, she lowered the shade.

He watched her window anyway. Even with her shade down, he could see her moving about. Suddenly she came close to the window again. Her shadowy womanly form was silhouetted in the center of that golden rectangle as she began to undress for bed.

He stood statue still, unable to stop himself from watching her. When she grabbed the bottom edges of her knit shirt and pulled it off over her head, his heart began to beat violently in his throat.

He watched her strip off her shirt and toss it carelessly onto the floor. Lazily she began to run a brush through her hair. He imagined its silkiness, its fire flashing against her slender neck. When her fingers came around her back and unhooked her bra, he began to shake.

Her breasts swung free. Dear God. The sight of her, knowing that she was half naked behind that shade, rocked his senses. He ached to hold her, to touch her, to know if those shapely breasts felt like warm velvet. He shuddered, his pent-up emotions in violent upheaval as he viewed the shadowy curve of bosom, waist and the voluptuous swell of her hip. The memory of the time he'd kissed her moved through him like electricity.

She was such an alluring mixture of defiance and fear and sweetness. More than anything he wanted to call her, to hear her voice, to talk to her—just one more time.

Only when she turned out the light was he released from her spell. Only then could he go back inside and pick up his phone.

He set it down again—hesitating. He felt insane with some fierce male need to claim, to conquer, to possess. But he would only hurt her.

Was it his ghetto breeding that made his blood run hot and wild despite his decision to be noble? Or was it just because he'd told himself he couldn't have her that he wanted her so much?

His fingers tightened in a stranglehold around the receiver. Then he set it down and pulled a slim black book out of his drawer.

Instead of Honey, he dialed Simone and asked her out for the next night, hoping sex would help him forget the woman he *really* wanted.

Joshua's date with Simone was the final disaster of his disastrous week.

Instead of taking her to bed, he took her home after dinner and told her goodbye forever. The next morning he had his secretary shop for a very expensive parting gift for Simone. He opened the black velvet box, scribbled a terse goodbye and his initials on a crisp card, inserted the card in the necklace's center and snapped the box shut.

Simone called the moment she received the diamonds.

But not to thank him.

"Who's the lucky girl, J.K.?" Her voice was husky, knowing, amused.

"My daughter's moved home."

"There's more to this than your daughter. You're different."

"In what way?"

She laughed huskily. "Not so sure of yourself. Perhaps, *cheri,* this time you've met your match. I'd like to meet the new woman."

"Simone—there is no new woman."

"Really? Why don't I believe you, J.K.?" Simone hung up laughing at him in that infuriating way that reminded Joshua of Midnight.

Sharks die if they don't keep swimming forward.

Dark suited, paisley tied, Joshua marched into his office Monday morning determined to let no distraction stop him from moving forward, determined that he was done with dwelling on the past and the absurd desire he had for a woman who was all wrong for him.

He glanced at his watch impatiently. He had a meeting with Midnight—they were supposed to go over the legal problems of the Wyatt takeover. But Midnight was late.

Suddenly from outside his office, he heard Midnight's laughter. Ticia giggled. More warm laughter from Midnight.

Midnight was never too busy to take time for women. Even though he hadn't devoted himself to one woman in particular for years.

The door swung open and Midnight stepped inside. He was holding a glass of iced cola. Sensing Joshua's dark mood, Midnight's smile died instantly. He set his drink down on a sunlit table.

"You're late."

"I got a ticket. The cop gave me a long lecture. Then I got hung up up at the hotel, too." Midnight yanked off his black leather jacket and tossed it onto a chair. He shrugged toward a boy of about nineteen who was lounging in the doorway behind him. "Come on in, kid. No matter what you've heard, Mr. Cameron has probably had his breakfast. I don't think he'll eat you alive."

"Thanks for the character reference, Midnight," Joshua growled.

Midnight shrugged. "Anytime, J.K. Kid, I said come in."

The haggard kid behind Midnight was dark and tall and unshaven. His old jeans and even older-looking running shoes made him look poor—ghetto poor. He moved in that faintly edgy way rangy kids from dangerous neighborhoods moved, head down, hands out of his pockets. His eyes were older than the rest of his face, and he took in everything with quick, restless glances even though he didn't dare stare.

"Meet Tito Pascale," Midnight said.

Tito shifted uneasily, lowered his black head and stared at his grubby shoestrings. There was an ugly yellow bruise beneath his left eye. His lip was cut and swollen.

"Why should I bother?" But Joshua was interested in spite of himself.

"He works for us, and he works twice as hard as the next best welder we've got. He's from our old neighborhood."

"Memories from the old neighborhood hardly warm my heart."

"So? What does?" Midnight smiled grimly.

"Midnight, are you going to tell me what the hell's going on here?"

"Tito wants to take off for a few days. His mother's sick."

Joshua studied the kid's black eye and swollen lip. "You know my policy, Midnight. I fire people who lie to me and demand special favors. I'm running a business, not a charity. We're behind on construction. I'm not some softie who can afford to fold at every employee's petty demand."

The kid broke in. "This is life-or-death. I swear I just need two days, Mr. Cameron. I like my job. I need it. I can't afford to lose it. My mother—"

Joshua leaned forward. "It's bad taste to lie about your mother to get something you want, kid. You've been in a fight. You're in some kind of trouble. You gonna tell me what your real problem is?"

The kid would have run, but Midnight had edged himself between the boy and the door. "You came here to talk to Mr. Cameron," Midnight murmured.

For an instant the kid looked desperate and lost. "I can't tell you, Mr. Cameron. I need the time. You've got to help me."

"I don't help people."

The furtive eyes grew resentful as they moved swiftly from Joshua's face across the plush opulence of the mauve office. "I guess you've been rich so long, you've forgotten what's it's like to be poor—to be someone like me."

Joshua went white. His body tightened. He turned away abruptly, but not before a terrible rush of the old helplessness swamped him. He felt the kid's hate. Hell, it felt like his own.

"No," he said quietly. "I haven't forgotten."

"Mr. Cameron—" The boy's fierce, desperate voice came from behind Joshua. "I've gotta have the two days to find my mother a new place to live. My stepfather beat her up bad—she looks worse than I do. He took everything we had. He's said he's coming back with a gun. I've got to stop him."

Joshua felt slightly ill. The kid would rob, maybe even kill, to get the money he needed—if someone didn't help him. He would kill his stepfather too, if the guy really came back and pushed too hard. Joshua knew because he'd been there. Only he'd been lucky.

Joshua turned around slowly. "Okay, kid. Will you get out of here if I give you your two days and enough money so you don't have to do anything crazy?" Joshua pulled a checkbook from his pocket, ripped out a check and scribbled on it. "This is a loan. It's not charity."

The kid took the check and eyed the amount. His eyes flickered with new hope and then an even fiercer determination. "I promise I'll pay it back."

"With interest. But use it to stay out of trouble, kid."

Midnight watched the stunned kid back out of the room. Then with a half smile he turned back to J.K.

Joshua spoke first. "You find that jerk of a stepfather and bring him here—to me."

"Will do." Midnight's smile broadened.

"What the hell are you looking so pleased about, Midnight?"

"You tell me, J.K."

"He came to you for help, didn't he, the way my men always get around my rules by going to you—because beneath your tough exterior you're a sucker for their sob stories? Why didn't you help him yourself? Why did you bring him to me?"

Midnight shrugged, lifted his cola to his lips, sipped and frowned. "Must be a warm day. The ice seems to have melted in my drink." He hesitated thoughtfully.

"What the hell were you doing, Midnight, bringing that kid here?"

Midnight set his drink down. "I was checking you out.
You've been different ever since you tangled with Wyatt's
daughter. Softer."

"Damn it. Soft is the last thing I want to be. You know
what I went through better than anyone."

"Other people have it just as bad."

"I don't give a damn about other people."

Midnight's eyes grew darker. He edged closer. "That's
always been your main problem, J.K. I'd just about given
up on you until lately."

"I'll be back to normal soon."

"You call hating everyone that lives and breathes on
Mother Earth normal. Hey, don't change on my account. I
like the new you. But what I can't figure out is how Miss
Wyatt got under your skin when you never even went out
with her?"

"Cecilia Wyatt has nothing to do with it."

Midnight stared at him, clearly puzzled.

The old Joshua never confided. The new Joshua surprised them both. "There is someone though—a woman,
who's been on my mind."

"That's great."

"It's hell!"

"Who is she?"

"A redheaded neighbor of mine. Nell's new apartment
manager. But it's over." Joshua took a quick breath. "Hell,
it never even started. She's not my type."

"Call her up, J.K."

"No!"

"Then give me her number and I'll call her. I'm not as big
a snob as you when it comes to women."

"You stay the hell away from her!"

Joshua looked dangerous and jealous. His hard voice held
that threatening note Midnight remembered from their
leaner, meaner days.

But Midnight just laughed as he lifted his glass in a
mocking salute. "It ain't over with you and her, boss," he

murmured. "Not by a long shot. I'll lay you fifty to one that she's melting your heart faster than the sun melted this ice."

"Go to hell, Midnight."

"Hey, that's where we both got our start, remember? No way am I going back. Not even for you." As always Midnight clung stubbornly to his point of view. Grinning, he grabbed his jacket and slung it over a broad shoulder. "Call her, J.K."

Seven

Why did the Bomb have to die today of all days?

Honey almost felt like crying as she lifted the grimy phone from her Chinese mechanic's filthy counter and called Mario. She still couldn't believe Foon Lew wanted five hundred dollars to fix the Bomb.

Mario didn't answer till the seventh ring, and at first all she heard was the pounding of his drums. Then he mumbled hello and grunted indifferently when she told him their problem.

"Mario, we don't have five hundred dollars—" *Why was she trying to explain? Mario lived in his own world—girls, his music, his motorcycle, his job, school—in that order.* "Just come get me," she said at last, hanging up in frustration before he could protest.

Honey went wearily over to her car. The Bomb was jacked up. All she could see of Foon Lew were the frayed cuffs of his blue jeans and his dirty tennis shoes sticking out from the front end.

"Foon Lew, please, isn't there something cheaper you could do? I don't have five hundred dollars."

"Then you don't have no car."

Her redheaded parrot, Emerald, began to dance on his perch in his huge cage which she'd set on the garage floor. "You don't have no car. You don't have no car."

Honey leaned down to her bratty bird and pinged a fingernail against his cage. "Be quiet." Her voice was schoolteacher firm.

For once Emerald obeyed and pecked docilely at his perch.

Foon Lew jumped out from under her car. "You want car fixed?"

Honey had to pace for a minute. The shop was so noisy she could barely think. From one corner a radio blared rock and roll. The concrete floor was so littered with tools, she almost tripped over a tire iron. Tattered photos of Foon Lew and his sons on their fishing trips fluttered from tacks on the walls. The place reeked of grease and gasoline.

She stopped suddenly, opened her purse, and got out her checkbook to inspect her dismally low balance. The magazine with Joshua's photograph on the cover fell out. A faint tremor went through her when she found herself staring into his brilliant ice blue eyes. Just his picture brought a melting wave of emotion that was so strong she felt she could reach out and touch it.

Her trembling fingertips brushed his lips. Then she swallowed on a deep, anguished breath, slammed the magazine shut and threw it back into her purse. She was so upset, she forgot to check her bank balance.

"Okay, Foon Lew, you can fix the car."

He smiled, very pleased.

She would have to charge the repairs. The thought depressed her, but not as much as thoughts of Joshua did.

If only she could solve her problem with him as easily. Her shoulders slumped as she picked up Emerald's cage and walked outside to wait for Mario.

She had moved to Telegraph Hill to confront Joshua, to stop him. Not to hide from him. But for ten days she'd parked at the bottom of the hill and climbed the steep Filbert Steps, deliberately using the back way to avoid him.

And the reason she was scared was because she'd expected him to be a monster and she'd found out he wasn't.

Dear God. It was worse than that. She knew she was crazy, but everything about him drew her—both his fierce ruthlessness and his gentleness. One angry kiss and she'd wanted to stay in his arms forever.

She'd married Mike to prove she wasn't some spoiled, little rich girl. When he'd died she'd buried herself alive and pretended she was in love with his memory. Joshua made her feel wild and vibrant and young; he made her feel real—honest. One kiss and she knew how unbearably lonely her sham of a life was.

Honey had wanted to discover J. K. Cameron's human, vulnerable side. Instead she'd discovered her own.

Now her father wasn't the only one in danger of being destroyed by J. K. Cameron.

He was a seducer of women, and she ached for him to ply his skill. There was no way she could help her father without risking herself.

The roar of Mario's powerful motorcycle broke into her troubled thoughts. She stepped out onto the curb and flagged him.

Dust and bits of paper garbage swirled as the big bike braked, skidding to a terrifyingly abrupt stop one inch in front of her. Flying rocks hit Emerald's cage and the parrot danced and squawked in frantic terror.

Two teenage girls in miniskirts squealed delightedly, impressed.

"Show-off," Honey accused.

Mario ignored both the admiring girls and the parrot. He took off his helmet and flashed Honey his warmest male smile, as foolishly pleased with his dashing arrival as she was annoyed by it.

"What took you so long?" Honey asked, lifting Emerald's cage from the ground.

Mario was stunningly handsome, having inherited the dark good looks of his beautiful Italian mother. He had olive skin, a white-white smile and auburn hair. He was all too aware of the effect he had on most teenage girls. He shook his head and his thick mane of dark hair—which Honey was always after him to cut—shone with red highlights as it rippled to his shoulders.

"Sorry I'm late. I stopped off to get you something." He unzipped his leather jacket and pulled out a torn paper sack. "Hungry?"

When he handed her a freshly baked croissant, she realized she was starving. Only when she began to eat the moist warm bread, did he bother to smile nonchalantly at the girls.

"I ate three of them," he admitted which didn't surprise Honey. Mario had been eating like a horse since he was ten.

"Did you go to your classes today?"

Suddenly tense, he looked away uneasily. "Not to English."

"Mario! What am I going to do with you? You can't major in girls—" She bit back a nagging maternal lecture—one he'd heard already countless times and remembered her new plan to be more positive with him. "Thanks for the croissant and for coming so quickly. Now remember, you've got to drive slowly because of Emerald."

Mario relaxed and handed her a helmet. "Because of you too. Tell me, am I supposed to park at the bottom of the hill again tonight and walk up?"

The thought of running into Joshua filled her with dread as she reluctantly eased herself onto the back of Mario's bike. With one hand she held onto her purse and Emerald's cage. She slipped her other around Mario's waist.

"No." She bit her lip. "Let's park at the top."

His dark head jerked around. He whistled admiringly. "So, you're finally going to beard J. K. Cameron in his den?'' Mario stomped his boot down hard on the gas several times. ''Brave lady.''

The motorcycle roared and then rocked backward. Honey strangled a scream as the big bike jumped out in front of a garbage truck.

A taxi honked—swerving at the last moment.

Brave lady—Mario had that right.

A big black motorcycle revved its motor and shot past Joshua's low-slung sports car, streaking recklessly up the steep grade of Union Street.

''Idiots! Heather, you're not to be stupid like that girl and ride behind some leather-bound madman on a motorcycle!''

Heather who'd been sulking ever since Joshua had picked her up from school and taken her to the grocery store, snapped to attention. She was mad because he'd refused to let her have a friend over for the night.

The motorcycle stopped ahead of them at a red light. Joshua pulled up right behind the couple. The punk kept revving his motor. A pretty girl in a pink ruffled dress waved at him from the sidewalk.

Heather sighed. ''Anybody would ride behind him, Daddy. He's pure hunk. Wow!''

Pure hunk! Did Heather say things like that just to goad him? She didn't have the vaguest idea what guys like that were like. What they were after from girls. At least he hoped she didn't.

Instead of snapping back at Heather, Joshua disciplined himself to taut silence. His grip tightened on the leather steering wheel.

''Daddy—''

Joshua ignored his daughter. They were only a few blocks from the house. It seemed safer to let his gaze wander to the voluptuous hourglass figure of the girl in the green shorts on the back of the motorcycle.

GREAT FREE GAME *Play* 421

AND HIT THE JACKPOT!

Up to 4 free Silhouette Sensations, a Teddy and a Mystery Gift.

HOW TO PLAY 421

GREAT FREE GAME WITHOUT OBLIGATION TO BUY

1 With a coin, scratch the 3 silver dice opposite and discover in an instant whether you will receive... 2, 3 or maybe 4 free books and perhaps 1 or 2 extra gifts.

To claim the Jackpot, it is sufficient that your dice display 4, 2, 1 in any order.

2 When you return the card to us, you will receive as many free Silhouette Sensations as you have revealed and perhaps also a cuddly Teddy and a Mystery Gift.

3 If we don't hear from you within 10 days, we'll send you 4 brand new Silhouette Sensations for just £1.99 each every month. You will of course be under no obligation and may cancel or suspend your subscription at any time by simply dropping us a line.

Silhouette Reader Service, Freepost, PO Box 236, Croydon, Surrey. CR9 9EL.
Registered Office: 18-24 Paradise Road, Richmond, Surrey. TW9 1SR
Registered in England No. 100449

Here is the cuddly Teddy that you could receive if you hit the Jackpot!

If you claim your free books we'll also send you this appealing little Teddy absolutely FREE. Soft and cuddly, he's a favourite with everyone.

PLAY 421 WITH SILHOUETTE

Scratch the 3 silver dice and see instantly which gifts you will receive.

YES! Please send me all the free books and gifts to which I am entitled and reserve me a Reader Service subscription. I understand that I am under no obligation to purchase anything ever. If I do not wish to receive 4 brand new Silhouette Sensations every month for just £1.99 each, I simply write and let you know within 10 days. If I choose to subscribe to the Silhouette Reader Service I will receive 4 brand new Silhouette Sensations for just £7.96 every month. There is no charge for postage and packing. I may cancel or suspend my subscription at anytime simply by writing to you. The free books and gifts are mine to keep in anycase. *I am over 18 years of age.*

MS/MRS/MISS/MR _____

ADDRESS _____

_____

POSTCODE _____ SIGNATURE _____

2S4SS

4 FREE BOOKS + A CUDDLY TEDDY AND A MYSTERY GIFT.

4 FREE BOOKS + A CUDDLY TEDDY.

3 FREE BOOKS.

2 FREE BOOKS.

<u>**To claim**</u>
<u>**421 can be in any order**</u>

MAILING PREFERENCE SERVICE

THE SILHOUETTE GUARANTEE

- You will not have any obligation to buy.
- You have the right to cancel at any time.
- Your gifts remain for you to keep in any case.

Silhouette Reader Service
FREEPOST
P.O. Box 236
Croydon
Surrey
CR9 9EL

TEAR OFF AND POST THIS CARD TODAY!

A wisp of silky, shiny red hair fluttered from beneath her black helmet against her skintight green knit top. Why, the kook was even holding a huge bird cage.

There ought to be a law. There probably was—in California.

The light changed. The biker and his girl raced up the hill. Tires screaming, they made a quick left on Montgomery Street.

Joshua made the turn as well and was surprised when the biker parked in the vacant space right behind his own garage.

The girl got off first and set down the bird cage very carefully. She seemed a bit shaky as she stretched. She had shapely legs. Slowly she took off her helmet.

Her glorious tangled hair gleamed even redder in the afternoon sun. When her dazzling green eyes met his, she started.

He should have known.

Honey Rodriguez! He recognized her instantly, staring at her for a long, silent time until she looked agitated and a little afraid. Staring at her until the bones in his hard jawline bunched painfully. He forced his gaze away from her tight, flushed face.

He was hurt. And surprised. His profound disappointment felt like a fist jammed hard in the gut.

Almost immediately his unwanted emotions jelled into hatred for her and her muscle-bound punk.

She could do better, Joshua thought disgustedly as he punched his automatic door opener.

She could have had me.

No, she couldn't.

Joshua couldn't believe that he'd nobly resisted her because he'd thought her wholesome. Then she went for a kid, a punk biker.

The punk had taken off his helmet and was leaning over his bike. He had pretty hair that fell to his shoulders. His arms were brown and muscular. He appeared all of twenty-two.

"Boy!" Heather said. "Would you look at that?"

"What?"

"The hunk—cute, huh?"

Joshua felt fresh horror when he realized Heather was staring fixedly at Honey's muscle-bound companion.

"I wonder where they live, Daddy."

The punk was done with his close inspection of his motorcycle. He eased himself up off his muscular haunches. Heather waved wildly as he did so and he waved casually back, his dark eyes appraising. Then he gallantly picked up the heavy bird cage and put his other hand against Honey's back to escort her down the Filbert Steps.

Joshua bristled with rage at the way the punk had looked at Heather, at the way his possessive brown hand had nudged the small of Honey's spine in such a free-and-easy fashion, as if he thought nothing of touching her.

Joshua stepped on the gas and swerved into his garage, punching his automatic door opener to close the second they were inside.

He turned angrily, "You're to leave that guy alone, young lady. He's already got a girlfriend."

"She's way too old for him, Daddy."

"Sweetheart, you've got that right."

From his kitchen window, Joshua could see the bay. He also had a clear view of Honey's bedroom window.

Joshua wasn't looking at the bay.

Nor was he paying much attention to the filet mignon smoking on his grill. Nor to the two potatoes he was microwaving. Neither he nor Heather liked microwaved potatoes, but neither of them was much good at real cooking.

Joshua tore his furious gaze from Honey's window and went to his liquor cabinet where he poured himself a drink—straight scotch on ice. Lots of scotch; not much ice. The scotch had been a gift. He'd kept it around to serve his guests because he rarely allowed himself a drink.

Heather's wild rock music throbbed loudly two stories beneath him. Usually he hated her music. Tonight he liked the way it pulsed angrily in his blood.

The light in Honey's bedroom window came on, and as before Honey came to her window and stared up at Joshua's house for a long minute. Then the young punk joined her there. She turned slowly, touched his face with deep affection. They talked passionately for a long moment. A muscular brown arm pulled the shade down. And the shapes of their bodies lingering against the lighted shade drove Joshua mad.

Had she let that young punk move in with her?

Joshua downed his drink and poured himself another. He bolted it too, and it hit his empty stomach and burned through him like acid. He didn't like to drink because it unleashed his demons and made him remember his father and how bad things had gotten before he'd shot himself.

Her bedroom light stayed on. From time to time two shadows loomed against the shades. He tried not to imagine what they were doing in there together. It was very late when the light went out and Joshua tore his gaze from the window. By that time he had burned their steaks and had drunk way too much.

As he climbed the stairs to his office, he felt faintly sick.

And mean.

Very mean.

Eight

Joshua felt worse than mean the next morning. He was queasy from a hangover, and his brain felt on fire as he grabbed a cup of black coffee, the newspaper and the thick stack of legal papers dealing with the Wyatt chain that Midnight had prepared. Joshua dragged himself slowly up the winding stairs to his terrace.

Before Heather had moved in, he'd gone to his office Saturday mornings. Now he worked at home.

Heather's friend had come over anyway last night—right after dinner. Her father had driven off, dropping her at the door, suitcase in hand, before Joshua could object. Since he'd been in no condition to drive the stranded girl home, Heather had won another battle.

Joshua sat down at his patio table and scanned the newspaper. A headline at the bottom of the front page caught his attention.

Sam Douglas Shot
Lacy's husband.
Midnight's Lacy.

This could change everything.

Sam would be no loss to the world, Joshua thought bitterly. Then he thought of Lacy. Maybe she wasn't as cold and self-serving as Midnight believed. Maybe she'd really loved the bastard.

Joshua read the article. Most of it dealt with Douglas's accomplishments in the senate and the ongoing investigation into his murder; apparently his mentally disturbed son, Cole, was being sought for questioning. Only the last sentence made faint mention of the fact that the assets of the Douglas estate had been frozen while the Internal Revenue Service looked into Sam's financial affairs. There seemed to be some question concerning the misappropriation of money from Sam's campaign fund.

Lacy was the only woman Midnight had ever loved. She'd seemed like an angel until she'd jilted Midnight for Douglas. Midnight had never gotten over her.

Still, Joshua wondered if she needed anything. He would call. Midnight would be furious if he found out. Damn Midnight. Lacy had been Joshua's friend, too. She'd had it tough, the same as he and Midnight had. Maybe she'd had her reasons for doing what she'd done. Regardless, Joshua had to know if she needed anything.

He set the paper aside and began to flip through Midnight's highly detailed documents that dealt with the legal complexities that might arise over air rights, massive construction contracts, tax easements and disputes regarding the environmental consequences of several of Wyatt's hotels.

Joshua yawned. Midnight was thorough, too thorough at times. It would take all day to get through the papers, but the house was quiet. So was the neighborhood. Maybe he'd be able to concentrate.

But the girls got up—way before noon, hours earlier than he'd expected since they'd played music long after he'd gone to bed. All too soon the smell of chocolate-chip cookies baking in the oven distracted him.

Chocolate-chip cookies were his favorite. But for breakfast? He smiled in spite of himself, wondering if Heather was cooking them especially for him. With an effort he forced his attention back to his work.

A few seconds later a frustrated male yelp from the Filbert Steps distracted him again. When the yelp was followed by a crash, Joshua set down his coffee and leaned over the railing. An open guitar case was sliding down the wooden steps. Honey's punk boyfriend was leaping down the stairs three at a time like a great agile monkey.

Joshua snorted in cynical amusement and gulped down more coffee.

Then he saw the boy's weights, his big guitar and his drums stacked on Honey's front porch, and the hot black coffee ate into his empty stomach. The boy was moving everything he owned into Honey's apartment.

For a minute Joshua couldn't breathe. He felt an indefinable element of disappointment right before his temper skyrocketed out of control. .

Joshua leaned further over the railing and watched with a jealousy-crazed mind. Which was absolutely absurd. Joshua had told her he never wanted to see her again.

He clenched the wrought-iron railing. *He'd lied.*

He remembered Honey's marvelous eyes, her flame-silk hair, her lush body. It didn't seem to matter that she wasn't glamorous, that she couldn't possibly fit into his life. He wanted her.

He'd wanted to save her from himself. But not for some punk who would be even worse for her than Joshua was.

Honey's bedroom shade was still down. Joshua thought of her lying there in tangled sheets, her fiery hair disheveled from lovemaking, still asleep, waiting for. . . that boy.

Joshua's mouth went hard and thin.

His headache sharpened and he felt even sicker at his stomach. He was about to grab his papers and go inside when Honey's mongrel cat scampered up the fire escape and leapt out onto the table, plopping himself squarely on top of them. Mr. Right flattened his ears and asserted his squatter's rights with an arrogant meow.

Joshua scowled down at the scruffy animal. The big cat's green rhinestone collar sparked back at him as brightly and defiantly as Honey's eyes.

Joshua was poised to rake the foul beast off the table when he heard Heather's bright giggle from the steps below.

Joshua raced to the balcony edge again. To his horror he saw that Heather and her friend were knocking on Honey's front door. The girls were scantily dressed in bright miniskirts and holding a sumptuous platter of *his* homemade cookies.

Interested, the long-haired punk swaggered slowly up the stairs and joined them on the porch. He set his empty guitar case down beside his drums and took a cookie. Several cookies. As he chewed, he eyed the girls with equal enthusiasm. He obviously had abundant, voracious appetites. Oozing charm, he leaned closer and said something that made both girls giggle. Then he held the door open, and the three of them disappeared inside.

Rage consumed Joshua.

It was bad enough that Honey was wasting herself on a boy who was obviously going nowhere. But Joshua wasn't about to allow his daughter to do the same.

There was nothing left to do but go after Heather.

Joshua pounded loudly on the wooden door. Mr. Right howled with equal determination. The damned beast had had the audacity to follow him.

From behind the door Joshua heard the soft padding of footsteps. Then the front door was gently opened. He caught the faint odor of fresh paint.

Honey's big, surprised green eyes met his. "Hi," she said, smiling, before she panicked and backed away from him.

Joshua drew in a deep breath, suddenly rigidly ill at ease too.

Honey stood barefooted in the doorway, masses of gleaming wet hair flowing like a river of flame to her shoulders. She was wearing an emerald-colored robe that came to her ankles, and she smelled deliciously of perfumed soap and shampoo. In one hand she held a half-eaten green bean which she was offering to a gigantic green parrot with a red head. The bird was prancing excitedly on her shoulder. In her other hand she held the last bit of a chocolate-chip cookie.

Damp, fiery tendrils were glued to Honey's forehead; more of them clung to her neck. She was so enchantingly sexy looking, so fresh and lovely, Joshua had to force himself to remember he was not glad to see her, that he had come for the sole purpose of laying claim to his wayward daughter.

"I see you've brought Mr. Right," she murmured. "I saw him climbing up your fire escape."

The parrot nibbled at the bean and then spit out his bite onto the threshold and shook his head disgustedly. The cat sniffed at it with equal disgust.

"Oh, dear," Honey said, concerned. Then to Joshua: "Emerald's been very sick. He has stress molt from the move."

Joshua warmed to the bird. *So, the parrot didn't like the bike or the biker, either.*

"I've been cooking all his favorite foods—pinto beans, corn—"

The parrot strained toward her cookie, and she gave it to him.

"I guess I didn't need that anyway." Honey smiled at her bird and then looked up appealingly at Joshua. "Why are you here? I thought we were off-limits to each other."

"This isn't a friendly visit," he said, remembering why he'd come.

Her eyes widened again with fear.

"Oh. Then I'd better take my cat and shut the door."

Joshua held the door open with his hand. While she tried to force it closed, Mr. Right dashed inside. Honey looked startled. The bird began to squawk.

Realizing her strength was nothing against Joshua's, Honey let her hand fall from the door. "What do you want then?"

His insolent gaze devoured her body and then returned to her face. She was paler. Her wide eyes stared uncertainly into his. She looked like a doe at bay, fearful that the predator was closing in for the kill.

"I came after my daughter," Joshua said grimly.

Honey sagged against a wall, a little of her tension easing. "Oh. The girls came down to welcome us into the neighborhood. They took Mario on a walk."

"So, his name's Mario?" Joshua sneered, coming nearer. "Mario what?"

Her voice quivered. "Rodriguez."

Joshua towered over her. "The same as yours?" His gaze fell to her left hand. For the first time he saw the wedding band glimmering there.

"His mother was Italian. His father, Hispanic." Her frightened whisper was barely audible. "Sometimes that adds up to a volatile combination."

"Rodriguez—you're not married to that macho punk?" Joshua's voice had grown even colder.

Honey laughed shakily, beginning to understand him at last, but too incredulous to take him seriously. "Married—to Mario? Don't be absurd. He may look mature, but he's still very young."

"Oh, so he just lives with you?"

Puzzled, she looked closely at Joshua. "You think that Mario and I—" she broke off awkwardly, confused, distraught.

"Naughty boy," screamed the bird.

"Excuse me." Honey's voice was quick and urgent as she dashed toward the bird's cage. "When Emerald says that, he needs to go back to his perch over newspaper."

The bird jumped dutifully onto his perch.

"Why does he live with you?" Joshua had followed her inside. His hard eyes slid over her with fresh contempt.

Her back was to him. "Who? Emerald?" Her voice was too casual. "I told you—I like pets."

"Mario! Damn it. Why does he live here?"

She turned around very slowly. "Because he's my stepson, and I've taken care of him since he was a little boy," she said quietly. "My husband, his father, died two years ago. Mario's had some problems. If I hadn't kept him, he would be out on the street. I know he looks kind of wild, and his sole ambition right now is to be a rock star. But if you look past the bike and the long hair, if you can stand the drums and his friends, he's a terrific kid."

"What were the two of you doing in your bedroom till all hours last night?"

"Were you spying on me?"

His question was louder. "What were you doing?"

"See for yourself!" Furious, she spun away from him and opened her bedroom door.

The scent of new paint filled the room. Joshua saw fresh white walls, apple green windowsills and baseboards and a protective layer of paint-splattered newspapers spread over her bedroom floor. His eyes returned to her indignant white face and lingered there for the space of another heartbeat.

Slowly his anger began to drain away. "You were painting—"

She pulled the door closed.

"You look too young to be his stepmother."

"I was too young when I married Mike."

Feeling very foolish, Joshua sank down on her couch. Even though he was too embarrassed to look at her, at the same time he was wild with relief.

Not knowing what to say or what to do, he studied the scuffed floor for a long, awkward moment. He had grossly misjudged her. There was nothing to do but to collect Heather and go.

Honey's soft voice filled the tense silence. "Mario has girlfriends his own age—lots of them. I think you owe me and him an apology."

Joshua started guiltily. At the same time he was non-plussed that she had assumed the upper hand so quickly.

She came to him and leaned down, her sweet-smelling body temptingly, dangerously near. "It was obvious you were thinking the worst of me."

He didn't bother to deny it, but he didn't bother to apologize either.

"I'm surprised you were so morally outraged," she said, needling him and bending even nearer. So near, he caught the scent of jasmine and fresh soap. "I mean you're the last person I would expect to be shocked by the thought of a woman taking in a younger lover."

"I wasn't upset." He kept his black head lowered and ground out the lie harshly.

"Then why did you barge in on me with that I-could-kill look on your face?"

"Because I was worried about my daughter."

"So, you came down here...only because of your daughter? That's probably why you just happened to notice that Mario and I were busy in my bedroom for hours last night."

"Damn it. Why are you pushing me? I was determined to stay away from you. I know you're wrong for me, and I'm all wrong for you. You know it, too."

"Yes," she said in a sad, small voice that somehow he knew would haunt him long after he'd gone. "Yes, I know it, too."

But on some deep level she wasn't so wrong. And she made him feel crazy with the way she was standing so close to him wearing that robe and maybe nothing underneath it. So crazy he couldn't stop himself from reaching up and putting his hands around the back of her waist. His jealousy was gone, but in its place was a mushrooming need.

Her muscles tensed. She drew in a deep, desperate breath, but the light pressure of his fingers around her waist was so gentle and undemanding she didn't struggle.

"Relax," he murmured, anguished longing in his tense voice. "Just relax."

"That's hard to do around you."

Slowly, silently he drew her closer and buried his head against her belly. For a long moment he pressed his face hopelessly against the soft green robe that covered her stomach.

He felt the delicious heat of her. Her sweetness enveloped him and filled him with fresh longing. He ached to pull her down on his lap. To kiss her. To do more.

Gingerly one of her hands came down to caress his thick black hair. Warm fingertips moved hesitantly over his brow.

"Joshua, I wanted to see you, too," she admitted in a low, shaken tone that sounded sad and lost. "I look up at your house sometimes, too."

She was every bit as afraid as he was.

"I'm sorry," he said. "For what I said. For what I did."

"For what you thought," she whispered.

"For what I thought," he admitted.

She laid her hand against his cheek for a long moment. Her fingers were warm and light, irresistible. He turned his head and blew a kiss into her open palm. She jumped back, startled, as if he'd jolted her with an electric current. He felt a thrill in the pit of his stomach—as if they'd connected in some body-to-soul way.

"You probably date someone beautiful," Honey said in a small voice.

Joshua looked up at her for the first time. "Not any more."

Honey stood very still. "Why not?"

"Because I don't want to."

"So, what do you tell a girl you don't want any more?"

"Goodbye."

Honey's exquisite eyes were fastened on his dark face.

"Look," he muttered guiltily. "She wasn't hurt. We weren't in love. She understood."

"You don't seem like the kind of man to do without a woman for long."

"I don't do without anything I need—for long. Does that bother you?"

"A lot of things about you bother me," she said.

"Yeah . . . I hate myself most of the time too." He got up slowly to go. "When Heather comes back, tell her to come home."

Honey nodded stiffly. "You don't have to worry about Heather and Mario. She's not his type—I mean not that way. He goes for more sophisticated girls."

Not his type. Joshua's gaze locked with Honey's and he felt his blood heat. *Somehow that was hardly reassuring.*

Joshua was at the door when Honey awkwardly switched the subject. "I—I was wondering if there's someone new in your life. I mean . . . a new woman?"

He shot her a quick look, and she blushed, as if aghast at her boldness.

Her interest in him was so transparent that he couldn't help smiling faintly. "I'm afraid there is."

"What's she like?"

In the soft light Honey's eyes sparkled with fire. Her silky, damp hair clung to her graceful neck.

He bared his teeth in a seductive smile. "She's very lovely—in her own way."

"Who's the lucky girl?" came that sweet, sad, lost voice.

Simone's words. They made him hesitate. "Don't you know?" Before he could think, he crossed the small room in a single stride and folded her hand into his.

Their fingers touched, mating hotly like fire and water shot through with electricity. When he pulled her to him, he felt her shiver. He wanted to kiss her hard on the mouth, to open her robe and kiss her everywhere, to taste hot, voluptuous woman flesh. But she had some quality that made him feel vastly out of his element, that made him go much slower than he wanted. So, he just looked at her delectable lips for a long moment and then into her eyes.

"Do you sail, Ms. Rodriguez? I keep a boat at the yacht club—"

"Mrs. . . . I told you before that I'm a widow." She turned her face away as if the thought of her dead husband still upset her.

"Yes . . . I remember that now." Gently Joshua touched her chin and tipped her face nearer his, so that he felt her breath, hot against his skin. "Are you still grieving? Is that why—"

Her long lashes flickered. Guilt darkened her eyes. "I haven't dated anyone. Not since my husband's death." She was trembling. The fear was back in her voice. "Mike is only one of the reasons why I don't think we should become involved."

Joshua lifted her left hand and studied her ring silently for a long time.

"Right," he whispered bitterly, letting her go. "I shouldn't have asked you."

In that first moment of total rejection he felt hollow.

Women had said no to him before, but it had never felt this awful.

Thank God his pride saved him from begging her or from saying something utterly stupid. Thank God he just walked silently toward the door and shoved it open.

A cool, damp wind blew inside.

Her parrot squawked. Honey called Joshua's name, but he went out onto the porch. Up the wooden stairs. Away from her.

It was only later that he was aware of the awful expanding emptiness inside him, of the deep and burning need for this woman that was so all-consuming there was no room in his heart for anything else except the bleak, cold knowledge that she didn't want him.

Nine

Joshua's throat was dry and painfully tight as he edged restlessly nearer the window of Tito Pascale's new apartment to check to see if that skinny kid he'd paid to keep an eye on his car was still there.

His car was his escape out of there.

The kid was leaning against a lamppost sucking on a Popsicle in the foggy street. Joshua's elegant black sports car was still down there. So was the litter and filth and the broken glass on the sidewalk and in the gutters.

His old neighborhood. The fog made it seem worse. Why the hell had he come—even for this brief, perfunctory visit? Just the short drive through the narrow dilapidated streets had brought the past back, brought the terror of that time when he'd felt he was less than nothing—when there had been a threatening thug on every street corner ready to take him on.

Even now, when he knew he could return to the wealth and security of his new life, he felt that some part of him had never escaped. For an instant he was so harrowed by the old trapped hopelessness, he felt almost laid naked by it. He remembered the terrible time after his mother had died—the foster homes, running away, living in filthy back alleys for days at a time. Would he ever really get away from his past?

Joshua gripped the freshly painted windowsill and then forced himself to release it. He dusted his hands on his jeans.

Idiot! He was safe now, or at least as safe as anyone could be. He had everything he wanted.

Then he thought of Honey, her fiery loveliness, her mystery, her passion. Most of all he remembered her rejection. His mouth thinned in a tight, unhappy line.

He forced his mind from her, back to the Pascales. At least they seemed happy with the way the interior of their apartment had turned out. The place was small, but it was clean. And they were safe now from the man who had threatened them.

Joshua had loaned Tito the money for the new paint and furniture. He'd dealt with the stepfather by paying him to leave San Francisco for good, by giving him a chance to start over in Vegas and warning him not to come back.

"I've gotta go now," Joshua said abruptly to Tito and Mrs. Pascale as he moved away from the window to the door.

They joined him there, clinging to each other, their faces shining with happiness and hope and pride in their new home. Joshua grimaced at the thought that Midnight would probably ride him forever about this and might expect more good deeds. But for the moment, Joshua didn't care.

"We'll never be able to thank you." Mrs. Pascale pressed Joshua's hand as he opened the door.

Joshua felt embarrassed by their gratitude. He hadn't done much, but then a little went a long way down here. To Tito he said, "Any more problems—you come to me. No more fights. And you enroll in night school like you promised."

"Yes, Mr. Cameron."

The Pascales shut the door slowly, smiling after him until he reached the stairs.

After the new brightness of their apartment, the hallway seemed damp and crumbling. In the dim light of a bare low-wattage bulb, Joshua saw the depressing gloom of peeling paint and moldy wallpaper. He strode carefully because of the sagging wooden stairs. The banister was loose. On a lower floor a shadow moved in a darkened corner and Joshua tensed, instantly alert to danger. He sighed with relief when he saw it was only a rat skittering across the floor.

Joshua remembered the congestion of his childhood, the lack of facilities, the cold and the unreliable water supply, the rats, the roaches, the indifference of landlords, teachers and the outside world.

Most of all he remembered the way his mother had given up and died—four years after his father. After that Joshua had lived on hate. He might drive away today, back to his safe, clean neighborhood, but he knew that deep down he could never really get out—and all because of Hunter Wyatt.

His thoughts were black as he stepped out into the chill of the foggy street. The last person he expected or wanted to see was Honey Rodriguez driving slowly by in her chartreuse Bomb looking for a parking place.

He stared after the green abomination with surprise and fury and not a little fear. Then he started running after her.

Was she crazy to come down here alone? She was driving so slowly, he easily caught her. *Anybody could have.* He lunged out in front of her bumper and slammed his hands—palm open—against her fender.

She braked and honked. When he yanked her unlocked passenger door open, a chemistry text tumbled out. He caught it before it hit his foot and heaved it onto the back seat, which was messily crammed with a dozen boxes, filled with books, manila folders and student notebooks.

In her soft green knit blouse and skirt, Honey looked pretty amidst the jumble of boxes. Too pretty to be down here alone.

He was curious, but more than curious he was possessively angry. "What the hell are you doing here? And why the hell don't you lock your car doors?"

Her green eyes flashed back at him. "Nice to see you too, Joshua."

"I asked you a question," he growled.

She lifted her chin and stared defiantly down its pert length at him. "I'm going to my school to store some stuff that I don't have room for in my apartment."

"Where is your school?"

"If you must know, it's right around the corner."

"You teach down here? This is a dangerous neighborhood."

"It's not *that* dangerous. I've worked here ten years. A lot of nice people live here."

He grimaced. "I grew up here."

"See what I mean about nice people," she said lightly.

"I'll drive you to your school."

"The last thing I need is you around, acting like everyone you see is a criminal."

But before she could finish he had walked around her car, opened her other door and gotten in.

When she threw up her hands in a gesture of mock surrender and scooted out of his way, he smiled grimly across at her. "What if I was a bad guy? You'd be in real trouble."

Every sensory receptor in his body flashed red hot at her languid look.

"Maybe I already am," she said softly.

"You should lock your doors," he warned gruffly, snapping his own lock. "I mean it."

"Are you always so sure you know everything?"

The instant he slammed his door, he knew he was in just as much danger as she was. He caught the scent of jasmine and felt a primitive, hot-blooded response at finding himself locked into such a tiny space alone with her.

And she knew it.

His hands gripped the steering wheel. "So why the hell do you have to teach these kids, Honey?" he asked bitingly, keeping his fierce eyes on the street because it was too dangerous to look at her.

"They need me more than some kids do. Because there's a losing battle going on in the streets of our big cities and in their schools, and I'm trying to save as many kids as I can. It's hard, more frustrating than I can say, but someone has to show them there's a way out."

She'd hit a raw nerve with that one. He stomped down hard on the accelerator. "Honey, there's no way out. And there's little chance that someone like you could show them the way if there was."

"You got out," she whispered.

He laughed derisively. "Did I?"

"You're successful."

"It's all surface. I'm still running, Honey. Make no mistake about that. And hating." He eased the car around the corner. "The hate stays forever."

She pointed at a dingy red two-story building on their right. "There's my school."

"There's a parking place."

"It's too small."

"No problem. The one thing San Francisco will teach you is how to park." He touched the turn signal. "Nobody ever really gets out," he persisted as, despite her objections, he began the seesaw process of parallel parking her large car into the tiny space on the steep hill. "Nobody. Do you understand me? The ones that do—they're like me—they just pretend they do." He paused, concentrating on backing the car for a moment.

She gasped as her fender slid past the bumper of the car in front of them with less than a millimeter to spare. "You almost hit him!"

"A long time ago I thought I could," he continued. "But all the self-hate, the despair, the misery, the desire for vengeance against anyone you can find to blame—it sticks. It goes deep, deeper than anything else. Deeper than all the nice things that happen to you. You don't ever forget places like this. You take them with you. No matter how high you climb, you can't escape it. And you can't ever fit in anywhere else. I believe in hate, not love. In saving myself, not others. In taking all I can and giving nothing to anyone. People like me keep people like these down here, but if these people had the chance they'd stomp on me too."

"Joshua, you don't have to be like that."

She was an idealist. You couldn't reason with idealism.

He put the car in park and set the emergency brake. "Feed that line of garbage to your students, Honey." He cut the engine and smiled. "I told you the space was big enough."

She wasn't about to feed his ego. "Barely... I do try to encourage them."

Two lean, ill-kempt teenage boys with narrow, restless eyes rode aimlessly down the middle of the street on battered bicycles. When they saw Honey, they waved and she waved back.

Bitter memories from his youth made Joshua frown. "But I bet the kids know better?"

"Some of them think they do, the way you say you do. They act tough, the way you try to act tough."

Did she think this was a game? Furious, he tore the keys from the ignition and dropped them into her outstretched palm, careful to avoid touching her. "It's not an act. You leave your real life somewhere else when you come here. That's something none of us can ever do."

Her trembling fingers closed around the keys. "I take this home with me at nights, too, Joshua."

"You have a choice though. I don't."

Careful to keep her eyes lowered, she edged nearer her door.

Away from him.

He wanted to seize her, to pull her back. To forget this ridiculous too-personal conversation.

"Maybe you're not so tough, Joshua. Maybe you're just scared like a lot of the kids I teach. Maybe you just want love and safety... and..."

Yeah. He'd wanted those things. He still did. His stomach twisted in knots.

She touched his shoulder hesitantly, and her unexpected warmth sent a shaft of desire through him.

"Maybe it's not too late... even for you, Joshua," she said ever so softly.

He seized her wrist. When she recoiled, he let her go in disgust.

"And who's going to give them to me—you? You can't wait to get away from me."

"Maybe if you weren't biting my head off at every opportunity, I wouldn't feel that way." She leaned quietly toward him again, and he was aware of her dizzying scent as she picked up her purse and put her keys inside it. "Thanks for parking my car. And thanks for the dog-eat-dog pep talk." She bent down, her breasts swaying against soft cotton. "I guess it's goodbye for now. I've got real work to do. I'm sure you do too."

He felt on fire with frustrated longing. "Yeah, you're out to save the world and I'm out to destroy it." He gazed cynically at the filthy neighborhood. "Looks like I'm a hell of a lot better at my job than you are at yours."

She picked up a heavy box of files from the floorboard and put her hand on the door handle. Hesitating, she forced herself to look at him.

His blue eyes were so savage and hot she gasped.

"Joshua," she said faintly. "It's easy to give up on life. That happens everywhere, not just down here. You could change, if you really wanted to. But only you can do it. Maybe you already have and you don't like it. Quit feeding your hatred and your desire for vengeance. You're a very talented man. Live your life positively."

Hatred and vengeance were the last things on his mind at the moment. Her red hair was on fire. So were her eyes. *So was he.* He wanted to drag her into his arms and silence her with his lips.

"You make it sound so easy, but you don't know what you're talking about," he muttered, struggling to sound coherent. "The world's full of two kinds of people—winners and losers. Quit wasting your time on losers."

"Which kind are you?"

He stared at her hard, almost hating her because he'd sworn he'd leave her alone.

"Why do you enjoy holding such a cruel view?" she asked, misinterpreting his expression. "Not just of this place but of yourself? Is it so wrong to believe we can make the world a better place if we try? That we can be better people if we try to be? That we can make neighborhoods like this safer places?"

"It's not wrong," he said in a hoarse, low tone. "But it's cruel to feed it to kids down here."

"Cruel? How?"

"Why feed people dreams of a fairy-tale world they can never be a part of and wouldn't like if they were? They're better off the way they are."

"Then why were you so determined to get out?"

"It was easier for me because there was a man I was determined to destroy." His mouth was drawn into a grim, forbidding line. "I couldn't take him on when I was poor, because I didn't have the right weapons to finish him off."

She had begun to shiver, and he realized he'd gone too far. All she said was a quick, "I've gotta go."

But he knew she meant—goodbye for good.

It was for the best.

The hell it was.

Before she could open her door, he dashed around to her side and helped her out. "You little fool, do you think I'm going to leave you down here alone?"

"Really, Joshua. I don't want you here. Not after—" Her face was very white, her tone cool, while his own heart was pounding crazily. "I mean I've got to carry all this stuff inside and store it. It's going to take a while. I'm sure you're way too busy getting revenge on the world to have the time to help me.''

He seized the box she was holding. "I'll make the time."

She tried to wrest her box back. "Look, this is ridiculous. I want you to go."

"I told you I'm not leaving you down here alone."

Her green eyes smoldered. "There's no winning against you, is there?"

"Not when I really want something," he told her quietly, a hot challenge in the dark look he gave her.

"Look, I thought I made myself clear Saturday—"

"Very clear!" he snapped, remembering her rejection. "Don't flatter yourself. You're in no danger from me—not in that way." *Liar*.

She picked up another box and marched away from him in hostile silence. He smiled grimly, stacked several more boxes on top of the one he had and followed her inside.

He was setting his stack down on her desk in the front of her empty classroom and about to go after more, when her quivery voice stopped him.

"I'm surprised you'd even care I was here. I would have thought that by now you'd already have a new girlfriend."

His gaze jerked swiftly to her white face. "So—what if I do?"

She arched an eyebrow and tried to look merely casually interested, but she was too still.

He felt a bolt of warm excitement, a half-formed hope as he hesitated before replying. "Would you care?" he demanded arrogantly.

"No, I—I was hoping you'd found someone—so you would leave me alone." But her lashes fluttered and she wouldn't look at him.

He felt a powerful hunger to go to her, to touch her, to pull her into his arms and assure her there was no one else. But it was smarter to let her wonder. So he left her inside her classroom and went out to bring more of her things in. It took her an hour to arrange everything in storage the way she wanted it.

When they had finished, she sat down at her desk to write
in her calendar. He tried to act casual as well and went out
and got a drink of water from the water fountain in the hall.

She made the mistake of following him.

She stood right behind him, so close that he felt her
body's warmth, so close he caught the smell of her fragrant
perfume. When he was done, she took her turn. He watched
her bend gracefully over the porcelain fountain. Sunlight
slanted through a high window onto her fiery hair, which fell
all over her shoulders. He watched the water glisten against
her soft, wet lips. He studied the way green cotton molded
her body.

The fierce need to touch her was too much. His hand shot
around her and he eased her against his body. Her soft
warmth set him on fire. When she gasped, he leaned over
her and whispered into her ear, "Baby, if I forgive you for
last Saturday, will you date me?"

She tried to jerk herself free of him, but he held her fast,
liking the way her every movement ignited sparks in him.

"You said I was in no danger—if I let you stay."

"If that's the only lie we ever tell each other, we'll be
luckier than most," he murmured, savoring the sheer, un-
adulterated pleasure of holding her.

She paled. His hands tightened, and he pulled her harder
into his body. Her lush, warm legs slid against tough thigh
muscles. She set him aflame.

"I'm not skinny. I know you like skinny—"

He was blistering hot. "Hey, I like you," he whispered.
"You feel good. Too good."

"Joshua, no," she murmured breathlessly.

"Someday I want you to say yes in that same breathy
voice."

"I never will."

He laughed knowingly. "I'm too conceited to believe
that."

His amusement seemed etched in every carved line of his
face, but he let her go—unfolding his big hands slowly.
When she was free, she stood trembling for a long mo-

ment. There was no sound other than his own pounding pulse. Then she scampered away from him into her classroom. She was gathering her purse and her notebooks from her desk when he stepped inside.

He stood grimly at the door, blocking her only escape. Carelessly he flipped the dead bolt. Her horrified little cry echoed in every corner.

He laughed softly. Their eyes met across the shadowy room. Hers were wide and alarmed; his burned with a hot, expectant light.

"Joshua, no—"

He strode toward her. "Yes."

"Not now. Not here."

"Now," he whispered huskily. "Here."

Even as she began backing away, he stalked her, grinning when she darted this way and that, trapping her easily against the blackboard behind her desk.

"You're through running," he rasped. "So am I."

"Are you out of your mind?" She tried to twist out of his grasp.

His iron fists closed over her wrists and he lifted them high against cold green slate. Chalk dust crumbled to the floor. "I told you this was a dangerous neighborhood."

She moaned and turned her head away. "You only want to go to bed with me."

He smiled insolently. "Would that be so awful?" His deep voice had softened dangerously.

Panicked, she kicked at his shins, little knowing that every time her leg rubbed his powerful thighs and torso she sent fresh waves of hot excitement charging through him until he was so wild it seemed unbelievable he could want any woman this much.

His whole body tingled. "Baby, if you're smart, you'll stop doing that," he muttered in a fierce, shaking voice. "You're just turning me on."

She stopped instantly, but his body was already as hot and hard as a brick fired in a kiln. His uneven breaths were more ragged than hers.

"You and your materialistic, self-serving values and your quest for revenge are everything I've spent my life running away from. I never want to see you again. Do you understand me?" she cried, her own breath heavy and hot and sweet against his throat.

"You think you're so noble, so different from me," he taunted, pulling her closer, so that his muscled body seared her softer flesh. "But, Honey, I wonder." He threaded his fingers through her hair and forced her face nearer his, so near that her lips were a mere fraction of an inch from his. "I think you're as attracted by my dark side as you are repelled by it. You get a vicarious thrill out of slumming down here with people who are toughened because they have to live on the edge."

"No." But she was breathless. Her eyes were glued to his lips as if she were mesmerized. She drew her tongue cautiously along the edge of her parched mouth.

"No?" He laughed. His warm fingers touched her throat and her fluttering heartbeat there. "Your pulse is beating even faster than mine. You like this jungle, Honey. You're too real yourself, too alive to be the saintly type you pretend you are. You like the jungle wildness in me. Because it's in you too."

"Let me go."

"Besides, if I'm such a lost soul, and you come to the jungle to save souls, maybe you can save mine."

"I want you out of my life." But when she looked at him, the hunger in her gentle eyes sent a different message.

"Do you?" His fingers moved down her throat. With expert ease, he began to unbutton her green knit blouse. His hand slid inside her lacy brassiere to cup her breast, to knead a velvet nipple until it grew pert and taut. He laughed again at her body's quick, involuntary response. "I think you're a liar. If you really wanted me out of your life, you wouldn't have moved onto my hill when I warned you not to."

"*Your* hill? You arrogant, conceited..." At his slow, erotic kneading of her nipple, her voice grew faint, dying away.

"I never pretended I was perfect."

"Please—don't—" she muttered shudderingly as his hand moved over her belly and he molded her body to his. Frantically she dug her fingers into the hard muscles of his arms and strained to push him away. And yet he knew she wasn't really fighting him.

"You should have escaped when I gave you the chance." He felt hot, hard and pulsating. His nostrils flared. "You know the kind of man I am. Sooner or later, I always take what I want. And I want you."

"You don't. Not really."

"Yes. I do." He lowered his black head toward hers. She would have turned away, but he caught her chin and held it still. Then his mouth came down on hers, his tongue sliding across the soft fullness of her lower lip, demanding admittance. After that his ravishing kiss seemed endless to them both. With his lips and tongue, he took possession of her mouth, of her.

"You're beautiful, so beautiful," he whispered. "You can't fight me any more than I can fight you."

Their mouths joined again. Their tongues mated. Slowly, surely, his deepening kisses saturated her with the same fiercely hot rapture that ensnared him.

"Joshua. I feel like I'm throwing my whole life away, but I can't stop myself."

"I'm not going to hurt you," he whispered.

Her hands touched his raven hair uncertainly. She ran a caressing fingertip down the hard length of his cheek and jaw. Then she locked her arms around his neck and arched her body willingly into his powerful muscular frame as if she craved the same total oneness with him that he craved from her. She was with him on this ravaging journey—all the way.

Her response made him hungrier than he had ever been, and his mouth left her lips to kiss the rest of her face, her brows, her nose, her ears. Then he pulled her soft knit blouse apart and brought his head lower, suckling each voluptuous breast hungrily in turn, tasting honey soft, ripe flesh, until she was as wildly hot and breathless as he, until he knew nothing mattered to her more than his touches and kisses, until he was sure that she was filled with the same keen delight and exquisite excitement that filled him.

A mad darkness seemed to swirl around them. He was whispering things to her he had never said to any woman. He was feeling emotions no other woman had ever made him feel. Honey tried to speak, but his mouth closed over hers again. And as he pulled her down, down into that thick blackening, destroying whirl, he sensed that he had lost something of himself, too.

"I'm afraid," she said.

Strangely, he was too.

Their hotly fused, shaking bodies slid against the blackboard wall to the floor. Joshua knew a wild need to have her, to take her.

To conquer. To possess. To make her his. Forever.

Now. On the cold tiled floor of her empty classroom.

As he held her crushed to him on that hard floor, she sighed in soft surrender. He felt himself shudderingly near the edge—almost crashing over it as if he were being swept in the violent surge of an avalanche.

"Do you know something crazy?" she whispered gently, her big eyes glowing with a strange, rapturous light. "I've never felt like this about anybody. I'm afraid of you, but I'm more afraid that I'll never feel like this again."

Use or be used. Take or be taken.

She was sweet. She almost made him feel sweet when she looked at him like that.

His old philosophy jarred.

His hands retraced the path from her shoulders to her breasts, and her little shiver of delight thrilled him too.

Outside two kids screamed and began to bounce a basketball against the brick wall. Joshua heard the ball thud again and again. At first the dull, repetitive vibrations seemed far away and no part of his hot, sensual mood. Only slowly did that change.

He pulled so hard at her blouse that a button came loose. He watched it roll across the floor, and as he did he became aware of what he was doing, of how hard and cold the floor they were lying on was, of how rough he had been. He opened his eyes wider and saw the badly scarred legs of Honey's big wooden desk, the rusty casters of her chair. He forced his gaze up to the dusty blackboard, to the tattered edges of the world map that hung on the opposite wall.

She was an idealistic teacher who wanted to help poor kids. This was her classroom. He admired her.

He picked up her button and turned it over in his palm. The cold reality of what he had done, of what he was about to do, sank in.

As he looked down at her, he thought her lovely with her eyes passionately closed, with her lashes still against her sensually flushed cheeks, with her delicious lips expectantly pursed. Her soft breathing was irregular. For a moment he watched the gentle rise and fall of her breasts. How trustingly innocent she seemed.

A great tenderness welled up inside him. She was too lovely to take, to exquisite to use.

He didn't want to stop. He wanted to make wild, violent love to her. He couldn't, because she meant more to him than he understood.

He kissed her fiercely and then gently. When her whole body arced with abandoned longing, her hands tightening on his body, he knew that she was as highly roused as he. But she was too sweet to defile on the floor of her empty classroom.

She began undoing the buttons of his shirt. His hand closed over hers, stopping her. For a long moment neither of them moved.

Then he tore himself free and lunged a safe distance away from her to lay doubled over against her desk, his fists clenched, panting in an unreal state of tortured frustration and pain. At the same time he felt a burning desire to crawl back and take her.

If she'd come to him, if she'd touched him or spoken to him, he would have lost all control.

Instead she leaned against the tiled beige wall beneath the blackboard, staring at him with blazing hurt eyes while her nerveless, shaking fingers slowly buttoned her blouse and fumbled to smooth her tangled hair.

Then she got up like some bewildered wild thing and ran from the room—from him—as if she were suddenly terrified for her life.

Ten

She was terrified of him. Because she was so on fire for him.

Honey's heart beat in sharp, pounding little throbs that seemed to vibrate painfully in her temples and fingertips. Two hours had passed since she'd run from Joshua, but the memory of the way she'd willingly ended up on the floor beneath him burned her with shame.

Even in the silent peace of her own home eating her favorite kind of chocolate bar for comfort, she felt threatened. Both from Joshua and from herself. From the knowledge that the sacred memory of Mike's love would never be enough to satisfy her again. She wanted more.

She wanted Joshua. She wanted to soothe away his anger and his pain, to bring out his gentleness, to know the wild thrill of his passionate lovemaking.

Why had he let her go? He had told her the kind of man he was. Had his punishing kisses been nothing more than a warning? Was he giving her one last chance to escape?

It was a lazy, ordinary summer afternoon. The fog had vanished, and the bay was glistening sapphire blue in the

sunshine. On his perch near a screened window, Emerald
preened green wing feathers, stopping occasionally to stare
at the tiny new apples dangling temptingly from a low limb
by the window. Tail flicking, Mr. Right was watching Emerald through slitted eyes from the windowsill. Mario was
outside on the porch tuning his guitar, getting ready to sing
something he had written to Heather and to Tina, one of his
girlfriends.

Honey was wondering how she could want a man who
intended to destroy her father. A man who would deliberately destroy her, too, when he discovered who she was.

When her teakettle whistled, she gathered her two candy
wrappers for the trash and got up from her couch like a
zombie. Clumsily she brewed tea in her favorite china cup
and went into her bedroom where she set it down and forgot to drink it.

She looked out her window up at Joshua's house and her
eyes filled with a sort of shrinking dread. He was standing
on his terrace, his long legs spread widely apart, as he stared
down at her, his blue eyes hotly searing.

The instant he saw her, he backed away from the ledge.
She jumped back just as quickly, fighting her panic, snapping the shade down so that he couldn't watch her, so that
she couldn't see him either.

When she returned to her living room, she felt no safer.
She couldn't erase the knowledge that he was up there—
waiting for her, wanting her. Nor could she erase the memory of the heated glory she had known in his arms, of the
hurtling sense of pleasure he had given her.

Nothing in her marriage had prepared her for the dark,
frightening power of Joshua and the passion he ignited in
her. And Joshua knew it.

Mario began to sing. His melting, smoky baritone intensified the ache of longing in Honey's heart. Honey wanted
to go outside and shout to him to stop. She wanted to order
Heather home and tell her never to come back. And yet in
the same moment that Honey arose, she sank once more to
her chair, helplessly torn, not only because she liked Heather

but because she sensed that the motherless girl was lonely and hurt and in need of real friends whom she could trust. But at the same time Honey hated to encourage the child of her most dangerous enemy. When the truth of their relationship became clear, Heather would only be hurt again. No, Honey must encourage Heather to try to become close to her real mother.

The longer Honey sat in the darkened stillness of her living room, the more hysterical she felt. Her plan to tackle Joshua on a personal level had been hopeless from the start. Not only had she put herself at risk, but she was endangering Heather who was too fragile to sustain another betrayal. Not to mention the very real danger of how Joshua would retaliate when he discovered Honey had deliberately tricked him.

She saw now that her move to Telegraph Hill had been a mistake. The only smart thing to do was to call Nell and quit this charade before it was too late for them all.

Then the phone rang, and the instant she heard the shaking vulnerability in Joshua's husky voice, her fierce resolve to leave him melted like butter over a hot flame.

"Don't hang up," he whispered in a low, anguished note.

She was powerless to do anything other than listen.

There was a long moment of silence.

"I'm sorry...about this afternoon," he said at last. "For the way I treated you."

"It's all right," she said weakly. "I—I'm not proud of the way I acted either."

"You have nothing to be ashamed of. What happened was my fault." He paused. "You seemed pretty shaken when you ran out."

Sweat beaded along her upper lip and she licked it away. She ran trembling fingers through her hair. She rubbed the tense muscles at the back of her neck. "I'm okay now."

"Honey, I want to see you again. Not for—I mean just to talk. Maybe we could go sailing. You'd be safe on my boat—even with me—because *Enchantress* is sixty feet long and a lot more than I can handle alone. And I don't have a captain. It's cold out there, and we'd be too bundled up in wet gear to touch each other."

Joshua was asking her out again.

Some unwise, traitorous, feminine side of her wanted to forget about Nell, wanted to surrender to the swift, hot urgency in his low, emotion-charged tone.

Fortunately her wiser side primly asserted itself. "I—I don't think that's such a good idea."

"I'm sure you're right," he admitted, but his tightly coiled voice was tinged with dark disappointment.

"I—I was about to call Nell and resign as apartment manager," Honey forced herself to continue briskly.

"So..." That old edge of bitterness that she hated had crept into his voice. "You're giving up on me... Just when you were beginning to make progress."

"Progress?" Honey asked quietly. "What do you mean?"

"No one's ever affected me the way you do."

No one had ever affected her the way he did either.

"That could be bad for both of us."

"Maybe. We'll never know if you move away." He hesitated. "I've been different lately—since you."

The memory of his mouth on her lips and body stirred hotly through her. "In what way?"

"You said you wanted to motivate me to be nicer. Well, maybe you have...just a little. The other day I helped a kid who works for me out of a jam. It felt good." He hesitated. "I'm helping a widow, an old friend, who was broke and alone and in trouble with a kid to support. She's going to sing in one of my hotel clubs till I can figure out what else to do. And yesterday I called my ex-wife and apologized for the way I treated her during our marriage. I told her how much Heather still needs her. She called Heather."

Honey twisted her wedding ring around and around on her finger. "Joshua, I—I really don't see—"

"I've even decided I can live with my view. I'll leave Nell's building and her tenants alone. I'll let you win. That is,

Ms.—I mean *Mrs.*—Rodriguez, if you stay for the summer.''

"I thought you didn't want me on your hill?"

"You were right when you said I was conceited to think of it as my hill. I want to share it . . . with you."

A desperate lump rose in Honey's throat. "Why would you back off? You said you never give up when you set out to do something."

"And you said a man could change."

"But have you? Really?"

"If you leave, we'll never know."

"And if I stay—" As she twisted her ring, it came off in her hand.

"I can't promise. All I know is that my priorities are different. I want to please you."

She knew she shouldn't listen, but somewhere inside her hammered the persistent advocate for his defense. "I—I don't know what to say. I feel all mixed up. I guess I can't really believe I've made any real difference to you."

"Oh, but you have. I've been chased by demons for as long I can remember. When I'm with you, they seem a long way behind me. I don't always feel the need to attack everybody like I used to."

"I don't know what to say."

"Just go sailing with me."

She wanted to. Still, she hesitated.

A balmy, all-enveloping coolness was drifting up from the waterfront, stealing up the hill into her open windows. She could almost smell the salty tang of the bay, she could almost feel the freshening wind. Mario's raspy, sensual voice and music drifted inside too.

Now was the time to say no to sailing. To say no to Joshua forever. She tried, but somehow the word stuck in her throat.

Instead it was his name, a whispery velvet invitation laced with sadness and longing, that escaped her lips.

"Joshua—"

He sensed her hunger. It was in his voice, too. "Honey—"

They both laughed nervously, huskily—together.

"I can't seem to say no," she said simply. She opened a drawer and threw her wedding ring inside.

"Good. I'll call you Saturday." Then he hung up.

She set the receiver in its cradle and put her hands to her face. She felt cold and hot at the same time. What had she done? Why couldn't she be smart and let Joshua go?

Because the mere thought was torture. Because without him, her future stretched ahead of her like a bleak and empty wasteland.

She had spent most of her life running from her father's coldness and materialistic cynicism. She had married Mike to prove she was not that kind of person. How could she embrace a man who was even darker than her father, a man who espoused all her father's worst characteristics—who in fact went further than her father with the same stifling, abhorrent views? A man who threatened everything she had always tried to believe in, all her most sacred ideals? A man who would show her no mercy when he found out she was Cecilia Wyatt, when he found out she had deliberately tricked him.

The mainsail was tight and full, but the jib spilled air as *Enchantress* tacked to windward. Normally Joshua would have trimmed the sail. Today he was too distracted by the woman at his side.

Joshua still found it hard to believe Honey had come out with him. He watched the wind and the sunlight play across her eager face and he was filled with pleasure and wonder. She smiled—that special smile that both charmed him and mystified him because it always gave him a curious feeling of familiarity. Yet if he had known her surely by now he would have placed her.

She was a natural sailor. She liked being out on the bay as much as he did. It was odd, but for a working girl, she hadn't seemed impressed with the yacht club or the fancy yachts as his dates usually were.

Honey was leaning against the lifelines, wearing his bright yellow foul-weather gear which swallowed her, not minding as Monica or Simone would have minded that she didn't look fashionable, that the humid wind tangled her hair. When an occasional wave doused her with frigid saltwater, she ducked and laughed.

San Francisco looked beautiful from the water. On one side the hills swept down to the purple Pacific like giant folds of red-gold fleece. On the opposite shore the buildings were tinged with slanting pink light.

The sun was going down and the cold breeze was picking up. As the lavender evening began to darken, so did his mood.

His brown hand spun the wheel all the way to starboard, and he shouted, "Coming about. It's late. We have to go in."

"I wish we could stay out here forever," Honey said wistfully.

When they turned back toward the club, the skyscrapers glowed even redder from their new angle. So did the waves. It looked like they were sailing across fire.

His eyes met hers, and in that unguarded moment he knew she understood that he felt even more reluctant than she to return. He always felt freer on a boat, easier. That's why he'd brought her sailing. He'd wanted to be with her just once without his fierce tensions taking over.

"I had a wonderful time today," she said. A dolphin sprang out of the glistening water, and she laughed. Then she turned and smiled at him.

He knew he had known her before. But where? When?

"There's another one," he shouted.

The long sloop sliced gracefully through the white foaming waves toward the gleaming city.

"When I was a kid, I used to bicycle down to the waterfront and watch the little rich kids getting on boats like this

with their parents. I never dreamed I'd own one myself," he
said bitterly.

"She's beautiful."

"*Enchantress* is first class. Sixty feet of perfection. She's
got a tough, fiberglass hull that cuts through chop like a razor."

"And she's lovely down below. All that polished teak."

"I oil it myself—to relax."

He had already explained how each of the dozens of state-
of-the-art, high-tech nautical instruments aided in naviga-
tion. Honey hadn't laughed when he'd told her that some
day he wanted to sail around the world.

"I'm glad you're a sailor and not a mountain climber,"
she said.

"Why?"

"Because I'm afraid of heights."

She was looking up at him almost shyly, smiling *that
smile*. Was she saying it was important to her to enjoy the
things he enjoyed?

"This boat is the only thing I've ever bought that's given
me something back. When I sail, I leave all my problems
and anger on shore."

She stared at the glistening city, at the fiery skyscrapers,
then at him. There was an intensity about her expression as
she studied him, an anxious something in her eyes that he'd
never seen in other women's, a need for him that was much
more than physical. There was fear, as well.

"Maybe you should sail more often." She glanced past
him. Her frightened face grew still.

He was filled with guilt. "After the other day," he began
hoarsely, "at your school—"

"Don't—" She turned back to him and moved closer,
pressing her shaking fingertips to his lips. "I want to enjoy
this moment."

So did he. As always her slightest touch made him hot,
hotter than he wanted to be. He folded her hand in his,
pressed it against his cheek and held it there for a long mo-

ment before he let it go. "I wouldn't have blamed you if you hadn't come."

"I wanted to see you again," she said gently, her quivery voice betraying her fear.

"It's probably difficult for someone with your high ideals to understand a man like me."

She stared at him in mute dismay for a long moment. "Like you said—I'm no saint."

"Compared to me—"

"No." She swallowed. "You were closer to the truth before. I'm no angel. I wanted people to think I was."

"A mysterious woman?"

She smiled and shivered, a little nervously, not looking at him, and just for a second he almost believed she really did have something to hide.

He pointed out two buildings he had built, and she complimented them. He showed her the hotel he was renovating. "You can see the new tower going up—to the right of the Transamerica Pyramid."

"It's wonderful. So modern. I'm impressed."

He fought against the sudden warmth her praise brought. "So far, that's all my life has been about—owning, taking. Making money. That's all that mattered." He looked at her, and her soft smile set off every erogenous nerve ending in his body. *Until now. Until you.*

He stopped himself. He didn't want to push her again too fast. "I'd better shut up," he finished awkwardly.

"No, I really do want to know more about you. How did you get the hotel?"

He trimmed the mainsail. "Like I've gotten most things— in an unfriendly takeover." His face darkened. "The same way I'll get that one—over there."

When he pointed toward the Wyatt Hotel, her whole body tensed. Her white fingers went taut on the lifelines.

Joshua scarcely noticed because his fiercest demons were back. He was a little boy again playing with his toy locomotive on that long ago rainy Sunday morning when a violent gunshot had exploded, shattering the silence, the peace, his life—forever. He had run down the narrow basement stairs only to scream endlessly when he found his father's lifeless body crumpled over his shotgun and broken whiskey bottle in a pool of blood. Joshua had dropped the locomotive and run all the way to the church so his mother would come home and make everything all right again. He remembered the horrors of the hospital, the funeral—how he'd felt cut off from it all, how his mother hadn't cared about anything ever again, not even her son. He remembered how he'd gone up to Hunter Wyatt's gigantic desk only to cower with impotent terror when Wyatt laughed at him and blurted out the awful truth—that he was a spineless wimp, just like his father.

Joshua's narrow blue gaze had iced over. "I'm going to buy the Wyatt chain and sell it off piece by piece until there's nothing left of Wyatt but the memory of his name."

"You mean another hostile takeover?" Honey asked faintly.

"Very hostile." All his seething tensions had returned. "Sometimes I think my whole life's been about that hotel—getting it back, destroying it. But what I really want is to destroy Wyatt himself."

"Why?" Her low voice was choked, thready. Her tongue came out and wet her lips.

"Revenge. As a kid, I wanted to kill him. I had to get some years on me before I realized killing's never any good—"

"Thank God—" Her eyes were frantic.

His deep voice was glacier cold. "I meant killing's always too easy."

"But why? Why are you so set on this? Have you thought of his family? His wife? His children?"

"Why should I give a damn about them?"

"Because they're human beings. Because you are too." She scrambled against the cabin, away from him. "Let Hunter Wyatt go, Joshua."

"Are you crazy?"

"I'm not asking you to do it for me. Do it for yourself."
Her wide, panicked eyes held incomprehensible misery, and
yet at the same time she stood her ground, challenging his
entire code of living. "Let him go, Joshua. Go forward with
your life."

"You have no idea what you're asking," he yelled before
he remembered he shouldn't blame her.

She was too sweet and gentle, too altruistic to understand how guilt and grief and hatred could twist a person.
He had probably frightened her by revealing his dark am-
bitions so forcefully. But before he could explain why he
could never do as she'd asked, his radar's alarm went off.

Three loud squawks.

He looked under his sail and felt an immediate jolt of
alarm. His pupils dilated. His dark face went white. Honey
screamed.

Hell.

An enormous megayacht, on a collision course with *Enchantress,* was bearing down on their port side.

Joshua was under sail and on a starboard tack which
meant he had the right-of-way on two counts. Not that
right-of-way rules mattered when his hull was about to be
crushed like a matchbox beneath a roaring freight train
which could easily kill them both.

Joshua forgot everything but the deadly, frothing bow
wave crashing toward them. His hand tightened on the
wheel.

"Tacking! Now!" He spun the wheel to starboard and
held it there.

Enchantress careened clumsily into a tall wave and was
stopped dead by the wall of water and strong current. Her
jib backed, and she heeled over. Water and spray broke
across the bow and decks, flooding her cockpit.

The power yacht charged relentlessly toward them. Honey
groped her way forward through the water and struggled to
loosen her jib sheet from the winch and bring the big sail
across.

Just when Joshua thought all was lost and he pulled Honey into his arms to shield her with his own body, the pilot of the other yacht saw them, veered and passed underneath them, missing them in that last split second by no more than a few inches, the huge yacht's churning wake rocking *Enchantress* violently.

Joshua let Honey go and watched the yacht speed recklessly away. *The bastards were either drunk or on something.*

He turned wild, furious eyes on Honey. She could have been chopped to pieces. That thought and how much he cared scared the hell out of him.

"That was close. Too close," he whispered, softening when he saw her fear.

Joshua had completely forgotten Hunter Wyatt. "Those bastards could have killed us, but you were great, the way you handled that sail—a natural," Joshua said, setting the automatic pilot, reaching for her.

She came into his arms, soft and small and seeking his strength like a frightened child. Their heavy foul-weather gear crinkled.

"I was a little scared," she admitted.

He could feel her shaking. Hell, he was shaking, too.

"It's over," he murmured softly. Her wet hair flew against his face, and he brushed it aside. "Nothing like this has ever happened out here to me before, but we're okay." His hand lingered against her cheek before he pulled it away. He was so glad she was safe he wanted to gather her closer and kiss her hard, but he remembered how he'd treated her in her classroom and held back.

"I hope we are—okay," she said, shaking, still afraid, clinging.

"Honey, Honey." His low voice soothed as he framed her face in his palms and drew her even closer. For a long time he held her, until she quieted and he felt his body tighten in a hot male way that told him he'd better let her go.

"So tell me about yourself," Joshua rasped, to distract them both, gently pushing her away.

"What do you want to know?"

"Everything." He made his voice casual. "Start when you were a little girl. I'll bet you were cute."

The wake of another boat caused *Enchantress* to rock. He steadied Honey with his hand.

"I was a brat. I made a terrible childhood even worse than it needed to be."

"You were poor?"

"No. I was rich. Very rich. We had mansions, servants, yachts, cars."

"You were lucky then."

Her eyes were huge. "No. You should know such things don't matter much."

"They do when you don't have them."

"My mother died," she said quietly. "My father remarried. My only brother was deeply disturbed by everything that happened. Instead of helping him, my father drove him away. After that I was alone with my father. When he wasn't ignoring me, he made my life miserable in other ways."

"What was he like?"

Did he only imagine that she flinched? That she was afraid again?

"I—I really don't want to talk about it." But after a while she did. "I was very unhappy after my brother left. I tried to find him, and when I couldn't I went through a rebellious stage. Then I got married—deliberately—to a man my father didn't approve of. After that I was totally estranged from my family. I guess I was fairly happy, until Mike died. And Mario started acting so wild. I tried to find my brother again, but it's like he disappeared off the face of the earth." Her sad voice trailed off.

"What happened then?"

"I kept Mario with me. Maybe because he reminds me of my brother. You see, my father should have taken my brother in hand, but he was too busy making money and trying to make his young wife happy. Nobody but me cared, and I was too young to help him. Sometimes I think I've spent most of my life trying to right the wrongs of my childhood.''

"Tell me about it! My life has been a one-man vendetta since my father died.''

"Why?''

Joshua tried not to see again the shrunken body of his father on the basement floor, but the vision overpowered him. Suddenly his chest felt tight, constricted, but when he took a deep gulp of air it just got tighter. He remembered the hospital, his father's strange stiff face, the coldness of his father's big hands that had once been so gentle, the dead, lost eyes in his mother's living face. At the funeral Joshua had wished that he could crawl in the coffin and be buried too.

All the dark grief and anger came back like it was yesterday. "It was a long time ago,'' he muttered bitterly. "It shouldn't matter any more.''

"But it does.''

"Yeah.'' His throat worked convulsively. "He was good to me. It still hurts.''

"Maybe you should fight harder to let it go,'' she said in a stricken tone. "He wouldn't have wanted you to grieve forever.''

His gaze shifted to touch her animated face—her lovely pale skin, her fiery hair, her big, luminous green eyes. Then her mouth. God, how he longed for the sweetness of it melting against his lips.

She was sweet. No one had ever seemed so sweet, so honest. All his life he'd been starved for the taste and touch of a woman like her. But she didn't understand. How could she? He was afraid to let go of the hate.

A twisted, churning rawness knotted his insides. He leaned forward and touched her face, tilting her chin back. His wayward caress of her silken skin was dangerously comforting to him, dangerously pleasurable. She made him know how lonely he was—how he craved her, only her.

"I'm not very good at letting go of intense feelings," he muttered. "Once they get a grip, they're like acid eating me alive on the inside—till I do something about them."

He shouldn't have touched her again. But now that he had, he couldn't stop.

His hand moved possessively lower to the base of her throat. He felt her pulse wildly fluttering beneath his fingertips. The waves rocked the boat and they fell against each other, their bodies intimately locking as the yacht heeled.

"Joshua, you have to let go of the bad feelings to have the good ones," she said in a hushed voice, holding on to him.

"It's not that easy." His hand, which had become tangled in her flying hair, tensed. "Anyway, I'd rather feel nothing."

"You keep saying you don't want love—" There was a throbbing ache in her voice.

"Because I don't. Love is a hook set deep in your heart that sooner or later rips you to pieces." Before he thought, he grabbed her by the shoulders and pulled her into his body. As always she felt good. So good, his insides curled with pleasure. So good, dark, hot desire throbbed through every male cell.

"Then why did you ask me out?" she whispered.

"Because I want this." His fingers dug into the tender flesh of her shoulders and he eased her closer against the supple strength of his male body.

She drew a deep worried breath. "So, nothing's changed?"

"Why do you want to complicate something that can be good for us both?"

"Joshua, I can't live on hate the way you can," she whispered, lifting a shaking hand so that her fingertips could gently trace the iron line of his jaw.

"Maybe you won't have to very long." He was surprised at the vehemence in his voice.

She seemed to swallow between heartbeats. "Because you only want me for a night or two."

When he didn't deny it, her eyes misted; her hand fell slowly away from his rugged face. "Joshua, if this is your best offer, please, do me a favor. Don't call me—ever again."

His hushed laughter was harsh. "You want me just as much as I want you." His hard hands drew her nearer. "You know you do."

"Yes, but every time you touch me you're setting your hook in me. I don't want to be hurt any more than you do." She tried to shake him off. "If you can't try to feel something for me, let me go, Joshua. Please—"

Take or be taken. His large hands tightened on her waist.

"Oh, Joshua. Are you really so selfish? So brutal? Do you really think you're the only one who's ever been hurt? All my life I've wanted love. I've felt so alone ever since my mother died and my brother ran away."

He'd been alone too. "You were married."

She winced. "I never felt this way about him. And I feel terrible because I couldn't. Mike was so good, so decent—"

"Damn it. The last thing I want to hear about is how unfavorably I compare to your saintly husband!" Joshua's hands were making their way inside her foul-weather-gear jacket. He wanted to crush her against the cabin and smother her with kisses. To kiss her until she begged him to take her.

"Joshua, I don't think I was meant to love a saint. I think I could love you. But if you can't even try to feel something for me, be kind and let me go."

Be kind? He laughed harshly.

Take or be taken. Use or be used. Desire pulsed through him like a volcanic river of fire.

Suddenly he kissed her hard, fusing his hot lips to hers, his mouth and tongue claiming fierce possession.

The yacht rolled down a wave.

"Please, Joshua, let me go."

He didn't want to, but when he looked into her terrified eyes, he realized it wasn't so easy to apply his old code of

living any more. How could he take her or use her—when
he knew she would never do those things to him?

Somehow, inexplicably, her softness had softened the hate
in him. He remembered how he'd nearly made love to her on
her classroom floor and had forced himself to stop.

As his grip slackened, she wrenched herself free and
scurried down below into the cabin as though she were truly
terrified of him now. She slammed the hatch shut, leaving
him in the cockpit to sail the rest of the way to the marina
alone.

Damn. Was he a monster? Or was he just as scared as she
was? If she took away the hate, what the hell would he have
left?

The velvet, icy darkness seemed to swallow him. He
turned on the running lights. The night grew colder, so cold
that Joshua felt chilled all the way to the marrow of his
bones.

Eleven

Two weeks. Honey had lived two weeks without him. Without his touch and with the terrible feeling that her heart was encased in ice. But somehow she had managed to go on, even though she'd thought of Joshua almost constantly.

Today had been especially bad until Mario had accidentally let Emerald escape and she'd been so preoccupied trying to catch her bird that she couldn't think of anything else. Thus, Joshua was not on her mind as Honey pried the thick leaves apart and peered through them.

Emerald was sitting high up in the apple tree, smug as could be, munching calmly. He had been there five hours and was in no mood to leave. Honey was frantic to catch him before it got dark, but as she nudged the ladder against the thin trunk which grew precariously close to the edge of the cliff, she heard the whir of traffic a hundred feet below.

She had assembled her parrot-catching kit too hastily. It consisted of Emerald's cage, her green bedspread and a pair of gloves. Unfortunately, she hadn't been able to find her net—a crucial item. So, she would have to climb.

When she put a foot on the bottom rung, the whole tree shook. Rocks tumbled down the sheer wall of the cliff. Emerald squawked and jumped to a higher limb. The ladder wobbled as she climbed to the second rung.

She looked down—all the way down—to the pavement and cars below. Bits of apple plunked onto her head. When her foot missed the third rung, her heart fluttered. Another bit of apple bounced off the tip of her nose. Emerald was probably taking deliberate aim. The higher she climbed, the louder Emerald squawked and the dizzier she felt.

Mario saw her predicament and jumped up, leaving Tina on the porch, to come over to help. He was instantly bombed by apple bits. "I bet next time you won't put off clipping his wings."

All Honey's frustrations zeroed in on Mario. "The last thing I need from you right now, young man, is advice. You shouldn't have left the door open while I was trying to collect Mrs. Conklin's rent."

He shot her a dazzling smile. "Sorry, but when Tina came by I forgot."

More apple whizzed past them, hurtling all the way down the cliff, splattering onto the street.

"Why don't you make yourself useful and hold—"

Mario was about to brace the ladder, when the phone rang.

"It's probably one of your girlfriends," she hissed.

He smiled. "Hang on. I'd better answer it—so Tina won't."

"Mario, she'll call back—"

But he was already gone. She looked down at the cars again and got dizzy.

He returned a minute later. "It's for you."

Honey crawled down the ladder and took the cordless phone.

"Cecilia, darling—"

"Astella—"

"I hope I didn't take you away from anything important."

More chunks of apple rained down.

"My parrot got loose."

"Guess who called? J. K. Cameron—with an offer to sell us all his Wyatt stock over the next few months—at a low price we'll be able to afford."

"Joshua? I don't understand. I begged him to do that two weeks ago, but he refused."

"Well, something must have changed his mind." Astella's voice was cool. "Maybe you did."

Honey could feel her heart beginning to thump with excitement. *Had he done it for her?*

"Cecilia, we've won. You can move home. I think your father is grateful even though he's not about to admit it. However, he did say he wants you away from Cameron—at once. Mario can come, too."

"What if Joshua changes his mind again?"

"The only thing that might make him do that is if he finds out about you. You've got to back off, Cecilia. Fast. If you stay, you jeopardize everything."

Leave Joshua? When he might be starting to care?

Quite suddenly all her happiness vanished. "You're right, I suppose." Her voice was soft and sad.

"You should be thrilled! We won! I think your father is even on the verge of forgiving us for interfering."

"Thrilled . . ." Honey's low tone was muffled as she said goodbye.

Joshua's five-story house cast a long shadow over her house. She looked up at his bedroom window. His blinds were drawn. She would never see him again. She felt bleak, empty.

She had won. She had everything she had wanted and more. Why then did she feel so cold that she had begun to shiver, so cold that she was afraid something vital and fragile had died inside her forever?

From the hill above she heard a sound. A tall man with a lithe, muscular body was descending the Filbert Steps with the easy, silent grace of a large predatory cat.

Joshua. She tensed expectantly as she remembered that first day when she'd been so terrified after she'd left him that note. He'd come down those same steps toward her. He had kissed her and her lips had burned for hours afterward.

Joshua stepped into the open, looking darker and more dangerous than ever. He wore black slacks and a black silk shirt that showed his lean, powerful build.

Their eyes met and held across the late afternoon shadows.

The wind blew his black hair across his tanned brow. In his eyes she saw profound emotion.

Her heart gave a leap of pure happiness. She gasped, clutching the ladder because she wanted to fly toward him, into his arms.

No, she didn't have everything she wanted.

Not any more.

Now she wanted a cold, dark man who didn't know how to love and didn't want to learn. She wanted a man who'd spent his life living for revenge, a man who was everything she wanted to run from—the one man her father hated more than all others.

Her father had forgiven her Mike. He would never forgive her Joshua.

But as she stared into the dazzling warmth of Joshua's blue eyes, it didn't matter.

Nothing mattered except Joshua.

"Looks like you could use some help," Joshua murmured in an odd voice. "I brought a net."

"Hey, that's great," she answered weakly, feeling heady with delirium and shy too.

Mario moved back to the porch. Heather, who had followed her father, joined Tina and him there.

Joshua came up to Honey. His gaze roamed her shapely body. "God, how I missed you."

Never had such simple words been filled with more erotic longing.

Her warm green eyes sparkled. Then she felt shy again.

"Don't you know it's not safe to look at me like that," he muttered, his cynical voice slightly hoarse, even as her adoring eyes stayed fastened on him defiantly.

"Oh, Joshua," she moaned helplessly. "I thought I wanted you to stay away and leave me alone."

"I know." His eyes were hot as hers; his voice was tender. "It's hell with you. It's hell without you, too. I don't know who I am or what I want. Everything that used to matter doesn't matter any more."

She held the ladder for him while he climbed the tree and caught her parrot.

Three passing tourists descending the Filbert Steps applauded when his net snagged Emerald just as the parrot was spreading his wings to take off for a towering pine. The teenagers on the porch laughed as Emerald squawked and jumped furiously in the net as he was brought down and carried inside.

Honey shut the door and opened the net, and Emerald flew to his perch and stared out at the apple tree sulkily.

She turned to Joshua and was struck by the force of his bronzed virility and his startling blue eyes. "I owe you. How can I repay you?" she asked, feeling a little faint.

"I think you know." His voice was a husky caress tingling down her spine. "By giving me another chance."

Radiant confusion colored her face as she turned away.

"You have all the rare qualities I never knew I wanted in a woman. You're sweetly loving, honest—"

The color drained from her face. "Joshua, there's something I'd better tell you."

He caught her to him. His fingers smoothed the worry lines between her brows. "Don't. No problems now. We can always talk. I'd rather not spoil the mood. We've both waited for this—too long."

He was right. The sweetness of their new beginning was too fragile. So, she opened her lips as his sensual mouth moved tantalizingly nearer and let him kiss her in that wild, hungry way that made her want much more.

* * *

The hotel bar was bathed in candlelight as Honey stepped out of the elevator on Joshua's arm. She wore a sleek green silk gown. Her red hair fell against her pale neck in a satiny pageboy. Her cheeks were aglow. She knew that tonight would be a night she would want to remember always.

Later. After they had tonight, there would be a right moment to tell him who she really was.

Then she saw the tall, dark man with the distinctive spray of silver in his jet black hair and the warm, surprised, cat-stole-the-cream grin that came over his face the instant he saw her. Honey froze as Johnny Midnight made his way toward them, thick legal papers stuffed into one dark hand, a scotch and soda in the other.

Midnight looked at her wrists and grinned knowingly when she blushed at the humiliating memory of their first meeting. "Now this is a surprise." Midnight turned to J.K. "Sorry I'm late with these. Look them over before your meeting with Mrs. Wyatt."

Honey stared at both men, her heart thumping, her mind paralyzed.

"Thanks, Midnight. I'll call you tomorrow, before the meeting."

Midnight didn't leave. Instead his smile warmed. "Aren't you going to introduce me to the lady?"

Honey felt doomed as Joshua's possessive arm moved her forward. "Honey Rodriguez, Johnny Midnight, my lawyer."

"My pleasure, *Miss Rodriguez*," Midnight said smoothly as he folded her icy, shaking hand in his warm one. When she tried to pull away, he held it a second longer than he should have. "You must be J.K.'s new *neighbor*."

"She's off limits, Midnight. She's very special to me."

Midnight shrugged, "So I see. You two look good together. Hey, why don't you both join me for a quick drink?"

No. No. No. Terrified, Honey stared numbly into Midnight's determined dark eyes.

Joshua shrugged. "Why not? If that's okay with you, Honey?"

Honey swallowed, miserable, and nodded mutely, not looking at him.

Midnight stared straight at her. "Joshua's been different—since you."

She sucked in a quick, sharp breath. "Oh?"

When she nearly tripped as she followed both men to the table, Midnight rushed to help her regain her balance. She was so flustered she let him seat her beside the window without even noticing the fifty-story drop. Then she looked down, and grabbed onto Joshua's arm. His hand closed over hers so protectively that she almost felt safe. Till she saw Midnight absorbing the tender moment.

Midnight paid for the first round. Honey gulped her white wine frantically while the two men talked.

All too soon Midnight turned to her, pretending no more than polite interest. "When J.K. told me he had a new girlfriend, I never expected it to be you—I mean someone like you."

Honey spluttered something inaudible as she choked on her wine.

Joshua patted her back and said smoothly, "She's a refreshing change."

The centerpiece of their table was composed of golden roses nestled around a single candle. Honey reached nervously for a rose and knocked over the burning candle. Midnight grabbed it just in time.

"Careful. It's always dangerous to play with fire," came Midnight's knife-edged, satin drawl. He eyed her steadily and blew out the flame.

Joshua's hand closed over hers. "Midnight, it took forever to get her to trust me enough to date me. Don't scare her away."

Midnight got up. "That was never my intention."

"She's in no danger from me."

"Maybe from herself then."

Midnight's soft words terrified Honey. Any minute Joshua was going to sense Midnight's not-so-hidden agenda.

Instead Joshua got angry. "What the hell are you driving at?"

Midnight ignored Joshua and leaned toward Honey. "He's one dangerous guy. Play it straight."

She was too terrified to speak; Joshua was too furious. In the confusion Midnight relit their candle and made a swift exit.

Joshua's arm circled her shoulders protectively. "What the hell was that all about?" A dark, angry note lingered in his low tone. "You two know each other?"

"No..." As Honey looked across the golden glow of their candle into Joshua's swarthy face, she felt thoroughly shaken. But she couldn't tell Joshua, not yet.

The band began to play—soft, romantic music.

"Do you want to dance?" Joshua asked, as if he was as ill at ease as she was.

The candlelight made her eyes sparkle like fiery, dark emeralds. "Oh, yes." Anything to forget Midnight's dark warning.

When he wrapped her in his arms, she felt the heat of his body and the hardness of his muscles. She laid her head over his violently thudding heart. Soon she was floating in a dream as he swirled her on the dance floor.

Other dancers twirled past them in a blur. After a while they were alone, dancing in the darkness near the sheer glass windows with the city and the bridges and the hills sparkling beneath them. She was breathless. Not from the height, but from being in Joshua's arms. His hot mouth found her silken nape, and she felt an electric quickening radiate every time his lips nuzzled her skin.

The hours passed like minutes and all too soon the candle at the center of their table had melted to a nub, its flame glimmering darkly from its crystal saucer. And still they danced, their bodies swaying rhythmically, aware only of their escalating need.

At one point Joshua led her away from the bar into a dark corner. She looked down—fifty stories down—and then breathlessly into Joshua's eyes. He took her fingers in his and brought them slowly to his lips. She felt his calluses and was reminded of his brutality even as the warmth of his lips caressed her fingertips.

The flickering candlelight accentuated the unrelenting harshness of his carved face.

Suddenly she was terrified. Could a man really change when he'd lived as roughly as Joshua had?

"You're afraid—of me?" he whispered, letting her go.

She struggled to smile. "I don't want to be."

His gaze fastened on her lips. He drew a deep breath. "Do you know," he began, "that sometimes I have the strangest feeling we've met before. I felt it the first time I met you—when you smiled."

She looked out the window and began to tremble violently. "Perhaps in another life—"

"No! This life."

His handsome, dark face was dangerously near hers; his vitality vibrated across her nerve endings, making her sharply, dangerously aware of him. And dangerously aware of her lie.

"I could never have forgotten you, Joshua." The half truth burned her lips and her conscience. "Never."

"I could never have forgotten you, either. That what's so damn puzzling." He lifted her chin, tilting her pale face to his. "Don't worry, one of these days it'll hit me," he whispered as his mouth descended toward hers. "Just like that!" When he snapped his fingers she jumped away from him.

"Hey, there's no reason to be afraid." He took her tremulous lips in another slow, hot kiss. It was as if he instinctively sought to erase her terror and guilt with melting passion, to make her know that he was a lonely man who craved her as no other man ever had.

She shivered, more afraid than ever by the completeness of her intimate longing for him. There was no way she could let him go. No way. No matter what it cost her.

Her hands circled his neck and clung. She wanted to be with him, tonight—forever.

When he felt the shuddering upheaval of her breasts that betrayed her inner torment, he pulled his mouth from hers. With a hot hand he brushed her cheek. "Let's get the hell out of here."

Careful not to touch, hardly daring to look at each other, they stepped into the elevator just as a beautiful woman with long golden hair began to sing from the stage. Her husky, smoky voice had a hauntingly lovely velvet sound.

"She's good," Honey said as the bronze doors closed, seeking what she thought was a safe neutral subject.

"She's Lacy Doug—Lacy Miller, an old friend, fallen onto hard times, dangerous times," Joshua said harshly. "She's not a professional singer, but she's good enough to be one. I'd introduce you to her some time, but I'm arranging for her to leave the country. Midnight was in love with her once."

"And?"

Joshua's expression darkened. "Same old story. She left him for a richer man. He was Johnny's former...boss. Lacy knew Johnny had grown to distrust and detest Douglas, and she still betrayed Johnny to him anyway."

"How?"

"She lied," he murmured, the old bitterness in his voice. "And now he hates her. Douglas was murdered, the assets of her husband's estate have been frozen, and she thinks Douglas's killer is after her. She's running for her life, and I'm trying to help her—a fact I don't dare tell Midnight since he's so inflexible once he makes up his mind."

Something in his dark, derisive look terrified her. "A-and was her lie . . . so terrible?"

"Midnight thought so," he muttered in a violent undertone. "That's what counts, isn't it?"

Joshua's eyes and voice were so coldly piercing that her secret breathless hope died. She cowered from him in the darkest corner of the elevator, so he wouldn't read her guilt and suspect that she too was a liar.

Tell him.

But his face had been ravaged by the unhappy memory, or by some loneliness all his own.

Her body felt icy, all its heat gone. She fought against her rising panic.

He sensed her distress and drew her into his arms and kissed her violently, demandingly. "There's so much I want to forget," he muttered in a low, tortured tone. "So many demons from the past that haunt me." His mouth descended once more in a long kiss that left her breathless.

Her hand went up, wavered, and then curved timidly around his neck to hold him closer. "I love you," she whispered.

A little bell went off and the elevator stopped at a floor. Reluctantly they drew apart before the doors opened.

No one was there. The doors closed.

Joshua drew her against himself and ran his hand across her smooth cheek. His fingers ruffled through her hair. He looked at her with eyes that hungered for more than her body, with a need that seemed to shake him. But he couldn't speak. He could only lower his mouth and search for the rapid pulse beating at her throat.

His lips were so gentle and hot they made her sigh. His pain was her pain because she loved him, and it thrilled her that he sought comfort in her arms.

Dear God, she had to tell him the truth. But as his mouth moved to her lips again and his kisses deepened, she didn't know how she could.

Twelve

——

Joshua's powerful sports car roared up and down through the sparkling hills. He was driving fast, dangerously fast, and yet with consummate skill. He downshifted, his headlights arcing off the walls of closely stacked Victorian houses as he whipped around a sharp turn, his tires shrilling as they burned the pavement. He frowned at the narrow street ahead lined with parked cars, his eyes concentrating on the flying dark. Honey felt his wildness, his willingness to embrace danger, and she gloried in it because the same volatile aphrodisiac pulsed in her blood.

The rush of cool wind and the moonlight was in her hair. His hard, possessive arm tightened around her shoulders as the car made the final climb up to Telegraph Hill. She felt an almost physical pain deep in her belly.

He made her feel wild—wild enough to stand on the edge of the highest precipice and take a flying leap over the side.

The car snarled up the hill. When he swerved to an abrupt stop in his darkened garage, he cut the engine and pulled her close, gripping her fiercely against his body.

Then he pushed her against the back of her leather seat, his body pressing into hers as he kissed her so hard she couldn't breathe. His large brown hand tunneled through her tangled hair, smoothing it back against her neck. Callused palms shaped her face, traced the slender length of her nose, her lips, her throat, and then trailed over her breasts. His heated lips followed the path of his hands, and she returned his kisses with fevered ones of her own.

"Heather's gone to her mother's," he had said huskily on the drive home.

The garage door rolled down noisily, sealing them into that vast tomb of silent, velvet blackness. At last they were alone—cut off for the rest of the night and from the rest of the world. His shaking hands slid down her body, undoing the buttons at the back of her gown, the rhinestone clasp at her shoulder, yanking her bodice halfway down. As he molded her to him, he was breathing fast and hard. She felt an urgency in him that she had never known before, and the same all-consuming madness was in her as well.

His voice was low and hoarse. "Let's go upstairs."

She could not speak. She did not want to. When he let her go the imprints from his fingers burned her skin, and she had to hold her clothes on as she got out of the car.

She grabbed his tie and pulled him back. Her hands slid inside his waistband and tugged out his shirt, so that her fingertips could explore him, first his muscular back and chest and then lower. His soft laughter was urgent when, at last, she let him go.

Inside his house, she grabbed him again as he unset his burglar alarm. Her hands moved under his clothes, across rippling muscles, bristly chest hair and warm, bare skin. His breath caught as hot, splayed fingertips trailed down his body. He had to key in the numbers twice, to get the code right.

From the bottom story, his spiral staircase wound up five stories to his bedroom. She looked up shakily into the blaze of moonlight that poured through his domed skylight at the top.

Silvery light and shadow distorted the modern paintings that hung against the soaring circular walls. Weird, frightening faces loomed warningly out of the canvases. And she was afraid.

He was Joshua K. Cameron, her father's enemy. *Her enemy.* This was madness. But stronger than her fear of him was her need to be with him.

His intense eyes were on her still white face.

"You're house is so huge," she said. "I feel . . . sort of funny, like I'm lost."

"It's always been a lonely hell," he murmured. "Until tonight. Until you."

"I've been lonely too, Joshua. Longer than you'll ever know."

Something smoldered dangerously in his eyes. "Now you've got me." Then he pulled her into his arms and she opened her lips to receive his reckless kiss, his searching tongue. A long time later he whispered, "My bedroom is on the fifth floor. I have an elevator."

Her arms slid around his neck. Her hands moved over his broad shoulders, down his muscular torso to tug at his belt buckle. "I'm having fun out here."

His hard mouth touched hers again, this time softly. But it was as if he had set off a fire storm. "Joshua, you're the last man on earth I should feel like this about, the very last man."

"I feel the same way about you." But he kissed her as if he were starving for the taste of her mouth even though he had tasted it only seconds before. She answered his ravening hunger with a need as intense as his.

Her eager hands moved back from his loosened belt to the lapels of his coat, and when she pulled he shrugged out of it. She dropped his coat heedlessly on the stairs and ran past him, up to the second-floor landing where she pretended to admire the magnificent sculpture of a naked woman.

"She's very beautiful," Honey said.

His raspy voice teased from behind her. "Indeed she is."

He caught her to him again, spun her around and placed her against the railing, kissing her again, hard, harder than before. "Very beautiful. And hot. I've never known a woman so hot."

She felt the nothingness falling away behind her and was terrified. The railing seemed deceptively fragile. But his strong arms held her tightly, and more than terror she felt passion as he opened the last of the buttons at the back of her gown. His warm hand moved against her naked back, around her waist, up across her breasts. Then he tugged at her soft dress, and the silk folds slid weightlessly down the length of her voluptuous body. He arched her away from the railing and let her go.

She was wearing a backless green satin slip that clung in all the right places. When his eyes raked her, she laughed a little breathlessly, leaned down and removed each green high heel, one by one and tossed them at him before she raced up four more flights.

He was right behind her, panting hard when they reached the top. She leaned over the edge and gasped at the dizzying drop to the terrazzo floor. He dangled her glittering shoes over the railing before dropping them, and she watched them fall—down, down, like shooting stars until they were lost in the darkness. Her hair swung loosely against her white throat. She turned her wild gaze toward him.

"I thought you were afraid of heights," he murmured.

She stared defiantly into his eyes. "I've decided to live dangerously." She nipped at his mouth wantonly with eager lips. "It's more fun."

His voice was almost gruff. "Not always."

"You would know."

He touched her smooth spaghetti straps and lowered them over her creamy shoulders. "I don't want to hurt you."

But you probably will—maybe you'll even destroy me. She glanced down into the spiraling darkness and then into his dark face. Tonight it was her mood to defy fate. All that mattered was the blazing desire she felt for him.

He was a man shut off from love, from everything bright and safe and truly glorious in the world. A man who took, a man who used. He was everything she'd always run from. And yet she felt his loneliness as if it were her own.

He saw her doubt and her fear; her desire and her defiance. His lips curved into a bitter smile. He would have edged away, but the fierce, lonely need in his eyes drew her like a beacon. Even his terrifying darkness drew her.

She rushed into his arms, and when her body melted into his and she laid her head longingly against his chest she felt him go rock hard. When her shaking fingertips reached up and lovingly traced the rough-edged features of his carved face, he drew a ragged breath.

For a long moment he stood statue still.

Then, very gently he tipped her chin so that he could look into her eyes. They were frightened and yet they sparkled defiantly with passionate fire. He saw her doubt, but he saw her tenderness too.

There was an intensity in his long silence that sent shivers down her spine.

Her fingers loosened the knot of his silk tie. Without a word they began stripping off the rest of their clothes. When they were naked, they lay down on the Aubusson carpet by the stairs, as he covered her with his immense, muscled body, his heat burning her, his mouth devouring her.

She moaned when his hands found her breasts, when his lips greedily raced over her body, sucking her nipples, kissing her everywhere until she felt as torridly on fire as he was.

Even before he thrust wildly inside her, he had swept her away on a burning dark tide, and she knew a total, bewildering oneness with this hard, bitter man that was unlike anything she'd ever felt before—a shattering loss of self that was almost like dying and yet was nothing like dying.

In the white fire of his passion she was reborn.

Until this night, until him, she had never known who she was or what she wanted.

Now she knew.

She knew as well that nothing would ever matter to her more than Joshua.

When the final explosion came, it shook her to the core. Her arms wrapped around his neck and she arched her body into his, pressing her lips into his chest to muffle her scream.

Afterward when she began to cry soundlessly he held her close, and she lay in that tender, silvery darkness against his hard body, which was moist with perspiration, and wondered if he had been as shaken as she.

If he was, he didn't say so. He held her tightly and stared broodingly up at the skylight as though he were studying the moonlight. She reminded herself that he was a man who had had many women—women far more desirable than she, women who would demand far less, women who were not the daughter of his hated enemy.

Joshua was hard and bitter. She was probably a fool to dream that she could change him, a fool to dream that her love was enough to soften him. He would probably hate her when he found out who she was.

But she had wanted tonight even if it was all she could ever have. And even though she would never be sorry, now that it was over all her old terrors were creeping into ascendancy and she was more terrified of him than ever.

When he fell asleep, she lay beside him for a long time. It was nearly morning when she arose and gently covered him with a blanket.

She got dressed slowly and walked sadly down the stairs because she knew that when he found out who she was, she would be the last person on earth he would ever willingly love.

Joshua knew that he wanted the huge emerald the minute he saw it sparkling against black velvet in the jewelry store window. Because it exactly matched *her* eyes.

"How much?" he demanded from the saleslady who showed it to him.

When she named an outrageous figure, he didn't bat an eyelash.

He just pulled out his credit card and handed it to her. He'd been in a hurry to get to the Wyatt meeting when he'd seen the ring and known that it didn't matter if the stop made him late. He had to have it.

Usually he bought jewelry to say goodbye.

But this was different.

Because the woman he was buying it for was so different.

The memory of her erotic sweetness last night, of the way she had felt when he'd been inside her, made him ache for her. He didn't understand the power Honey Rodriguez had over him. All he knew was that he could not live without her.

Always before, sex had been something he had been able to keep in perspective. It was an appetite to be satisfied when he was hungry. There had been great pleasure, and he had spent a lot of time seeking that pleasure. But there had never been one woman he had had to have.

That was before *her*.

Last night her wildness and the totality of his own emotional response to her had caught him by surprise. There had been more of him involved than his body.

The hate was gone from his heart, and a new feeling that was even more powerful consumed him. He could not name it.

All he knew was that he was going to ask Honey to marry him.

The engagement ring was in Joshua's pocket as he strode toward the Wyatt Hotel with the legal documents Midnight had given him. There were several details he needed to work out with Astella Wyatt before he was willing to agree to sell out to her.

He paused on the steps that led up to the glass doors of the huge hotel. A dozen red banners with the Wyatt insignia waved from flagpoles. He couldn't bring himself to look up at the hated flags which would continue to fly over the hotel that had once been his father's pride and joy. He re-

membered visiting his father in his office here. He had been
treated like a crown prince.

Most of all Joshua remembered Wyatt buying out his father, destroying his father, his mother, his own life. He remembered the long years when he had lived with one
dream—revenge.

That was the past. Today, because of her, the past had lost
some of its terrible power.

Something had happened to him. He wasn't sure what.
He only knew that he valued the new feeling in his heart
more than the hate, that pleasing Honey mattered more than
revenge. He only knew that all the old, dark feelings stood
in the way of his new life.

Maybe his wounds were scarring over. Maybe in time the
demons' howlings would seem like distant whispers.

Honey had asked him to let Hunter Wyatt go.

Joshua was about to go inside the hotel, when he saw a
huge chartreuse car jammed crookedly into a tiny parking
space several yards in down the street.

The Bomb.

Her car.

He went back down the steps and smiled at the crazy way
she had parked. Honey must be somewhere nearby.

He forgot his meeting and loped toward the Bomb.

As always it was unlocked and untidily crammed with too
much junk. He would probably have to hire two maids when
he married her and follow her around locking doors and
setting alarms. But he smiled when he saw several chocolate-candy wrappers on the front seat and a used book she'd
bought, *Why You Never Have to Lose Those Last Ten
Pounds.*

The meter had run out. As he dug for a couple of quarters he scanned the street and sidewalk, but she was nowhere in sight.

He plunked both quarters into the meter. When he got
done with Astella Wyatt, he would come out and wait till
Honey came back because he couldn't wait to ask her to
marry him.

But when he returned to the hotel, Honey was coming down the steps. She stopped breathlessly on the third step, looking pale and a little scared.

He wondered why.

Then a red banner flapped, and she tilted her sunglasses up and smiled at him in that special way that always warmed him through.

Only today it rocked him like the coldest wave.

Because at last he knew why her smile had haunted him. Because at last he knew who she really was.

In his mind's eye he saw a blurred vision of a woman in white, of chocolate-candy wrappers, of her warm smile. Most of all he remembered her touch.

She was Cecilia Wyatt from the hospital.

It was all so obvious; why hadn't he seen it before?

Honey reached for him, and he backed away, his stomach tightening sickeningly. One frightened glance into his blazing eyes, and her outstretched hand seemed to freeze in midair.

God, she'd known who he was from the first. She'd sensed that she had some unique power over him even on that first day, that she could turn him soft, and she'd used it. So she'd made herself more attractive, gotten close to him and deliberately ensnared him.

Everything she'd done, everything she'd said was a setup—a lie. Like a fool he'd fallen in love with her.

He grabbed her by the arm and hurried her down the steps.

"Joshua, what's wrong?"

They were both panting when he positioned her against the stone wall of her father's elegant hotel. "You want to know what's wrong? You tell me—*Cecilia!*"

She closed her eyes in mute defense. Then her face tightened as if against some terrible pain, but the rage inside him built. She'd used her sweetness to enchant him, to change him, and all the time she'd been a lying cheat.

Use or be used. She had warned him she'd come after him. She was better at his game than he was. "You were good! Damned good! Your performance last night was the best of all! No wonder you ran out. I'll bet you laughed yourself to sleep last night.''

Red Wyatt banners whipped above them, making her still face go light and dark.

Scalding tears slipped from her eyes. "No. I love you, Joshua. I really do!"

"Don't!"

Did she know how her tears and desperately spoken lies tore at his heart? How he would have given everything he owned for them to be the truth? Because now that he knew who she really was, now that he knew she was lost to him, he knew that her love was the only thing he had ever really wanted.

If he despised her, he despised himself more. "You're just saying that for the same reason you've done everything else—to get what you want. I was a fool to think you were different."

She took off her sunglasses. Her tear-filled green eyes were so huge and stricken he would have winced if he hadn't known she was just playing a part.

He grabbed her shaking hand and forced Midnight's legal papers between her clenched fingers. "You tell the people you work for the deal's off." Then he reached into his pocket and pulled out a tiny black velvet box. "Here's something else. I always give the women I sleep with a parting present when I tell them goodbye." His fierce face grew even darker, his savage voice colder. "I spent more than usual, but never mind. Enjoy it. You earned it—*Honey.*"

All the blood drained from her face. The scarlet banners whipped again and held her face in shadow, causing the light to go out of her desperate eyes.

She swayed toward him. Afraid she would faint, he reached for her.

His hand touched hers and she held on to him for a long moment, trembling. He tensed at her touch, hating himself because he liked it, because he craved it. Only when she managed to steady herself, could he relax. Her hand fell away. As he drew back he saw that a single tear traced down her white cheek.

His hard gaze fastened on the sparkling tear. She was good. She was the best. She'd used him. She'd destroyed him. And he was such a wretch he still wanted her.

"Joshua, no... You're wrong. Please, you mustn't believe that I— Last night I wanted to tell you the truth, but I was afraid to tell you. Let me explain."

"I don't give a damn for your lies. I'm going to destroy your father." Joshua's voice softened to a hiss. "But know this—the person I really want to destroy is you."

He turned on his heel and was gone.

"Joshua, please..." Her voice seemed to chase after him—desperate, tear choked.

When she called his name again with a longing that bordered on pain, the husky sound tore his heart like a hook set deeply in soft tissue that was savagely ripped out.

The hardest thing he had ever done was to keep walking away from her.

Thirteen

————

A black flame burned Joshua's soul. He'd thought he'd been in hell before. But this time it was worse. All his demons roamed at will.

He hadn't shaved in two days. He hadn't worked. All he'd done was drink.

Not that whiskey ever helped. Joshua had learned that lesson a long time ago the hard way from his father. Joshua had always known he had his father's weakness. Today was no different. The liquor only made the terrible hatred and the pain and the self-loathing burn all the more fiercely.

He wanted to hate Honey. No. *Cecilia!* He wanted to hate himself, so he'd started the morning off by hitting the bottle especially hard. But the bottle had only made him want her more. For some reason Midnight had chosen today to come by to check on him around noon, when the alcoholic haze had been particularly thick and his hateful desire for her particularly acute. Joshua had greeted Midnight with the order to use every means in his power to destroy the Wyatts and Cecilia.

Midnight had yanked his bottle out of his hand, gone to his bathroom and poured his whiskey down his bathtub drain, yelling, "Hell, no! I won't hurt her *because* you love her, you crazy self-destructive bastard."

Joshua had gone to his bar and opened another bottle. "Then you're fired."

"Oh, no. You can't fire me!" Midnight picked up his leather jacket in disgust. "Because I quit. I'm not going to stick around and watch you rot up here like a street wino instead of trying to understand that she only did what she did because she *had* to. She came to our offices a dozen times to talk to us—no tricks. You called the police. She took you on because you were going to destroy her family."

"If you're so smart about my love life, why are you too damned stubborn to do something about your own? You still love Lacy, but now that Douglas is dead, the guy that killed him—probably Cole Douglas—is after her and her kid. Douglas's assets are frozen and I'm the one who's helping her, who's gotten her fake passports and tickets to Brazil—"

Midnight went sheet white. "Damn you. Who do you think you are—meddling in Lacy's life behind my back? After what she did, she's getting what she deserved from Douglas."

"Does she deserve to die?"

"You stay away from Lacy!"

"You're wrong about her."

"No, I was wrong about you."

Joshua froze at the inflexible rage in his friend's voice. The two men glared at one another with cold mutual dislike, each feeling he'd been stabbed in the back by the other. Only when Midnight slung his coat over his shoulder and raced out of the house, did Joshua's brain clear enough for him to see that he had started their inane quarrel. But when he tried to run down the stairs to stop him, the liquor made him stumble. He fell clumsily against his front door just as Midnight sped away in his latest fast red car.

Joshua felt a terrible guilt about their quarrel, a terrible premonition. He called Midnight's office, but he wasn't there. Nor was he at home.

Joshua's darkness got darker. Without Midnight he was completely alone. And an odd fear took root in the back of his mind and grew.

Joshua stood at his bedroom window and took a pull straight from the bottle. The house was as cold and gray and as hellishly empty as his soul. Since it was no place for a child, he'd ordered Heather move in with Monica for a while, maybe for the rest of the summer.

He stared out the window at Honey's house. She was the cause of everything, even the loss of his daughter and the quarrel with Midnight. Why the hell didn't she go on and move? Was she going to stay down there forever just to torment him?

He took another pull from the bottle. Then he heard his doorbell.

He ignored it. His answering machine was taking all his phone calls.

Whoever was down there pounded defiantly at a window. His doorbell rang again.

It was probably Midnight—determined to resume his defense of Cecilia Wyatt.

Hell. Now that his friend was back Joshua was afraid to see him, because in his present dark mood he would probably just make Midnight more angry. Tomorrow was soon enough to stop drinking and deal with Midnight.

Joshua went to his stereo and turned the music up, so he couldn't hear the pounding and the doorbell.

He jumped when a rock exploded through a glass windowpane and his burglar alarm went off. Shirtless and in old jeans, he staggered out to the landing like a huge, dark, tormented animal.

Honey was standing in the center of his foyer with a scratched wrist and a jagged piece of glass in her hand, looking up at him. As always she wore green.

Her voice was low and frightened, yet he heard it over the pounding stereo.

"Turn off your alarm, Joshua. It's only me."

"The hell I will. I'll let the police come and deal with you for breaking and entering."

"Handcuffs again? I don't think so." She punched in the code herself.

He leaned over the railing. "How the hell did you do that?"

"I watched you."

"Go to hell," he snarled.

She smiled *that* smile, the smile that so haunted him.

"Hey, no need to travel. I'm already there." She came up the stairs slowly, as if she dreaded reaching him as much as he dreaded her.

She was thinner, too skinny for her. How could anyone look so different after a week. Her face was gray; there were dark circles beneath her lifeless eyes. Her red hair didn't shine so much. Her getup was crazy, mismatched. The odd-looking gold bangles at her wrists and ears were cheap and ill chosen. He hated her flowered blouse. She looked like a gypsy, but somehow a very sexy gypsy.

"You look like hell," he muttered darkly. "What do you want?"

"Joshua, I came here because you said it was me you really wanted to destroy—not my father."

He laughed harshly. "Ever the sacrificial lamb."

"You once said you wanted me for a night or two—no complications. Well, you can have me, if you'll just let him go."

His hard gaze raked her body insolently. "I had you—remember? That makes you used merchandise. You don't look so good now. What makes you think I still want you?"

She lowered her lashes against his savage, burning look. But not before he saw that she was trembling, terrified of him.

"Because I can feel it, Joshua. I know you still want me."

He watched the way soft cotton flowers clung to her breasts, the way her skirt swayed against her hips when she moved. And it made his blood beat violently. He ached for her to come nearer.

Dear God, she was right. Had some demon created her just to torment him, to make him lose the last shreds of his sanity?

It had been a week since he'd made love to her, a week since he'd found out her true identity. Seven days of ever-worsening hell.

"Damn you. Go home." But in his imagination he stripped her naked.

"No!" She took off her hat and with a defiant flick of her wrist flung it sailing down the circular stairwell.

When she walked toward him, he wanted to seize her, to pull her beneath his body. Instead he recoiled and stumbled blindly back into his bedroom. "If you're smart, you'll go."

"I have no choice, Joshua," she whispered in that shaking tone. "I'm playing for keeps."

So was he. He willed himself to be unmoved by her terror, by her seductive power, by his own fierce need to take her and punish her.

"You wanted revenge—well, take it. Take me. Use me. Destroy me. Get it all out of your system."

Never in all his life would he ever be able to get her out of his system. He tried to tear his eyes from the voluptuous curves of her lush body, from her soft mouth, but his pulse was beating abruptly in his throat. *She had offered herself to him.*

When she swayed closer, he caught the scent of jasmine and was intoxicated by more than liquor.

"Joshua, please . . ."

Something inside him broke, and he grabbed her and threw her down onto the bed. He fell on top of her, his massive body crushing hers. Her skin was like warm satin, her lips provocatively near, her breath warm and fragrant against his naked chest. A remnant of sanity in his whiskey-sodden mind warned him to let her go. But he didn't listen. She felt too good. She smelled too good. Other needs were all powerful.

He turned her face to his. "Do you know who you are? Why I have to hate you—"

"Does it matter?" she whispered, fighting to smile, her lips quivering instead.

His male reaction to her voluptuous body mixed with the whiskey and his hatred, and the combination was as volatile as fire and gasoline. He felt hot and wild, wilder than he'd ever felt. Why did she have to feel so treacherously, dangerously good? Why did his pulse throb? Why couldn't he breathe? He wanted to hate her, to destroy her, but most of all he felt a volcanic rush of desire to make love to her.

"Your father killed my father! The Wyatt Hotel was my father's hotel. Hunter took it. And when he did, he took everything. My father felt like a failure after that. He started to drink. He abused me and my mother. He took risks. One day he was drinking and cleaning his gun. The gun went off and blew his brains out. Maybe it was suicide. That's something I'll never know." He paused for a long moment. His voice broke. "I—I found him. I was eleven. I blamed myself, because he'd gotten so mean I sometimes prayed he'd die."

"Oh, Joshua . . . I'm so sorry," she said gently, tenderly.

All his life he had craved gentleness, tenderness—love. Her pretense at those emotions and his craven need of them enraged him.

"Damn you. My father died because your father ruined him. My mother died, too. Hunter Wyatt put me in hell. Then you came along and finished the job."

She moaned softly. Fear and desire pooled in her wide eyes. "Because I didn't know—I'm sorry, Joshua. For what I did. For whatever my father did. The last thing I would ever want is to hurt you." She stroked his face very gently till he grabbed her hand and pulled it away. "But most of all I'm sorry for what you're doing to yourself."

"I don't believe you!" he yelled. "You're a liar! You don't give a damn about me!"

"No..."

But he couldn't bear to listen to more of her lies. When she tried to speak, his anger mushroomed like a spreading black haze. But so did his desire. He knew he shouldn't touch her; he knew he should throw her out before it was too late. But there was no way he could save himself. It was already too late.

Take or be taken. Use or be used. Destroy or be destroyed. She had done the same to him.

Her body lay beneath his. All he knew was that he could have her if he wanted her.

He ripped his jeans off. Then he stripped her, tearing buttons loose while she watched with big, frightened eyes.

When they were naked, he seized her hand and placed it on his thigh. "Touch me," he whispered. "You know the way I like it. Pretend again that you like it, too."

She flinched, wanting to draw back, but she didn't. Her hand went across iron muscle, circled him and moved with soft, sensual expertise until he groaned in an agony of savage pleasure. Tears slipped from her lashes and wet her cheeks.

Use or be used. He shoved her hand away and caught her in a powerful embrace and brought his mouth down to hers, his intention to ravage with bruising kisses, but when she kissed him, all the sweetness of her soul seemed to pour into his and become part of him. And it was as if he had entered a sensuous dream, and his fierce will was no longer his own but hers, too, and he could neither hurt nor destroy her. Some force that was stronger than his hatred made him gentle.

How could he hurt her when all he had ever wanted to do was love her? So he murmured velvet-tender love words as he gently kissed away her salty tears, which glistened like jewels upon her pale cheeks. He took his time until she was so eager she wrapped her legs around his waist and cried out for him to take her. He stroked her private satin flesh until she was ready and damp and clinging and arching her body into his, her need no longer sacrificial but a passion that burned with the same terrible, bright heat as his.

He made her wait, making love to her hungrily with his tongue, tasting her long and slowly until she shuddered with ecstasy against his mouth, until he drove himself mad. A long time later he drew her body beneath his and came inside her, at last, and again her body was like warm, writhing velvet. She was hot and tight and meltingly moist. And wild. Wilder and more wonderful than before. He knew that he would love her till he died.

When their crisis came together, they clung shuddering as if not only their bodies but their souls were joined.

Afterward, in the lengthening silence, they still held one another. It took a while before he fell back into himself, before he remembered her hateful identity. *Cecilia Wyatt!* How could he know her and still want her? She was the daughter of his father's killer. Her every word had been a lie. Her every kiss an act.

If he were a fool to still want her, he'd be much more of a fool to let her suspect how completely she had him in her power.

His frigid voice was low and harsh when he at last summoned the will to speak; his bitter eyes, blue ice. "Go home, *Cecilia*. You were good, but not good enough. I still intend to go after your father."

Her strangled cry tore his heart.

She was in his blood. He wanted the warmth of her skin next to his, the scent of her perfume every morning when he awoke.

He turned his back to her and lay still, feigning stony indifference as she got up, gathered her clothes and ran out.

After she was gone, the house was colder and lonelier than before. He was lonelier. He felt like a wounded beast whose heart had been torn out. The terrible silence almost drove him mad.

Then the phone rang, and his machine caught it.

The phone rang again.

And something told him to answer it.

A stranger's voice. A woman's.

What she said jolted him wide-awake like the most chilling scream of a nightmare.

His body turned to ice as her staccato words burst across his frantic brain.

"Terrible car wreck... His car rolled.... It took them more than an hour to cut him out. Marin County across the Golden Gate Bridge..."

Midnight was in the hospital intensive-care unit—dying.

And Joshua knew it was all his fault.

More than anything in all the world he needed Honey to help him face this nightmare. He hung up the phone and dialed her number, but when she heard his voice she made a low, almost inarticulate sound that contained all the loss and anguish in her soul.

The one broken word she spoke was his name. *"Joshua."*

Then the line went dead, and he felt as if her gentle voice had torn out his heart.

He remembered the last breathless, ravaging hour they'd spent together in his bed. The insidiously erotic power she held over him, his deep need for her and his fierce agony had nothing to do with hatred and everything to do with love.

He had been a proud, doomed fool not to forgive her, not to realize that he couldn't live without her.

But it was too late.

She was gone forever. He had driven her away just as he'd driven Midnight to his death.

Fourteen

———

"You can't go in there!"

The hell he couldn't. To hell with hospitals and all their stupid rules.

Joshua barged angrily through the shiny doors. Three gloved orderlies in masks and scrub suits rushed up to restrain him, but with deadly instincts honed in the gutter Joshua fought them off, slamming one against the wall and the others against a table, upsetting a tray of sterile instruments that clattered onto the tile floor.

That was the easy part. Then he saw Midnight lying gray faced and as still as death on a bloodstained stretcher beneath brilliant lights, and something inside Joshua shattered into a million pieces.

Doctors and nurses were speaking in hushed, urgent whispers, working frantically to prepare Midnight for surgery.

As Joshua slowly crossed the room, he realized he had never seen Midnight helpless before. His handsome features were slack. Black bruises circled his inky-lashed,

shuttered eyes. His nose was broken and his mouth was cut
and grotesquely puffy. There was a bloody patch on his
forehead where the skin had been abraded by the steering
wheel or the windshield.

A nurse was shaving his coal dark hair for brain surgery.

Joshua pressed Midnight's lifeless fingers and felt nau-
seated when he remembered that last time he'd touched his
father's hand. What finished him off was the small plastic
bag that a nurse stuffed into his hand.

Midnight's ring and watch.

Cold sweat broke out on Joshua's brow. The same
clammy stuff ran down his back. His temples throbbed.
Everything blurred. He felt as weak as a kitten, so weak he
had to be helped back to the waiting room.

Hours passed, but Joshua had no concept of time; only
of an ever darkening nightmare in which the horrors of his
past mingled with the horrors of the present. It was his
eleventh birthday and his first day at his terrible new school.
A gang of street kids twice his size greeted him at the water
fountain by slamming him against a graffiti-splattered
locker and laughing at him because he was small and new
and friendless and therefore defenseless. They made him the
butt of their humiliating jokes, knocking the locker door
into him at every punch line, shoving him mercilessly from
one bully to another, until he felt even smaller, until he got
dizzier and dizzier until he was so sick he threw up all over
himself. That had made them laugh all the harder. Then
Midnight was there, taller and tougher than any of them and
meaner too—except for his eyes. The bullies had slunk
away. And Midnight had been there ever since.

Till now.

Midnight had taught him to fight, had taught him to survive. Midnight had been the only one who understood his
pain, and Midnight had always wanted him to get past it. It
was a bitter irony that Midnight's last battle against the

darkness in Joshua's soul was probably going to cost him his own life.

And Joshua knew he had never been worth it. He had always been a lost soul. The demons inside him had made him drive his only friend to his death. Just as they'd driven him to use Honey when she'd come to him to save her father; just as they'd driven him to cut her heart out with the roughest words he'd ever used on any woman.

Destroy or be destroyed.

He loved Midnight. And he loved Honey. His own daughter didn't want to live with him anymore. He loved her, too.

But the dark demons that were destroying him had made him destroy them all.

He would have given everything he had to die in Midnight's place.

Then Lacy was there in that tiny waiting room, and everything was worse because beside her was a skinny nine-year-old boy with coal-dark hair and coal-dark rebellious eyes. The kid had a distinctive strip of white in his hair that dripped low over his brow.

Lacy looked tired and scared, and Joshua remembered the dangerous man who was after her.

"You're supposed to be on that flight to Brazil."

"I couldn't go after I heard," Lacy said gently. "I—I couldn't leave Johnny... because... I just couldn't." She nudged the boy forward. "This is Joe," Lacy murmured.

Joshua looked into the boy's black eyes and missed a heartbeat.

Midnight, who loved children, had a son.

And because of Joshua, Midnight would probably die without ever knowing. Lacy and his child would be in terrible danger. If something happened to them because they had stayed in the States, their deaths would be Joshua's fault as well.

"It's too late to tell him," Joshua muttered. "He's unconscious and they don't think he'll ever wake up."

Joshua buried his head in his hands and let the black, numbing despair close around him.

And as he waited, even with Lacy there, without Honey, he felt alone during those long, dark hours, and more than anything he wished he could die instead of Midnight.

Pink light was pouring into the waiting room, but Joshua was scarcely aware of it. He felt stiff as he hunched forward, elbows on his jeans, his dark head collapsed in his hands. He twisted his wrist and looked wearily at his watch. Midnight had been in surgery more than five hours.

Dear God. The waiting was killing him. Then the bitter thought came: *If only it would.* Lacy had taken Joe downstairs to get something to eat.

A door was pushed open. Soft, tentative footsteps alerted him that he was no longer alone. God, the last thing he wanted was company. But he looked up, his dark face, haggard and angry and lost.

A woman was backlighted by the glow of the pink dawn light so that she looked like an angel with a shining aura. Her hair seemed on fire. Her face was in shadow.

But he knew who she was.

She moved toward him in vinyl boots, with earrings that jingled.

"Joshua—"

The soft tissue of his heart seemed to tear as her velvet voice shivered through him.

"Go away," he muttered fiercely. Even as he said that some part of him wanted to get down on his knees and beg her to stay.

He hunched lower, into himself, fighting to ignore her. But she just tiptoed defiantly closer and smiled *that* soft smile that he would always love.

Dear God, did she know what she was doing to him?

"Why the hell don't you ever obey me?" he growled, drawn, as always by her defiance, by her loveliness, but determined not to show it.

He shut his eyes and buried his head in his hands to resist the temptation of looking at her.

"How the hell did you know where I was?" he asked in a thick, anguished voice.

"Heather called."

"She shouldn't have bothered."

Honey took a faltering step toward him. "I'm sorry I hung up on you. I—I didn't know about Midnight."

Joshua kept his hands over his eyes, afraid of the sick, tense eagerness that made his stomach churn.

"How's Midnight?" she asked ever so gently.

"Not good," he managed. "He's still in surgery."

"He's tough."

"Even the toughest guys are human," he said unemotionally.

"I'm glad you finally learned that."

A great stillness descended on him. All he could hear was his heart slamming against his rib cage. "Look, I don't want you here."

"I know that."

He heard the sob in her voice as she took another step toward him. He held his breath, more afraid than he'd ever been.

The silence lengthened. He didn't know what else to say, what to do. Some unbearable tension began to build like an explosive force.

Then a door was thrown open and Midnight's surgeon, a beautiful woman with red hair and tense brown eyes, walked into the room.

"Who the hell—?" Joshua demanded, looking up. Then he saw how her brown eyes were circled with dark rings of exhaustion, and he shut up.

Dr. Lescuer nervously thumbed a two-inch-thick chart and set it down. "We nearly lost him—twice." She paused. "But after a while, things began to go better for us. We gave him blood. Got him stabilized. Then we removed bits of bone and metal from the thalamus and hippocampus fibrous regions of his brain. He was lucky as hell—a millimeter away from death or vital brain functions being destroyed. His leg and ribs and the surface cuts on his face were easy after that. If he makes it through the night, I'd say he's got at least a fifty-fifty chance. The surgery went off better than we expected. But..."

"But?"

"Even though we don't think there's been any permanent damage to the brain, he's been shaken up pretty badly."

"What do you mean?"

"There could be problems, disorientation for a while, maybe even some amnesia," the doctor said. "In a case like this, you can never predict the outcome. He could be moody, different."

Midnight would probably live. He had a fifty-fifty chance. That was all that mattered for now. And Lacy would be with him.

When the surgeon left, Joshua looked at Honey for the first time. Her face was pale, her green eyes huge and luminous, concerned.

Honey's gentle, reassuring smile cut out his heart. Dear God— Maybe Midnight would live, but he'd lost Honey.

Anguish made Joshua's features hard and set. His voice was harsh. "Thanks for coming."

For a moment her throat seemed so dry she couldn't speak. "I—I can't stay." She too looked anywhere but at him. "My father was furious when I told him where—"

Somehow Joshua kept his voice calm. "Don't stay on my account."

She went very still. "I knew you wouldn't want me here." Then she swallowed. "Goodbye, Joshua."

His heart slammed in slow, painful strokes as he watched her walk away.

She was at the door.

"Why did you have to come today?" he whispered.

"Oh, Joshua—"

Scalding tears slipped from her eyes and ran down her cheeks, and he saw how terribly he'd hurt her.

He heard her passionate whisper as if in a dream. "I'm sorry, Joshua. For what I did—for hurting you. For coming here when you don't want me. I hope I didn't make this worse. I understand why you hate me."

Her white face held the same wild pain that filled his soul.

Let her go.

How could he? Then his life would be utter, soul-destroying desolation. He'd lived like that too long.

He got up slowly. "I don't hate you."

She swallowed a convulsive sob. "I—I just had to make sure you were okay." She pushed the door open. "Now that I know—"

He started running. "Hey, I'm not okay," he whispered fiercely, grabbing her arm in desperation. "I'll never be okay—not if you leave me." He pulled her back into the room, against his body.

"Joshua, what are you saying?"

"That I've been a crazy, stupid fool. Honey, I love you."

"I can't believe—"

"Believe it! I love you," he repeated in a low, tormented tone. "And I'm sorry, sorrier than you'll ever know—about a lot of things—for getting crazy drunk and hurting you the way my father used to hurt me. For quarreling with Midnight when he defended you, so that he drove so recklessly he damn near killed himself."

"Midnight and I were just as much at fault—"

"No— You both fought to save me." Joshua gave a deep sigh and drew her closer. "You are so beautiful. . . ."

"But I'm not glamorous—"

He felt a terrible, growing constriction in his throat. "In my phony world, you're the only thing that's real."

"I'll never be skinny and glamorous enough to wear skintight sequins."

His eyes blazed with unspoken needs. "You look perfect—naked. Instead of sequins, I'll give you emeralds—to wear in bed."

"All I ever want is your love." She clung to him, her face shining.

He liked the way her length fit his, snugly, warmly, securely. His heart thundered. A white heat swept him. His hands smoothed her hair, touched her face reverently. "I never knew I could want anyone this much," he whispered fervently.

Her lashes were lowered. A soft cry of joy escaped her lips.

"I think I loved you from the first," he whispered. "Even when I knew who you were. You made the hate begin to go away. You brought me closer to Heather. I was very set on revenge, but your love and idealism lit a bright path out of the darkness. Oh, Honey, there were so many years of darkness."

Their gazes melted together. She brushed her fingertips across his lips. "I couldn't bear the thought of losing you either," she admitted very softly. "That's why I came today. Because I had to see you. I was so afraid you'd blame yourself—"

"But your father—" he whispered.

"Oh, Joshua, I don't care if he ever forgives me. Astella is on my side now, and she'll try to win him over. But I love you too much to give you up—for anybody." Honey kept smoothing his hair gently with her trembling hands. "I wanted his approval and I could never have it. So I married Mike and pretended that I was good and morally superior like him and that what I really wanted was to save the world. Now...at last, for the first time, I feel like I'm beginning to know who I am and what I really want and I don't care if anybody approves. Because I know you are right for me. And this new belief in myself is something wonderful that grew out of my feelings for you. You weren't what I thought I wanted, but I love you anyway. I love you so much that everything, even my family...even wanting to find my brother, Raven, pales in significance. Mario will be better off. He needs a father."

"And Heather and I need you," Joshua said, kissing her, softly at first, and then with an intensity that left no doubt about the depth of his feelings. "I don't deserve you. I'll never be good enough for you."

When he kissed Honey again, wildfire pulsed in his blood. And as his searing mouth stole the very breath from her lips, he surrendered his soul to the only woman he had ever loved. She smelled sweet and wondrous. She was his. Only his.

They held each other, shuddering with delight as they kissed and nuzzled while the heat of their love and the fire of a new sun enveloped them in glorious flooding warmth.

There had never been a hotter or a wilder dawn.

Epilogue

Raven's gift arrived a month after Honey's wedding, three months after Midnight's accident, the first Saturday they got back from their honeymoon in Hawaii. It was huge and wrapped in shiny psychedelic *green* paper, her favorite shade of green. There was no return address, nothing but his first name written in a slanting, bold hand on the outside and the drawing of a tiny raven beneath the name. The mysterious gift was delivered by a special courier who would say nothing about the sender.

Honey began to shake the minute she saw her brother's name and the familiar line drawing. How had he known she'd married? Where she lived? Why hadn't he come himself?

She was dying to open his gift, and yet it was too precious to open without Joshua and their family and friends at her side. So, she carried it up to the terrace where everything was set up to honor Midnight, who was now living on his houseboat with Lacy and Joe.

The package was such a hot, brilliant green that she couldn't take her eyes off it. She could hardly wait to open it, but she waited. Only when Midnight walked slowly out of the elevator and onto the terrace with Lacy and everyone had laughed that so much green and so much clutter had crept into Joshua's home in just four weeks, only after the champagne corks had been popped and glasses filled, did she unwrap her present and gasp with pleasure when she discovered a long lost painting her mother had done of her and Raven.

Tears sprang in Honey's eyes as she looked at it, and she clung to Joshua. "It was the last thing Mother painted before she died. Raven knew how much I loved it," she whispered. "He loved it, too. That day was our last happy time together. I always wondered what happened to it."

"I like the way you wore your hair," Heather said, studying the picture.

"You were cute," Mario said. "But you had mischievous eyes."

"I was a brat," Honey replied.

Honey began to tear through the paper her brother's gift had come in. "H-he didn't send a note. Why—"

Joshua was silent.

"But at least I know he's still alive," Honey said. "Maybe some day soon he'll decide to come home. Until he does, I have you and Mario and Heather."

Midnight came closer and lifted his champagne glass to them. "To you, J.K., and to you, Honey, for finally doing what I'd been trying to do for years."

"And what the hell was that?" Joshua demanded.

"She saved your soul." Midnight's voice lowered, but he held his glass higher. "To your lasting happiness."

Joshua lifted his glass. "And to you, Midnight. You'll never know how I prayed for this day. To see you walk through my front door again, and with Lacy and Joe."

Midnight's expression darkened as he stared across the crowded terrace at Lacy, who seemed to be ignoring him. "Thanks. But they're not completely mine yet, J.K."

"Why not?" Joshua demanded.

"It's a long story. A lot happened while you two were away on your honeymoon. Last night Cole Douglas broke into my houseboat and scared the hell out of Lacy. He's in custody and I'm expecting a call from the lieutenant in charge of his case. We may have some answers soon about a lot of stuff that'll affect Lacy and me—I want her back, J.K." Midnight's expression was hard.

"Then what's stopping you?" Joshua asked.

"I'm not sure. A feeling in my gut. My brain's not working quite as good as it used to—"

"Good. Then maybe I can keep up with you."

Midnight set his champagne glass down with a tense smile. "I can tell from now on my life's going to be a living hell. Hey, I'd better look for Joe and let you two enjoy each other."

"Good luck, Midnight," Joshua said.

"He looks wonderful. He's going to be okay," Honey said reassuringly.

Joshua pulled her close and her nearness made him feel warm and loved. "I want Lacy and Midnight to find each other—the way we found each other."

"They will," Honey whispered.

But when the police called a few minutes later and Midnight dropped the phone and seized Lacy, dragging her away with a dark, shattered look on his face, Honey saw that Joshua was very worried.

Not that he mentioned his friend until hours later when their guests had gone and Honey and Joshua were alone in their bedroom getting ready for bed.

Joshua ripped off his cuff links. "Did you notice how upset Midnight looked with Lacy when he ran out? I thought things might work out between them until he did that."

Honey took off her emerald earrings. "Trust me. He loves her. He never took his eyes off her."

"But why did he run off like that looking like he hated her?"

"I seem to remember you looking at me once or twice like that," she said with a smile. "They're going to find each other—the way we found each other."

Suddenly he knew she was right. "When two people really love each other," he said huskily, "they find a way to work out their problems."

She laughed. "I can't believe this! You're beginning to sound like an incurable romantic."

Joshua opened a window and got into bed. "Hey, you were the one who taught me to believe in the power of love to work miracles. Lacy has come back to Midnight. They've both been through hell, but he'll accept her back completely in his life—he just needs time." Joshua turned out the light and the room melted into starry darkness. Cool night air that was scented from the flowers blooming in the garden drifted into the bedroom. "Come here," he said huskily.

"I was trying to have a serious conversation."

"I want to give you a hands-on lesson about the power of love. We'll worry about Midnight tomorrow." He took the phone off the hook and buried it under a pillow.

She got into bed wearing only her sparkling emerald ring. Her naked body slid into Joshua's warmth. Midnight and Lacy would have to work out their own problems the way she and Joshua had. And Joshua was right—the greatest power on earth was love.

Joshua's arms wound around her. His mouth found hers in the darkness. Her soft body nestled against his hard, muscular length. As always his skin was incredibly hot, his kisses stirring her to incredible heights. And what happened was something wild, something so shattering that it involved all her senses as well as her soul. And when it was over, it wasn't over at all because she lay in his arms the rest of the night, satiated and yet basking in the incredible security of his love, which she knew would last as long as they lived and forever.

*   *   *   *   *

COMING NEXT MONTH

THE SEDUCTION OF JAKE TALLMAN
Cait London

Morganna Larrimore had picked a dangerous area for her attempt at "bonding with nature" and Jake Tallman had to rescue her without appearing to do so. That was why he told her she wouldn't last a month on his ranch; it was a challenge Morganna couldn't resist!

COUNTERFEIT BRIDE
Christine Rimmer

Jordan McSwain swept Eve Tanner off her feet and then gave her an ultimatum. Eve couldn't believe that they were washed up just because she didn't want to get married instantly, and pretending to be Jordan's wife would give her the opportunity to change his mind.

IMITATION LOVE
Jackie Merritt

Cord Durant and Abbie Forbes had one unforgettable night of passion, which left Abbie with a choice between a scandalous end to her career or a commitment to a man she barely knew…

COMING NEXT MONTH

CASSIE'S LAST GOODBYE
Shawna Delacorte

Trent Nichols deceived Cassie Brockton about his background; he knew she wouldn't have anything to do with him if he told her who and *what* he was. And she *needed* him.

MOONLIGHT DREAM
Noelle Berry McCue

One glance told Shannon that Donovan Lancaster was way out of her league but something in those beautiful golden eyes tempted her to play with fire. What harm could it do?

BEAUTY AND THE BEASTMASTER
Carol Devine

Bram Masterson made his living in an unusual, flamboyant profession and lady lawyer Amanda Tarkenton just couldn't see herself marrying a muscle-bound *wrestler*! So why did she fall in love with him?

♒ Zodiac Wordsearch ♌
Competition

How would you like a years' supply of Silhouette Sensations <u>ABSOLUTELY FREE</u>?

Well, you can win them! All you have to do is complete the word puzzle below and send it to us by 30th June 1994. The first five correct entries picked out of the bag after this date will each win one years' supply of Silhouette Sensation romances (four books every month - worth over £90). What could be easier?

S	E	C	S	I	P	R	I	A	C	F
U	U	D	C	A	N	C	E	R	D	I
L	E	I	N	I	M	E	G	U	S	R
C	A	P	R	I	C	O	R	N	U	E
S	E	I	R	A	N	G	I	S	I	O
P	O	P	W	A	T	E	R	W	R	I
L	G	A	H	M	A	T	I	T	A	P
U	R	R	T	O	U	H	I	S	U	R
T	I	B	R	O	R	E	N	G	Q	O
O	V	I	A	N	U	S	A	T	A	C
I	O	L	E	O	S	T	A	R	N	S

Pisces	Aries	Leo	Earth	**Please turn over for entry details**
Cancer	Gemini	Virgo	Star	
Scorpio	Taurus	Fire	Sign	
Aquarius	Libra	Water	Moon	
Capricorn	Sagittarius	Pluto	Air	

How to enter

All the words listed overleaf below the word puzzle, are hidden in the grid. You can find them by reading the letters forwards, backwards, up and down, or diagonally. When you find a word, circle it or put a line through it. After you have found all the words, the left-out letters will spell a secret message that you can read from left to right, from the top of the puzzle through to the bottom.

Don't forget to enter your name and address in the space below then put this page in an envelope and post it today (you don't need a stamp). Competition closes 30th June 1994.

**Silhouette Competition
Freepost
P.O. Box 236
Croydon
Surrey CR9 9EL**

--- ✂

COMZW

Hidden message _____

_____

Are you a Reader Service subscriber?   Yes ☐   No ☐

Ms/Mrs/Miss/Mr _____

Address _____

_____

_____

_____ Postcode _____

mps MAILING PREFERENCE SERVICE